Dental Science In A New Age

AL LAOANG

DENTAL SCIENCE IN A NEW AGE

A History of the
National Institute of Dental Research

RUTH ROY HARRIS

Montrose Press   Rockville, Maryland   1989

Library of Congress Catalog Card Number 88-063744

All photographs are courtesy of
the National Institute of Dental Research
unless otherwise noted.

Frontispiece: *The Dental Research Laboratory Building at NIH*

Table of Contents

Illustrations and Charts

Foreword

History, according to Cicero, "illumines reality, vitalizes memory, provides guidance in daily life, and brings us tidings of antiquity." To those of us familiar with the early days of dental research, Ruth Harris's text satisfies all these criteria. For the first time a scholar has pored over the files of this government agency, the memorabilia of key individuals, the formal documents preserved in archives, and the informal accounts provided by human memory and the ephemera of newspaper and periodicals. The result is a comprehensive chronology of the forty-year history of the National Institute of Dental Research.

To establish the context, Dr. Harris "brings us tidings of antiquity" with a review of ancient beliefs about that most ancient of ailments, the toothache. The seventeenth century father of modern dentistry, the Frenchman Pierre Fauchard, is duly acknowledged, along with other European pioneers. The pendulum then swings to the New World, moving from colonial times to the advances in the nineteenth century, notably the discovery of inhalation anesthesia by American dentists, and the establishment of the first dental schools and societies of dentists in the United States. By the end of the nineteenth century European influence in biology dominated with the critical discoveries of Pasteur, Koch, and Ehrlich. Among those attracted by the intellectual ferment abroad was the American dentist Willoughby D. Miller, whose insights into the cause of dental caries would establish a permanent place for him in the odontological pantheon.

The beginning of the twentieth century marked the beginning of organized dental research, first under private auspices and later under the United States Public Health Service and the National Bureau of Standards. While work at the bureau was aimed at improving dental materials, Public Health Service dental research focused on the need to improve the dental health of children.

That need would eventually lead to one of the great sagas of dental research, the fluoride story, told here in full detail: from the earliest observations of McKay and Black, through the indefatigable efforts of H. Trendley Dean and his co-workers in the 1930s, and on to the clinical trials of water fluoridation that began in Grand Rapids, Michigan, in 1945. These trials would climax in one of the great success stories of dental research and mark the beginning of the movement of dentistry from repairs and restoration to prevention.

When Dean began his research he was the first dental scientist to be appointed in the newly named National Institute of Health (NIH). Dean's career would extend beyond World War II to his appointment as the first director of the National Institute of Dental Research (NIDR) when it was established in 1948. Dr. Harris "vitalizes memory" in her careful laying down of the political, legal, social, and economic factors that figured in establishing the Institute. She reminds us that it was the deplorable state of the dentition of army recruits in World War II that so shocked federal officials and raised the voices of organized dentistry, individual practitioners, and academics to the need for federal investment in dental research.

The chronicles of NIDR in the fifties and sixties marked the growth and expansion of NIDR into new areas of basic and clinical research while continuing the investment in fluoride and caries research. Forces opposed to water fluoridation engaged the energies of NIDR and the dental community in charges and refutations that would recur over the years. Economic woes delayed construction of a separate research facility for NIDR at the NIH, but in 1961 the structure was in place and NIDR enjoyed a healthy growth spurt. Concurrently, steps were taken to enhance dental research and research training in the nation's dental schools.

During the 1970s health research took on the metaphors of the military. To fight the "war" on caries, President Nixon adopted as a special health initiative the NIDR proposal to establish a National Caries Program (NCP). Dr. Harris delineates the life and times of the NCP over its ten-year existence, citing the program's accomplishments against the backdrop of a political climate that increasingly favored targeted research.

The latter parts of the text "illumine reality"—if we translate reality to mean the contemporary research scene. They document the emergence of dental research into mainstream biomedical research and the rapid pace of progress we are seeing, thanks to the adoption of the tools and techniques of cell and molecular biology. Here, then, are accounts of the contributions dental research is making to an understanding of the human genome, to the origin and metastastis of cancer, to genetic diseases, to infections like AIDS, as well as to basic studies of normal development, maturity, and aging of the tissues. These chapters also provide "guidance in daily life"—when we realize how dental research findings are being translated into better oral and general health for Americans. One thinks of the exquisite control of acute and chronic pain now possible, of the remarkable findings about the defense mechanisms present in saliva, and of the discovery of new factors that can promote bone growth and soft tissue regeneration. One thinks of the growing catalog of drugs, endogenous factors, biomaterials, behavioral therapies, and preventive measures that can now be brought to bear on oral and systemic disease—all as a result of oral health research.

The historian brings us up to the present, with a picture of dental research as a global enterprise. We can be proud of much that is narrated in these pages, pleased that in the span of forty years dental research has achieved such great improvements in oral health and that it has enjoyed an increase in both quality and quantity of research investigators. Now we see new challenges before us—challenges to understand the aging process, the genetic control of development, the interplay between the immune system and the oral microbiota, and the role of individual differences, environment, nervous system controls, and endocrine factors in oral health and disease. These are among the exciting frontiers ahead that will await the next generation of dental scientists and future historians to chronicle.

Harald Löe, D.D.S.
Director
National Institute of Dental Research

November 1988

Preface

Today Americans have fewer cavities and keep their teeth longer than their forebears. The nation's dentists, scientists, and public health officials played a significant part in bringing about such a change. This account recapitulates the human courage, persistence, and scientific skills of those associated with the National Institute of Dental Research (NIDR) who, over several decades, helped improve the dental health of not just Americans but people all over the world.

The origins of NIDR emerged many years before its official establishment in 1948 as the third institute of the National Institutes of Health (NIH). Consequently, this history examines the forces that helped create the Institute and the scientific, professional, and political influences that affected its forty years of operation. Where documentation is available, the inner workings of the Institute are disclosed. In this work, names of organizations, which often change, are those in use for each time discussed.

Thousands of Institute-supported extramural scientists and hundreds of NIDR intramural laboratory researchers published articles based on their investigations. Such a vast body of scientific accomplishments cannot be covered fully in a narrative history such as this one. Nevertheless, a few examples are introduced to demonstrate the extent and nature of the science produced under NIDR auspices. Both the extramural research conducted outside the Institute laboratories, which was extremely difficult to identify, and the NIDR intramural findings deserve a separate account of their own. As the selected accomplishments contained in this history indicate, the Institute has fostered much exciting and revolutionary scientific progress benefiting our children and grandchildren.

Preparing this history underscored the importance of preserving important records or "an institutional memory." The Institute information office maintained a helpful file, but over the years many essential documents vanished. Thanks to several individuals who kept their own records of Institute activities, we located important papers and copies of many of the first director's files. In addition, we found significant information in the files of the NIH director's office, the NIH Library, the National Library of Medicine, the National Archives, and presidential libraries. These contemporary materials, like eyewitnesses, helped in the recounting of the path taken by NIDR. And oral history interviews aided by filling gaps and capturing the flavor of significant events.

For future generations, histories of the other NIH institutes should prove useful in planning, managing, and conducting biomedical and behavioral research. In commissioning this history to celebrate its fortieth anniversary, the National Institute of Dental Research already has taken an important step to enlighten others about its past.

Acknowledgments

In putting this history together, a number of individuals provided valuable assistance. In particular, as the researcher for this history, Laura Kells of History Associates Incorporated contributed her superb research skills in ferreting out pertinent information from files at the National Institute of Dental Research and the National Archives. Ms. Kells also assembled the appendices, selected the pictures, and read and commented on the drafts for this history. Also from History Associates, Drs. Philip L. Cantelon, Ruth A. Dudgeon, and Barbara S. Kraft read the text and advised on changes from the viewpoints of historians and writers; Donna Wilkes prepared abstracts of the oral history interviews; Margaret Belke, Barbara Hunt, Gail Mathews, Kim Kilpatrick, DyAnn Smith, and Roberta Hahn handled administrative and word processing assistance. Dr. Suzanne Lowitt improved the manuscript with her editing.

Former directors Dr. Seymour J. Kreshover and Dr. David B. Scott and current director Dr. Harald Löe generously gave of their time for interviews and advice and provided personal papers and pictures for the preparation of this history.

Brent Jaquet, chief of the National Institute of Dental Research Public Inquiries and Reports Section, supplied invaluable help throughout the history's preparation.

The following Institute staff members opened their files and furnished useful advice: Anne Atlee, Carol Beasley, Dorothy Costinett, Mary Daum, Jody Dove, Carolyn Grolman, Mimi Henry, Susan Johnson, Bob Kuska, Rose McLaughlin, Ethel Roseman, Joan Shariat, Patricia Sheridan, Marcye Slaughter, John Small, Alma Tokarski, Nancy Walsh, Kirk Weaver, Sally Wilberding, Joan Wilentz, Mary Workman, and Kathy Wyckoff.

Institute scientists, administrators, and retirees who located records and patiently translated scientific terminology into lay terms included: Dr. Bruce Baum, Janet Brunelle, Dr. Patricia Bryant, Dr. James Carlos, Dr. Joseph Ciardi, Dr. Lois Cohen, Dr. Raymond

Dionne, Dr. Ronald Dubner, Dr. Robert Fitzgerald, Dr. John Folk, Dr. George Garrington, Dr. Arthur Hand, Dr. Matthew Kinnard, Dr. Dushanka Kleinman, Dr. Hynda Kleinman, Dr. Rachel Larson, Chad Leyshon, Dr. James Lipton, Dr. Preston A. Littleton, Dr. Kenneth Lynn, Dr. George Martin, Dr. Stephan Mergenhagen, Dr. Abner Notkins, Dr. Marie Nylen, Dr. Karl Piez, Dr. A. H. Reddi, Dr. Joyce Reese, Dr. Anthony Rizzo, Dr. Michael Roberts, Dr. Lois Salzman, Dr. Ann L. Sandberg, Dr. Robert Stephan, Dr. John Termine, Dr. John Townsley, Dr. Thomas Valega, and Dr. Sharon Wahl.

Mrs. Ruth Dean and Miss Ruth Dean, widow and daughter of the Institute's first director, donated a rich collection of Dr. H. Trendley Dean's papers to the Institute for use in the history.

Elsewhere, help was supplied by Aloha South at the National Archives; Dennis Bilger at the Harry S. Truman Library; Herbert Pankratz at the Dwight D. Eisenhower Library; Nancy Smith at the Lyndon B. Johnson Library; Harold L. Miller at the State Historical Society of Wisconsin; John Whittock of the School of Dental Medicine Library, University of Pennsylvania; Dr. Viron Diefenbach of the University of Illinois School of Public Health; Dr. Robert Genco of the Department of Oral Biology and Periodontal Disease Clinical Research Center, State University of New York at Buffalo; Dr. Ira Lamster of the Fairleigh Dickinson College of Dental Medicine; Drs. William Alstadt and Rafael Bowen, Sara Denney, Aletha Kowitz, Betty Presteman, Cindy Sims, and Drs. John Stanford, Anthony J. Steffek, and Carl Verrusio of the American Dental Association; C. Jay Brown of the District of Columbia Dental Society; Dr. John Tesk of the National Bureau of Standards; Wendy Ailor of the National Academy of Sciences Archives; Dr. Bruce Forsyth and Dr. Robert Mecklenburg, former chief dental officers of the Public Health Service, and the chief dental officer's assistant, Dr. William Maas; Dr. Thomas Louden, acting chief of the service's Division of Associated and Dental Health Professions; Anita Mills in the office of the Assistant Secretary for Health; Lillie E. O'Haro and David Porter of the Office of the Director, National Institutes of Health; Dr. Wyndham Miles, former historian of the National Institutes of Health; Peter Murphy, Prospect Associates; Dr. John Parascandola, Chief, and Dorothy Hanks, Reference Librarian, History of Medicine Division, National Library of Medicine; Dr. Victoria Harden, National Institutes of Health historian; Dr. Ben Z. Swanson, director, Museum of the Baltimore College of Dental Surgery, the University of Maryland; and last, but not least, Drs. Isadore and Jonathan Harris, and Geoffrey Harris, husband and sons, respectively, who served as volunteer advisors.

CHAPTER ONE

Dentistry: From Magic to Science

In Nature's infinite book of secrecy
A little I can read.

WILLIAM SHAKESPEARE

What caused the agony?

Scientists in the twentieth century searched for invasive microorganisms, but their ancient predecessors, Babylonian savants of 5000 B.C., blamed "the worm" for toothaches and bleeding gums. According to a clay tablet found centuries later in the Euphrates valley, the Babylonians recited an incantation to the god "Ea" and placed pulverized henbane and gum mastic on the sore spot to relieve the pain and exorcise the worm.[1]

For thousands of years humans assumed an intruding worm invaded and carved out cavities in teeth. Chinese medical texts prepared twenty-seven centuries before the Christian era cited worms as the cause of dental caries, commonly known as decay of the teeth. For treating toothaches, the ancient peoples and their descendants employed mixtures of magic recitations or gestures with practical mouth rinses, potions, and ointments.[2]

The Ebers Papyri, the famous medical tracts discovered by a nineteenth century German Egyptologist, and mummies also provided information about ancient dentistry. From his studies of those sources, dental historian Dr. Vincenzo Guerini found that dentistry emerged as a part of early medicine rather than as a separate discipline. Guerini concluded that from 3700 B.C. to 1550 B.C. the

1

Egyptians did not fill any cavities or perform any kind of dental surgery. Instead, the "Chiefs of Toothers and Physicians" only pre-scribed soothing recipes for the ailing mouth and provided false teeth.[3]

From about 1000 B.C. to 400 B.C. Etruscans introduced a more sophisticated restorative dentistry. The quality of their crowns and bridges favorably impressed Dr. M. D. K. Bremner, an American dental historian familiar with their work.[4]

Early medical practitioners tried to deal with the agony of the toothache even though they could not explain its causes. Hippocrates devoted thirty-two paragraphs of his writings to dentition and rec-ommended a mixture of cloves, pepper, and ginger to ease the pain of an aching tooth. Scribonius Largus, physician to the emperor Clau-dius and believer in the worm theory, recommended fumigating the aching tooth and rinsing the mouth with warm water.[5]

Surprisingly, the first physical evidence of a therapeutic tooth fill-ing turned up in the New World. Smithsonian Institution scientists discovered the filled tooth in the skull of an Indian woman who was buried in a mound near what was later called the Illinois River, north of St. Louis, Missouri. The scientists regarded the filling, which resembled cream-colored Portland cement, as skillfully crafted be-tween A.D. 900 and A.D. 1200.[6]

In the twelfth century the practice of dental surgery regressed in the Old World. For much of the Christian era, Catholic clerics performed most dental surgery because they could read the works of such instructors as Hippocrates. In 1163 Pope Alexander II prohib-ited priestly officers from performing any operation that caused the shedding of blood. As a result, barbers took over the practice of dental surgery.[7]

Ironically, during the 1300s dentistry first appeared in writing as a separate field. In his 1363 *Chirurgia Magna*, Guy de Chauliac, a surgeon, observed that tooth operations were performed by the *dentator* and barber "to whom physicians had abandoned them."[8]

While barbers continued to practice dentistry, the basis of modern dentistry was laid in the sixteenth century, especially in France and England. During the 1500s the University of France first admitted dental students, and Henry VIII granted a charter to the Barber-Surgeons' Company of England.[9]

Elsewhere on the European continent individuals prepared the

This eighteenth century engraving, "The Country Toothdrawer," provides a humorous depiction of the treatment of dental problems prior to the establishment of dentistry as a separate profession. Courtesy of the National Library of Medicine.

groundwork of modern dental science. Eustacius and Fallopius, scholars in the Venetian Republic, produced works that gave accurate, detailed descriptions of the anatomy, embryology, and physiology of the teeth and mouth. In 1530 the first textbook on dentistry was published in Leipzig. The Dutch student of natural history and microscope maker, Antony van Leeuwenhouk, wrote the first complete description of bacteria taken from teeth scrapings; his studies especially opened a new age for science.[10] Thus, toward the end of the European Renaissance dentistry benefited from that resurgence of learning.

The Beginnings of Modern Dentistry

Modern dentistry in name and practice appeared in France in the seventeenth century. The reference *chirurgien dentiste*, obviously the antecedent of the word *dentist*, was in common use by 1622 in France. Also by the 1600s dentists represented what Guerini called "a well-defined class." To practice dentistry in France by 1700, one had to pass a special examination.[11]

Such an intellectual environment and fate provided society with the father of modern dentistry. Pierre Fauchard's parents intended to educate him for surgery, but financial reverses ruined those plans. Instead, the Brittany native, encouraged by a mentor in the French Navy Medical Corps, took up the practice of dentistry at the age of eighteen in 1696. After achieving fame as a practicing dentist, Fauchard wrote *Le Chirurgien Dentiste ou Traite des Dents*, published in 1728. This two-volume work laid the foundation of modern dentistry, and for over a century after its publication, *Le Chirurgien Dentiste* remained an authoritative guide for western European dentists. Fauchard's work also provided the first complete treatise on odontology, the science of the development and disorders of the teeth. Fauchard was among the first to connect disease of the mouth with the health of the rest of the human body. Some of the remedies in his writings, including the use of oil of cloves or cinnamon to relieve toothaches, were still used in regular dental practice in twentieth century America.[12]

Fauchard's writings, translated into German in 1733, stimulated a profusion of dental research and writing in France and Germany in the eighteenth century. A French contemporary, Robert Bunon, published a book in 1743 that stressed hygiene, advocated measures to preserve teeth, and cited tartar as a primary agent in causing gum disease. In 1756 Philip Pfaff, dentist to Frederick the Great of Prussia, wrote the first German treatise on dentistry, which included a discussion of the anatomical and physiological notions about teeth. Pfaff further distinguished himself by introducing the use of plaster molds of teeth and by being the first dentist known to cap an exposed dental pulp. After 1757 another German, Jacob Christian Schaffer, investigated the worm theory, not disputed by Fauchard, and wrote a book disproving the existence of worms in decayed teeth.[13]

In part because there was no English version of Fauchard's works, English dentists and scientists independently produced scientific advancements in dentistry.[14] The British Isles' most notable research came from John Hunter, a Scottish anatomist who experimented with animals to determine the effects of diet on enamel and dentine. He concluded that enamel had no circulation but that dentine was vascular before it became calcified. Hunter published *The Natural*

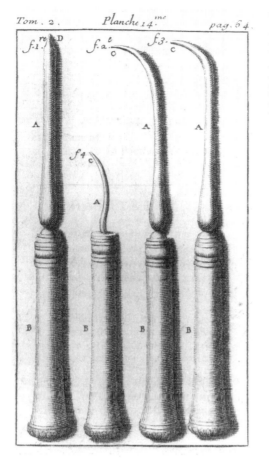

Tools to clean and scrape caries, from Pierre Fauchard's *Le Chirurgien Dentiste ou Traite des Dents*, published in 1728. Courtesy of the National Library of Medicine.

History of the Human Teeth in 1771, a book that became the basic English language work on the anatomy of the teeth and the jaw.[15]

Other revolutionary discoveries affecting dentistry accompanied the increase of scientific investigations into disorders of the teeth and mouth. A French apothecary started using porcelain for dentistry, and the English chemist, Joseph Priestley, discovered nitrous oxide, later known as the laughing gas used by dental surgeons.[16]

In the eighteenth century most dental progress occurred in the Old World. With the emigration of Europeans to the American colonies, some New World dentists also began to pry open the secrets of dental diseases.

The Rise of Dentistry as a Profession in the New World

Dentistry started modestly in the American colonies. In the third decade of the seventeenth century, William Dinly, a "tooth drawer," came from England to serve the Plymouth colony. Dinly was probably the first dentist to practice in the American colonies, which by 1625 included close to two thousand settlers. The French-trained Sieur Roquet, who arrived in Boston in 1749, may have been the first modern dentist to practice in the American colonies. In 1766 Robert Woofendale, a student of the eminent Thomas Berdmore, opened a practice in New York. Berdmore served as dentist to George III of England and wrote *Treatise on the Disorders of the Diseases of the Teeth*.[17]

Despite the modern training of some of the eighteenth century colonial dentists, the first known scientific publication by an American dentist did not appear until after the American Revolution. In 1790 a Philadelphia dentist trained in Europe, Jacques (James) Gardette, published one of the earliest American articles on dental decay and periodontal disease, "Remarks on the Diseases of the Teeth," in *The American Museum or Universal Magazine*.[18]

The first known American discussion of the cause of dental caries also occurred in the late eighteenth century. That question perplexed dentists, physicians, and scientists in Europe and the United States. Two opposing theories prevailed: one that the origin of caries was internal and was caused by a "humor" or internal body fluid; the other that it was external or introduced by some invasive element, such as a residue of food. John Hunter and Joseph Fox of England argued in favor of the internal theory, while John Greenwood, George Washington's dentist, suggested an external source based on his observations of patients' teeth.[19]

In 1796 disgruntled Scottish merchants unknowingly brought about the earliest recorded chemical experiment by an American on the origin of caries. Glasgow businessmen complained to the New York Chamber of Commerce about the poor quality of potash they received from the port of New York. The chamber asked Dr. Samuel L. Mitchell of Schenectady to conduct experiments on the potash. Mitchell, a physician and a professor of chemistry at Columbia University, cofounded the first medical journal in the United States and later became the first vice-president of the New York County Medical Society. In the course of his testing, Mitchell obtained tartar from a dentist, tested it, and concluded that the tartar included septic acid formed from fermenting food particles. Mitchell deduced that the acid corroded tooth enamel and in that manner formed caries.[20]

The fact that Mitchell was a physician and chemist, not a dentist, was symptomatic of the status of dentistry in the nation's early years. Although the first medical school in the country had opened in 1765, by 1800 no dental counterpart existed.

The growth of the nation contributed to an increase in the number of dentists and, eventually, to a demand for better-trained dentists. By 1800 the census counted 5,308,000 residents, an increase of 100 percent from the 1783 count. The country expanded west and south with the Louisiana Purchase in 1803 and with settlement later in the Midwest and Northwest. After the War of 1812 virtually every community along the Atlantic coastline had easy access to a dentist, although a contemporary, Dr. Charles Ballard, observed that the majority of dentists lacked adequate professional training. Some forty dentists, however, considered scientific knowledge and research so important that through learning and teaching they strove to enhance the profession of dentistry in the United States. Their efforts made a permanent impact.[21]

Levi Spear Parmly was one of the first dentists in the nineteenth century to show an interest in dental research. Vermont-born and Boston-trained, Parmly attended medical lectures in London where he became interested in the scientific aspects of dentistry. Upon his return to the United States after the War of 1812, Parmly collected thousands of teeth extracted from dead soldiers from that war, examined caries in various stages in those teeth, and concluded "that caries universally commences externally" when stagnated food penetrated through the minute apertures formed in the enamel. In 1819 he preached cleanliness as a preventive measure in a guide written for the public.[22]

Major progress toward making American dentistry a profession came several years after Parmly's publication. Formal schooling, research, experimentation, and discovery grew simultaneously. Two brothers, John and Chapin Harris, started the dental school movement in the United States. In 1825 John Harris used his home in Bainbridge, Ohio, for the first school of dentistry and dental surgery in North America. His brother, Chapin, graduated from there and, with Horace H. Hayden and two physicians, Drs. Thomas E. Bond and H. Willis Baxley, in 1840 founded the first dental college in North America, the Baltimore College of Dental Surgery. Opening with five students, the Baltimore institution set the precedent for establishing other dental colleges in the United States and formed the basis for making the profession educationally accountable.[23]

Dr. Chapin Harris and his colleagues also collaborated to encourage dental research through a journal and professional organization during this same period. In 1839 Harris met with Drs. Solyman Brown, Horace Hayden, and Eleazer Parmly to create the first dental periodical, the *American Journal of Dental Science.*

In 1840 the Chapin Harris group formally organized the American Society of Dental Surgeons, the first national dental society. At the society's initial meeting the members listened to deliveries of early dental research papers and then published the proceedings in the *Journal.* The *Journal* subsequently featured society papers and news. Later known as the *American Journal and Library of Dental Science*, the periodical published new articles and reprinted standard works on dental theories and practice. Both the society and *Journal* ceased operating in the mid-1850s.[24]

The movement started by Dr. Chapin Harris and his associates led the way for the establishment of additional dental journals, local dental societies, improved dental education, and dental research. The most important of the journals that followed, the *Dental News Letter*, began in 1847. Later named the *Dental Cosmos* (merged in the twentieth century with the *Journal of the American Dental Association*), this publication provided a forum for the works of eminent American dental scientists.[25]

State and local dental societies blossomed in the 1840s and brought educational and political improvements to the profession. Virginia dentists organized one of the first state groups in 1842. Created in 1844, the Mississippi Valley Association of Dental Surgeons served the country's western region and published the *Dental Register of the West* for half a century. After the Massachusetts Dental Society persuaded Harvard University to start the first university dental school in 1868, Dr. Nathan C. Keep, president of the Massachusetts group, became its first dean. The Harvard action encouraged other major universities, including the Universities of Michigan and Pennsylvania, to establish dental schools. A number of the state groups also started publishing their own journals and thus gave researchers, dentists, inventors, and scientists publication outlets. Most of the state and local societies, however, were formed after the organization of the American Dental Association (ADA) just prior to the Civil War.[26]

An episode known as the "Amalgam War" precipitated the dissolution of the major national dental organization in the 1850s. In that conflict one group of dentists in the society opposed the use of amalgam instead of gold in fillings. The amalgam opponents viewed the mercury in amalgam as dangerous, although they lacked scientific proof that the body absorbed the mercury, and they considered the use of amalgam fillings as quackery. In 1856 the American Society of Dental Surgeons members disbanded because those disputes drastically reduced membership and attendance at meetings.

Two national dental organizations formed in its wake: the American Dental Convention in 1855 and the American Dental Association in 1859. Following the Civil War, southern dentists from former Confederate states started the Southern Dental Association in 1869. In a period when some dental colleges also briefly organized to improve dental education, both the northern and southern dental groups aimed at upgrading the profession. Less discriminating in setting training standards for members, the American Dental Convention dissolved in 1882. The American Dental Association drew up an ethical code and encouraged formal education of dentists. It merged with the Southern Dental Association in 1897 to form the National Dental Association to continue the same policies.[27]

Improvements in Dental Education and Licensing

The statistics on the educational preparation of practicing dentists in the country supported the concerns discussed by the national association. Although national and local societies encouraged formal dental school educations for practicing dentists, a minority of dentists in the nation in the nineteenth century graduated from dental school. In 1870 only 1,305 of 7,839 dentists in the country, or 15 percent, held dental school diplomas. The dental schools and professional organizations encouraged dental school attendance and supported the establishment of a sufficient number of dental schools.[28]

Initially, dental school faculties taught scientific courses similar to those in medical schools and provided instruction in mechanical and artistic skills. Refining the profession of dentistry, dental college faculty members also fostered the development of specialties in dentistry. For example, through his teaching at the University of Pennsylvania and his book, *A System of Oral Surgery*, Dr. James Edmund Garretson helped to establish oral surgery as one of the first specialties in 1869.[29]

In 1884 ten of the nation's twenty-two dental schools formed the National Association of Dental Faculties to bring about a more uniform curriculum. The association extended the curriculum to three years by 1891, increased the course work in the mechanics of dentistry, and, by 1899, raised admission requirements.[30]

Changes in curriculum and admission requirements could not in themselves improve the quality and image of dentistry in the nation. Officials of the schools and the dental societies understood that legal requirements were necessary. As early as 1805 Maryland empowered examiners to issue special licenses to dentists, and Alabama legislation created dental licensing in 1841, but neither state enforced the available controls. In 1868 Kentucky established the first effective law that resulted in mandatory dental licensing. The state laws that followed Kentucky's allowed dentists already in practice to continue, but new dentists had to pass board tests or offer dental school diplomas. The licensing laws spawned the growth of dental schools, a number of which operated only for profit, according to one historian of dental education. The proliferation of disreputable dental schools in turn caused several state legislatures to alter their licensing laws so that all applicants had to pass examinations. By 1900 a number of states had tightened dental licensing, and some of the commercial dental schools had closed.[31]

A supplemental form of dental education also originated in this period. Dr. C. M. Wright of Cincinnati introduced the dental hygiene movement, which promoted the cleaning of teeth through education of the public by dentists. Later the National Dental Association established a committee on oral hygiene in which Drs. D. D. Smith and W. G. Ebersole played prominent roles. Although the mouth hygiene movement started in the nineteenth century, the campaign did not attract widespread support until the twentieth century. Then the occupation of dental hygienist was created after Dr.

Alfred Fones trained the first dental hygienist in 1906 and started the first dental hygienist school in Connecticut in 1913.[32]

Progress in Dental Research and Inventions

During this period of the Industrial Revolution abroad and at home, the inventor, the scientist, and the experimenter began to flourish. In some cases Americans went to Europe to study and brought back with them the latest in discoveries, experiments, and education. Influenced by European higher education, Americans established outstanding graduate schools, with one of the nation's first at the University of Michigan. At the same time, the self-taught and self-made man symbolized the fulfillment of the American dream. American dentistry progressed in such an atmosphere.

In the nineteenth century Americans led the world in experiments to relieve pain. Hoping to solve dentistry's most ubiquitous problem, several American dentists and physicians introduced various kinds of anesthesia for use in extracting teeth. While Dr. C. W. Long, a physician, first used sulphuric ether in 1842, he did not publicize it. Instead, dentists brought the use of anesthetics to the attention of the medical and dental communities in the United States. In 1844 Dr. Horace Wells demonstrated the efficacy of nitrous oxide (laughing gas) in quelling pain from tooth extraction. After 1846 Dr. William G. T. Morton promoted anesthesia for that purpose. After Europeans had already found novocaine safe and effective in cloaking pain, in 1910 Guido Fischer introduced the use of novocaine for dental practice in the United States.[33]

American advances also extended to scientific investigations into dental caries, an increasingly troublesome problem in the Western world. The cause of caries continued to mystify the dental community. In England the incidence of caries increased in the latter half of the nineteenth century. British historians attributed that development to widespread availability of refined sugar, which became so inexpensive that most people could afford it. A similar situation occurred in the United States. By 1882 the National Dental Association considered caries so important a disease that it offered a prize for the best paper showing original work on the etiology, or the scientific investigation of causes, of caries.[34]

Dentists and scientists from the United States benefited from the biological discoveries in Europe and applied them to dentistry. The introduction of modern bacteriology in the late nineteenth century in Europe contributed the most toward the rise of dental science in the United States. Foremost in bringing that knowledge to American dentists was Dr. Willoughby D. Miller, a dentist who studied under the famous German bacteriologist Robert Koch at the University of Berlin. Koch, winner of the Nobel Prize in physiology and medicine in 1905, and Louis Pasteur developed modern scientific bacteriology. Influenced by his work with Koch and theories on the decay process by Europeans, Miller in 1881 started over twenty years of publishing detailed explanations about the onset of tooth decay. He attributed decay to the destruction of enamel that then allowed germs to attack the dentine and form a cavity. Miller concluded that oral bacteria produced lactic acid from fermenting starch and sugar food particles lodged in the crevices around teeth. According to his theory, the acid dissolved enamel and thus made teeth vulnerable to decay. Miller deduced that caries occurred in stages: decalcification, infection, and putrefaction of the remaining organic matrix. Miller provided the first experimental data showing that tooth decay was an infectious disease. He established the scientific background for a chemico-parasitic theory of scientific investigations that continued long after his works were published. After the *Dental Cosmos* published Miller's thesis in 1891, the profession began to promote dental cleanliness. From that campaign the toothpaste and toothbrush industry thrived.[35]

Progress in applied dentistry covered a broader range than advances in basic research. In the nineteenth century dentists and nondentists produced inventions that eased the work of the dentist and the plight of the sufferer. In 1844 Charles Goodyear patented the rubber vulcanite process. The process proved especially useful for the making of rubber bases for false teeth. In 1872 James B. Morrison's invention of the first dental foot engine for drilling cavities introduced a new era for dentist and patient because it allowed the dentist to make more satisfactory crowns and bridges. Wilhelm Roentgen's discovery in Germany of the X ray in 1895 provided a major diagnostic tool for dentistry. Beginning in 1896 Dr. C. Edmund Kells and Dr. J. W. Morton were among the first American dentists to promote use of the X ray in dentistry. After the turn of the century Dr.

Dental education at the turn of the century. Students working at lathes in a dental laboratory at the Detroit College of Medicine, Department of Dental Surgery, 1904. Courtesy of the National Library of Medicine.

William Taggart of Chicago recognized the possibilities of the casting process used in general artwork and introduced it for making gold inlays. Taggart's development eased the dentist's task.[36]

The scientific work of Dr. Greene Vardiman Black especially affected the practice of dentistry throughout the world. One of the most distinguished dentists of the nineteenth century, Black came from a poor family, never attended a dental school, and instead learned his dentistry from a preceptor, or dentist-instructor. Black conducted experiments with machinery and instruments he made by hand. Best known for his work on the treatment of dental diseases, the Illinois native taught himself the scientific aspects of dentistry. Black's most important books, *A Descriptive Anatomy of Human Teeth* and *Operative Dentistry and Dental Pathology*, became the authoritative works on dental nomenclature and anatomy in the early 1890s. In 1895 he published another major dental treatise, "Physical Character of Filling Materials," in *Dental Cosmos* that standardized cavity filling and the manufacturing of amalgam. His peers considered him an outstanding educator, and in 1897 Black became dean of the North-

western University School of Dentistry. Black contributed to almost
every facet of scientific dental progress during his lifetime. The
American dental profession so revered Black that before he died in
1915, the profession had awarded him almost every existing dental
honor.[37]

Although many people still regarded dentistry as nothing more
than a mechanic's trade, American dentistry grew professionally during the nineteenth century. Through the combination of outstanding
and widely respected figures, such as Miller and Black, and advances
in research, invention, and legislation, dentistry in the United States
rose in stature. Dental historian Gardner P. H. Foley praised the
quality of that dental literature which, he judged, overcame handi-
caps and outshone contemporary dental education and organization.
Yet by 1900 there was one very important body that had failed to
include dentistry in its regular health operations—the United States
government.[38]

The United States Government and Dentistry, 1789-1865

Although George Washington used the services of a dentist, neither he nor his more scientifically inclined eighteenth and early
nineteenth century successors attempted to find a place for scientific
research in the federal government. Congress also displayed a reluc-
tance to dispense public funds for scientific purposes during the early
years of the nation. As Leonard D. White, the chronicler of United
States government administrative history, explained such policies, the
first administrations viewed science and accompanying intellectual
disciplines as "the undisputed domain of private citizens, or of state
and municipal governments."[39]

At least one local government, however, recognized the value of
public health dentistry in the first years of the new nation. In the
nation's first decade, the Board of Managers of the Dispensary of
New York City approved the appointment of Richard C. Skinner, a
dentist, to the dispensary, a medical institution. Skinner founded a
dental clinic in the city in 1792.[40] (Little information is available on
other dental activities of local or state governments during the country's early years.)

As for medical care, the federal government followed a precedent started during colonial days by the British government. In 1798 Congress and President John Adams approved the establishment of the Marine Hospital Service to care for stricken seamen as a continuation of the service instituted by the British. To pay for the service, seamen initially were taxed at twenty cents a month.[41]

Although a medical corps served in the United States Army in the War of 1812, the government did not establish the office of surgeon general until 1818. The United States Navy stationed medical officers on ships and at naval stations but without a central organization until 1842 when the navy formed the Bureau of Medicine and Surgery. Except for hospitals set up for the War of 1812, the army and navy operated small hospitals at their bases for care of the sick. Through the Civil War neither the army nor the navy conducted any kind of research nor did they employ any dentists.[42]

In the middle of the nineteenth century, major changes edged the federal government toward assuming medical and dental public health responsibilities. Among the most important was a growing government role in science and medicine. Before 1850 government approval of scientific research consisted primarily of laudatory statements by some government leaders and congressmen and financing of exploratory expeditions, such as the globe-circling Wilkes expedition of the 1840s. Undoubtedly, the 1846 establishment of the Smithsonian Institution, through the endowment of a generous British subject, kindled government interest in science.

Also part of the rise of science, the public health movement and the new technique of epidemiology originated in the mid-nineteenth century. In 1850 the Massachusetts Commissioners for a State Sanitary Survey prepared the basis for a national public health movement by issuing a report on dirty, unwholesome air. That report led to the first National Quarantine and Sanitary Convention in 1857. About the same time scientists in England started identifying diseases through the use of epidemiology, or the examination of epidemic diseases in large population groups. Perhaps because the federal government was not organized to handle either public health or epidemiological methods in the 1850s, it did not take on those responsibilities in that decade.[43] Nevertheless, the expansion and needs of the developing country brought about the most significant change in the government relationship with science.

Major government participation in scientific research started in the 1860s out of necessity. By 1860 the United States stretched from the Atlantic Ocean to the Pacific Ocean and from the Mexican to the Canadian border. The United States census of 1860 showed that 83.9 percent of the 31,443,000 people in the United States lived in rural areas. To accommodate the expansion and burgeoning population, Congress encouraged settlement and farming in public lands of the West and uninhabited areas. In 1862, to promote farming, the federal government brought into effect the Homestead Act and organized the Department of Agriculture. In establishing the agricultural department, the federal government created its first agency devoted primarily to scientific research and authorized the hiring of chemists, entomologists, and other scientists engaged in physical and biological research.[44] That change in government philosophy eventually was applied to dentistry.

Meanwhile, before the Civil War, dentistry's proponents unsuccessfully urged the federal government to hire dentists. Jefferson Davis, secretary of war from 1853 to 1857 under President Franklin Pierce, reportedly tried but failed to persuade the army to start a dental corps. Even the Civil War recruiting experience and soldiers' ordinary dental needs and dental injuries from battle did not move the federal government to take dentistry seriously.[45]

The war, however, provided the United States government with ample evidence of the sorry state of dental health in the country. For induction the Union army required a recruit to have six opposing front teeth "to bite the cartridge." In his study of Civil War recruiting, John R. Lewis reported that in 1863 the Union army rejected one in fifteen recruits and in 1864 one in ten because they could not satisfy that dental requirement. Inductees also needed treatment of routine dental problems as well as for injuries incurred in battle. During the Civil War officers and members of both the American Dental Convention and the American Dental Association urged the surgeon general of the army and President Abraham Lincoln to appoint dentists as assistant surgeons to service the needs of those soldiers. The surgeon general of the Union army and the medical department of the army opposed adding dentists for economic and professional reasons, according to Robert McCluggage's study of that period. Contemporary dentists charged that, as a result, medical doctors untrained in dentistry and charlatans performed dental work on

Union soldiers. The mortality rate reported for facial surgery to correct battle-incurred dental injuries among Union troops amounted to almost 12 percent.[46]

The Confederacy took a more positive attitude toward dentistry than the Union. In 1864 the Confederate Congress passed a law conscripting dentists. By the end of the war one historian estimated that some five hundred dentists served the Confederate army either with the rank of hospital steward or by contract. Impressed by a technique developed by James Baxter Bean of Atlanta to treat facial and jaw wounds with an interdental splint, the surgeon general for the Confederacy established hospital wards solely for the use of Bean's treatment. Nevertheless, the Confederate army, like the Union army, never gave dentists rank equal to that of medical doctors and never established a dental corps.[47]

The Rise of Dental Public Health and Science in the United States

The first federal government recognition of dentistry came after the Civil War. Although for the rest of the nineteenth century the surgeon general of the army refused to appoint dentists to his corps, his chief librarian, Lt. Gen. John Shaw Billings, acknowledged the importance of publications on dentistry and dental science. Billings, also a physician, proved to be a superb book buyer and library builder; during his service he amassed one of the world's great medical library collections.[48]

In 1872 Billings began an extensive effort to collect dental journals and asked the surgeon general's staff around the nation to obtain old and new dental publications. He also corresponded with Samuel S. White of the S. S. White Dental Supply Company in order to acquire the first issue of *Dental Cosmos*, the prestigious dental science journal, and sought copies of extinct dental publications, such as the *Dental News Letter*. The catalog published for the library between 1880 and 1893 included over one hundred pages of titles relating to dentistry.[49] The government, however, still lacked an agency with dental scientists who could put that collection to use.

At the same time that Billings was building up the nation's leading medical library, the American Public Health Association first met. At the organization's initial meeting in 1872 its members discussed the need to establish a central government agency to deal with public health. The only government entity then resembling such a body was the Marine Hospital Service, brought under the control of the secretary of the treasury by legislation in 1870. At its May 1873 session the new association joined the American Medical Association and Billings in approving a new system for keeping records of the incidence of disease in the service's hospitals. As a result of this action, the service adopted the use of the "Provisional Nomenclature of the Royal College of Physicians" in London to establish an international and standard nosology, or classification of diseases. Service officers chose the nomenclature so that the service could conduct comparative statistical health studies. That decision prepared the service for engaging in clinical research, or the observations of disease in individuals under study, and in epidemiology.[50] Both methods later became essential to the service's work in dental research.

With the adoption of this nomenclature in 1874, the service began enumerating specific dental diseases found in hospital patients. The Marine Hospital Service classified dental diseases under diseases of the digestive system. Stomatitis, later known as Vincent's disease or trench mouth, was the first dental disease counted by the service. By 1881 the service was reporting a variety of dental diseases found in patients, including dental caries and abscessed teeth.[51] The earliest biological research by the service, however, concentrated on deadly diseases.

A cholera outbreak in the United States in 1873 and recurring epidemics of yellow fever helped to further the appeals of the public health agency advocates. Congress passed a national quarantine act in 1878, appropriated funds to investigate the causes of epidemic diseases, and in 1879 created a National Board of Health to organize a federal medical research effort. The board provided the first government health research grants to university scientists. Congress allowed the board to expire but continued government-sponsored disease research. Consequently, the supervising surgeon general of the Marine Hospital Service chose Dr. J. J. Kinyoun to start bacteriological research in 1887 in Stapleton, Long Island. A disciple of Robert Koch and Louis Pasteur, Kinyoun used Koch's research methods and modeled the Stapleton laboratory, later called the Hygienic Laboratory, after that of Koch.[52]

In the meantime there was a growing recognition in the dental profession that organized scientific research was necessary to enhance the quality of dental care. The American Dental Association observed that, unlike the United States, institutions or governments in Europe sponsored dental scientific investigations. The association resolved to subsidize research five years before the American Medical Association discussed such an issue. While the federal government was forming its own biological research for human health care, in 1885 the American Dental Association began providing funds to encourage research in several fields of dental science including anatomy, histology, physiology, and etiology.[53]

By the 1890s both a strong middle class and a movement for social justice began emerging in the nation, and young doctors started preaching a scientific gospel that helped to create a permanent public health service to replace the Marine Hospital Service. This enthusiasm spread to the dental community and philanthropists interested in dental care.

Such a spirit complemented the aims of the national dental community, especially the National Dental Association, formerly known as the American Dental Association. The National Dental Association continued the policy of the American Dental Association to encourage the government to include dentistry in its interests. The association initiated a campaign for federal government employment of dentists for scientific research and for treatment of the military.[54]

In 1897 the Committee on the National Dental Museum and Library of the National Dental Association won support of the association membership to seek

> in the interest of public health, the employment, at government expense, in the Army Medical Museum and Library, of at least one dentist of eminent fitness, whose time, when so employed, shall be devoted exclusively to the advancement of dental science.[55]

With that decision the association initiated its effort to persuade the United States government to engage in dental science work.

But only another war remedied the army's neglect of dentistry. During the Spanish-American War, Lt. Col. Louis M. Maus, chief surgeon of the Seventh Army Corps based in Jacksonville, Florida, felt compelled to take matters into his own hands. He explained,

> On account of the large number of men belonging to the corps, who

suffered from toothache, bad teeth, and other troubles of the mouth, I determined to organize a department of dentistry. . . . It was almost impossible to realize the great benefit which resulted to the troops from this department. . . . Dentists were kept busy from early morning to late into night.[56]

The Spanish-American War also prompted association members to launch a vigorous effort to establish regular dental service in the army and navy. Although modest, the first success came on March 3, 1901, when Congress authorized the army to contract for the services of thirty dental surgeons without military rank. For the next ten years the association lobbied for a dental corps with officer rank for the dentists. The major breakthrough occurred with the March 3, 1911, law establishing the Army Dental Corps as part of the Army Medical Department. A year later, on August 22, 1912, President William Howard Taft signed a bill that authorized the United States Naval Dental Corps.[57] These successes, however, covered only dental care for the military. Persuading the federal government to undertake dental research and public health dental care proved to be more difficult.

An initial milestone for public health care and research occurred in 1902 when President Theodore Roosevelt signed legislation renaming and expanding the mission of the Marine Hospital Service to that of the Public Health and Marine Hospital Service. The act established the first federal agency to coordinate public health matters and provided an advisory board for the Hygienic Laboratory. The Hygienic Laboratory divisions resembled academic departments of chemistry, zoology, pharmacology, bacteriology, and pathology; the scientists used the title "professor." But the early administrators of the 1902 law did not interpret the act to include dental care or research.

Another trend began after 1900 with the inauguration of institutional sponsorship of dental public health and research. Dental public health meant studying, preventing, and controlling dental diseases in the population as a whole. Private interests, however, initiated those activities.[58]

One of the first to take such action, Dr. Thomas W. Evans, specified in his will that his estate be used to establish and support a museum and dental institute in Philadelphia. Dentist to Napoleon II and European royalty, Evans died in 1897 with many of his assets in Paris. A lengthy court battle with the French government over disposition of Evans's properties delayed the implementation of the Evans bequest. Although the American interests lost the court battle, Evans's Philadelphia holdings were sufficient to carry out his wishes. As a result, the University of Pennsylvania Dental School started the Thomas W. Evans Dental Institute in 1912. The agreement establishing the institute provided for undergraduate and postgraduate training for the dental degree and for the "opportunity and facilities for scientific research in subjects pertaining to dentistry."[59]

Organized dental research also started in the twentieth century, again through private initiative. While the legal aspects of Evans's legacy were being settled, the National Dental Association established a standing committee on scientific research in 1908. One of the committee's first acts was to commission work at the Harvard University chemistry department to develop a technique for saliva analysis. In 1913 the association created a research commission that provided grants and established an institute in Cleveland, Ohio, in 1915. The research institute conducted both biological and physical research and turned over patents for the use of platinum and platinum compounds substitutes to the Public Health Service. In the second decade of the twentieth century, dental clinics were founded and endowed for public dental education and scientific research by several philanthropists, including the Forsyth brothers of Boston; George Eastman in Rochester, New York; and Mrs. George Carter in the Hawaiian Islands.[60]

Meanwhile, philanthropists and the National Dental Association initiated other dental public health programs early in the twentieth century. In 1906 Henry Lomb funded the first dental inspection of schoolchildren in Rochester, New York, and inspired eighty-nine cities in the United States to follow that practice by 1911. Dr. Arthur Merritt of the National Dental Association in 1911 called for a nationwide campaign to educate the public to keep teeth and mouths clean to curb dental diseases. Tooth decay was so prevalent that Merritt referred to it as "The People's Disease." Consequently, dentists organized a national mouth hygiene movement that included dental inspection and hygiene education.[61]

Dental Public Health and the Federal Government

Through the efforts of the dental hygiene movement, American dentistry gained some recognition from the civilian federal public health agency. At the request of Dr. W. G. Ebersole, a dentist and physician and chairman of the Oral Hygiene Committee of the National Dental Association, the Public Health and Marine Hospital Service sent an assistant surgeon general to Cleveland, Ohio, in 1910 to monitor a dental inspection and hygiene instruction program. The inspection showed results similar to those conducted in other cities, according to Ebersole: 97 percent of the children had "defective mouths." Subsequently, in 1912 Dr. Rupert Blue, surgeon general of the Public Health and Marine Hospital Service, addressed a joint meeting of the National Dental Association, the District of Columbia Dental Society, and the newly formed National Mouth Hygiene Association. When questioned by the dentists, Blue considered adding dentists to the service and conducting some dental research. Later that year Blue agreed to accept dentists only if they had earned both medical and dental degrees. The service's examinations, however, tested individuals solely for duties as medical officers but, said Blue:

> It is the desire of the Bureau to forward the several lines of public health work, and an officer with the dual qualifications mentioned could render especially effective service. . . . An announcement of the opportunities for public health work by an officer having a dental and medical degree would be timely.[62]

There is no evidence to show that Blue ever issued such an announcement or that the service ever hired a dentist during the next five years. Blue may not have been adept enough politically and administratively to carry out his promise to the dentists. Victoria Harden, for instance, has found that Blue encountered numerous obstacles to obtaining sufficient funds and personnel throughout his term as surgeon general.[63]

Nonetheless, strengthened by a 1912 congressional act, the service did conduct its first dental research in response to requests from some dental societies. That legislation shortened its name to the Public Health Service (PHS) and authorized it to "study and investigate the diseases of man and conditions influencing the propagation thereof. . . ." After the law took effect, the District of Columbia Society requested Blue to undertake research on focal infection, or a limited infection in the mouth, including "infection being mechanically forced through the orifices of the roots." Western dental societies also asked for help after Dr. John S. Marshall warned their members of the dangers of introducing disease through use of unsanitary dental instruments.[64]

Subsequently, Dr. H. E. Hasseltine, a passed assistant surgeon[65] of the Public Health Service, subsequently conducted research on the sterilization of dental instruments as a direct response "to the officers of some dental societies." Hasseltine published the results of his experiments in 1915 and recommended procedures for sterilizing instruments. He urged dentists to sterilize their equipment for each patient to avoid spreading communicable diseases.[66] Meanwhile, other government bodies took more direct action.

In 1913 the federal government organized its first civilian dental unit, the Indian Dental Service, in the Bureau of Indian Affairs. The five dentists assigned to the unit covered specific districts and served Indian reservations with portable dental equipment. They also published their findings of unusual dental conditions and provided the Public Health Service with valuable information.[67]

Using the precedent set by citywide dental inspections in schools, several state governments also initiated public dental health services. Although the Kansas legislature first passed a law in 1915 requiring public schools to provide free dental inspection, the inspections did not take place because the act lacked enforcement measures. In 1916 Virginia became the first state to include a dentist on its state board of health. The North Carolina State Board of Health organized the first state dental health unit in 1918 and hired six dentists to work in schools through the North Carolina Division of School Medical Inspection. Other states followed the example of North Carolina during the next two decades. Disease-reporting requirements and clinical work varied according to state laws, but those states with dental health programs stressed education in dental hygiene and usually conducted inspections.[68] Subsequently, statistics collected by the state programs provided a major resource for future dental research by the Public Health Service.

World War I and Dentistry in the Government

The United States' entry into World War I in 1917 brought additional attention to the need for dental public health. By June 30, 1918, the Army Reserve Corps attracted 5,372 dentists, according to the American Dental Association. The 1,873 dental officers serving in France included specialists in maxillo-facial units qualified to perform face and jaw surgery, a service badly needed during and after World War I for individuals suffering from facial injuries. Civilian dentists formed the Preparedness League of American Dentists to help eliminate dental disabilities in potential recruits who would otherwise have been eligible for induction. In October 1918 officers of the National Dental Association and Col. Robert I. Rees and other War Department officials agreed to establish the Students' Army Training Corps in order to commission 10,000 dentists by July 1, 1919. The armistice of November 11, 1918, cancelled the training program, but the plan demonstrated that the army regarded dental officers as essential in its forces.[69]

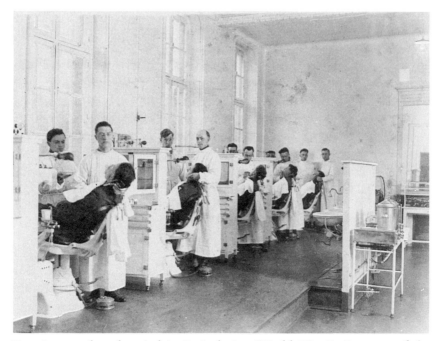

Dentists at a base hospital in Paris during World War I. Courtesy of the National Library of Medicine.

Congress agreed with the perception that the federal government needed to broaden its requirements for health care professional personnel. On October 28, 1918, President Wilson signed legislation that authorized the Public Health Service to establish a reserve corps that could include dentists and other professionals without medical degrees.[70]

Observations

Although almost seven thousand years separated the Babylonian savants and the bacteriological investigators of tooth disease, both groups suspected an invader as the cause of dental caries. Using a basis far different from that for ancient magic, scientists later disproved the worm hypothesis but suggested microscopic living organisms as contributors to tooth decay.

Through the centuries humans coped with the discomforts and aggravations brought on by dental diseases. They had tried everything from incantations to toothpaste to eliminate the various ailments associated with the mouth and jaw. Yet the most significant advances in dentistry started with the rise in professionalism and progress in scientific research that began emerging toward the end of the European Renaissance.

Until the nineteenth century most of the progress in dentistry occurred in Europe, but in the 1800s Americans exercised leadership. The world's first dental college opened in the United States, and dentists organized to improve the profession and encourage research. Dental societies and state governments strengthened licensing requirements for dental practice. In an age that included the Industrial Revolution and the evolution of modern bacteriology, American contributions to dentistry included experiments in alleviating pain, inventions that eased the dentist's task, and scientific advances in the biological and physical aspects of dentistry. Such achievements countered the popular definition of dentistry as merely a mechanic's trade.

The federal government health agencies, managed by physicians, were slow to accept dentists and dental research. Ironically, a dentist adapted the methods of modern bacteriology to dental research before the United States government started biomedical investigations.

Yet when the Marine Hospital Service opened the Hygienic Laboratory as a direct result of the new bacteriology, the laboratory did not include dental research in its first twenty-five years of operation.

Instead, organized team dental research and dental public health in the United States began under private initiative in the twentieth century. While the National Dental Association and concerned dentists recognized the importance of dental research, they lacked the power and the money to carry out adequate programs. Dental research still was in an early stage and was usually an individual effort by dentists in private practice and academics. Yet some of the small number of late nineteenth and early twentieth century dental investigators produced exceptional findings that profoundly influenced dentistry and prepared the basis for later research.

Finally, the dental needs of certain groups forced government in the United States to employ dentists. After the turn of the century, knowledge of the dental problems of U.S. soldiers in the Spanish-American War induced the United States government to include dentists in the armed forces. During the next fifteen years the navy, the Indian Health Service, and state boards of health added dentists to their rosters. The Public Health Service was one of the last major federal health agencies to employ dentists. Only after World War I ended did the United States Public Health Service begin to take on the challenges of dental public health.

CHAPTER TWO

The Federal Government Moves Into Dental Research, 1919-1945

We must not wait for favours from Nature; our task is to wrest them from her.

IVAN VLADIMIROVICH MICHURIN

In the aftermath of World War I several American scientific, dental, and medical leaders called for more emphasis on dental research. The earliest initiatives came from the private sector.

William J. Gies, a professor of biological chemistry at Columbia University, led the research movement. In 1918 he founded the *Journal of Dental Research*, a periodical featuring scholarly dental scientific articles. Two years later he organized the International Association for Dental Research. The association brought together dentists and scientists seeking to enhance dental research.[1]

In a special study Gies also encouraged research in dental schools. That work resulted from the 1921 decision of the Carnegie Foundation for the Advancement of Teaching to fund an examination of dental education in the United States. The foundation's administrators wanted a report similar to Dr. Abraham Flexner's influential and classic 1910 medical education study that contributed toward the reform of the nation's medical schools. Consequently, the foundation chose Gies to head the dental education investigation. Published in 1926, the Gies report urged dental schools in the United States and

Canada to improve their curriculums by using well-trained, full-time teachers, conducting and encouraging research, and providing adequate libraries. Recognizing the dearth of dental researchers, Gies recommended that each dental school should "encourage and support research by its teachers and should arouse and develop creative capacity and professional leadership among its most gifted students."[2]

During the postwar period support arose for federally sponsored dental research. As a consequence of World War I, the federal government had assumed new and more extensive responsibilities in health care. Medical leaders advising the government recognized the need for dental research and, for the first time, included dental scientists among their consultants. Concurrently, government agencies started conducting scientific dental research, and both private groups and government officials pressed for an expansion of government research in dental sciences.

The National Research Council and Dental Research

Established by a July 1916 executive order, the National Research Council of the National Academy of Sciences was one of the first federal government bodies to promote dental biological research. President Woodrow Wilson had created the council to coordinate the nation's scientific research facilities for defense work. In February 1918 the council formed a division of medical sciences to foster biomedical research on a national scale, support worthwhile research with grants, and advise government medical agencies on an ad hoc basis. Neither the council nor the division originally included dental research in their missions.[3]

The council's organization was such that it could easily promote dental research. In 1918 approximately seventy-five national scientific and technical societies belonged to the National Research Council. The council solicited philanthropic institutions and private sources for funds, part of which the division of medical sciences dispersed. In 1919 the division created the committee on dental investigations to encourage dental scientific research and appointed Dr. Thomas B. Hartzell as the committee's first chairman. A dentist in private practice, Hartzell also conducted dental research with scientists at the University of Minnesota. The formation of the committee represented the first attempt outside of the dental community to coordinate and support dental scientific research on a national level.[4]

Several political obstacles interfered with Hartzell's attempts to obtain adequate funding for dental research. During its first few years a lack of power hampered the dental committee's operations. Hartzell despaired over what he regarded as the ineffective support the National Research Council gave dental research. The council's weakness reminded Hartzell "a good deal of prohibition beer in that it hasn't a very great deal [of] authority."[5]

Professional prejudice added to the Hartzell committee's difficulties. In 1920 Dr. Henry Christian, chairman of the division of medical sciences, scoffed at the capability of the dental researcher. Unknown to Hartzell, Christian explained to a medical colleague how physician researchers could take advantage of dental scientists:

I believe that the dentists can help us with their cooperation. Of course, they can't do any real investigating of such a problem on their own hook, but in a cooperative thing I think we can make use of them, and the way to do it, it seems to me is to let them think that they are just as important cogs in the wheel as anybody else. . . . If eventually we get the money we will . . . have complete control of the whole thing.[6]

Christian's remarks provided a glimpse of the patronizing views on dentists held by some members of the medical profession. Inasmuch as physicians controlled most health care and research, attitudes such as Christian's probably led to such weak council support for dental research.

Only after almost five years of operation did the dental committee finally achieve success. In the meantime the committee's accomplishments had been limited to advising the American Dental Association Research Commission on research grants. The change occurred in 1924 when the Carnegie Corporation, a member of the National Research Council, awarded $85,000 to the University of California Dental School "to undertake, through the cooperation of a number of men in different fields of science, a joint study of pyorrhea and its possible relation to other human maladies." The American Dental Association Research Commission helped to plan the project. The Carnegie award marked the first large dental research grant in the

United States from a foundation outside the dental community.[7]

Yet the division of medical sciences board discharged the committee on dental investigations in May 1924 by explaining that it saw no reason to continue the committee. Despite a request from a respected army dental scientist, the National Research Council waited several years before establishing another dental research committee.[8]

In 1928 the division of medical sciences resurrected the dental research committee after Dr. Arthur D. Black, the dental representative in the division, proposed such a group on behalf of the American Dental Association. The division appointed Black, son of G. V. Black and dean of the Northwestern University School of Dentistry, chairman of a new advisory committee on dental research. Elected president of the International Association for Dental Research in 1929, Black was the first official of the dental research association and the only dental scientist to serve on the revived National Research Council dental committee. The remaining members were physicians and scientists.[9] Black's committee continued duties similar to those of Hartzell's group, namely, the approval of American Dental Association research grants.

In 1929, while assessing the research grant requests, the committee recommended that the association refine its grant policies. The committee advised the association to determine priorities in research, make awards to "men of known ability rather than to projects," support more extensive use of animals in experimental research, and find animals best suited for research. Some of the recommendations were controversial, especially the suggestion that grants go only to well-known investigators in a field that had few researchers. On the other hand, the committee understood the "exceptionally difficult problem" of locating appropriate animals for the study of dental caries. Although the committee wanted to encourage the American Dental Association to be more selective and more scientific in funding research, it neglected the problems stemming from a shortage of dental researchers.[10]

In later years more dental scientists joined the committee, which continued to support the growth of dental research in the United States. The group's most important role, however, was in lending recognition to the significance of dental research.

The National Bureau of Standards Dental Research

The first known federal dental research program originated at the National Bureau of Standards in response to dissatisfied U.S. Army dentists. After encountering difficulties in fitting suitable dental fillings in patients during World War I, two army dentists sought the help of Dr. George K. Burgess, director of the National Bureau of Standards, in preparing an amalgam alloy contract award. The dentists asked the bureau to develop specifications to improve adherence and retention of dental filling materials. Burgess turned to Dr. Wilmer Souder, chief of the bureau's thermal expansion section. With a recent doctorate in physics from the University of Chicago, Souder based his research on G. V. Black's recommendations to obtain a sensitive instrument for determining physical changes in amalgams. Souder and a bureau colleague, Chauncey G. Peters, used an interferometer, with a sensitivity of one-millionth of an inch, to measure the thermal expansion, dimensional changes, and crushing strengths of dental amalgams. They first presented their results at the March 1919 American Physical Society meeting in New York. The Souder-Peters measurements immediately influenced the manufacture of alloys for amalgam.[11]

Aware of the void in amalgam research since Black's death in 1915, Souder was so intrigued with the work that he founded the bureau's dental research unit in 1919. In the early 1920s Souder urged the American Dental Association to fund additional bureau research on dental materials, but the ADA Research Commission rejected Souder's request because it lacked adequate funds. Nevertheless, seeking a way to back Souder, Research Commission members decided to investigate the possibility of supporting some bureau research in the early 1920s. Meanwhile, in 1922 Dr. Louis J. Weinstein, president of the Weinstein Research Laboratory, financed a research fellowship at the bureau for dental materials research. That cooperative venture concentrated on the casting process and resulted in the development of castings that could be made to fit tooth preparations more accurately.

The efforts of Souder and the Weinstein laboratory gave the dental profession new information on the composition, properties, and techniques for proper use of dental materials. In 1926 Souder formulated a

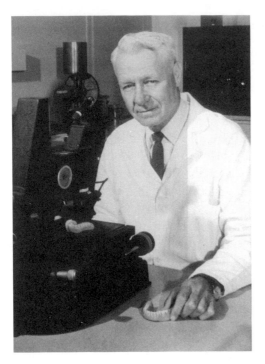

Dr. George C. Paffenbarger, the second ADA research associate at the National Bureau of Standards, was the first dentist to work full time in the NBS Dental Research Section. Courtesy of the National Bureau of Standards.

federal specification for procurement of amalgam, then the most commonly used dental material.

The bureau's work so impressed American Dental Association members that ADA Research Commission members conferred with bureau officials and, in 1926, with Secretary of Commerce Herbert Hoover about establishing a cooperative relationship with the bureau. In 1928 the association inaugurated its research at the bureau by assigning Dr. Norris O. Taylor, a chemist, as its first research associate. Dr. George Paffenbarger, the second association research associate, started as the unit's first full-time dentist in 1929.[12]

From 1929 to 1930 Taylor expanded on Souder's work on amalgam and produced physical and chemical specifications that served as a foundation for the first international standards of the Fédération Dentaire Internationale (FDI) and of the International Organization for Standardization. In the years that followed, the bureau and American Dental Association scientists broadened the scope of dental materials research to provide national and international standards for products ranging from dental cements to toothpaste.[13]

The success of the National Bureau of Standards dental research set an example for other government agencies and encouraged the American Dental Association to press in the late 1920s for government investigations into dental diseases.

The Army Medical School Dental Research

The earliest known federal dental bacteriological research took place at the Army Medical School. In February 1921 the Army Medical School assigned Dr. Fernando E. Rodriguez as an investigator in the bacteriology of dental diseases. A graduate of Georgetown University Dental School, Rodriguez practiced dentistry as a member of the United States Indian Dental Service until 1917 when he joined the army. Given a captain's rank, Rodriguez served in the United States and in his native Puerto Rico until assigned to the Army Medical School in Washington. The first known government researcher to conduct biological research on a dental disease, Rodriguez carried out his experiments in the dental section of the Army Medical School's laboratories division.[14]

Rodriguez isolated and identified bacteria connected with tooth decay. While some scientists thought that multiple kinds of organisms caused decay, Rodriguez believed instead that a definite species of bacterium was involved. He attempted to induce cavities into seventeen extracted caries-free teeth by suspending each tooth in fluids containing specific pure bacterial cultures. After observing changes in the specimens, Rodriguez found a distinctly high acid-producing group of bacteria in the deep layers of decay. When Rodriguez exposed normal, previously sterilized teeth to that bacteria, "caries-like lesions" developed. He named the group *Lactobacillus odontolyticus*. Rodriguez's work coincided and agreed with the August 1922 published report of the English team of James McIntosh, James Warwick, and P. Lazarus-Barlow. In December 1922 Rodriguez reported his findings to the American Society of Bacteriology.[15]

Rodriguez gained recognition for his research throughout his remaining years as an army dental scientist. In 1923 the Executive Board of the National Research Council honored him for his 1922 bacterial experiment with an appointment to the Committee of Dental Investigation of the council's Division of Medical Sciences. Also elected as a Fellow of the American College of Dentists, Rodriguez was the first government dental scientist to serve on that advisory committee. After Rodriguez's death at forty-four years of age in 1932, the army supported only sporadic dental research until after World War II.[16] Rodriguez's career in dental caries experiments provided an example for future government dental research.

Dentistry Enters the Public Health Service

Despite lobbying by the dental community and the military's organization of dental corps, by the end of World War I the Public Health Service neither had hired more dentists nor conducted any dental research. That neglect ended at a most unlikely time. In the immediate postwar period the government had to deal with an influenza pandemic that killed approximately five hundred thousand Americans between 1918 and 1919. Public Health Service scientists desperately searched for a way to isolate the influenza bacillus in order to develop a vaccine. In the midst of pressures to concentrate on the influenza emergency, the service added dentistry to its responsibilities.

Public Health Service medical officers in the Child Hygiene Section were among the first to succeed in convincing the service to employ dental personnel. After finding "dental defects in numbers far in excess of the combined total of all other physical defects," concerned Child Hygiene Section physicians decided to investigate mouth hygiene problems in the field by assembling a mobile dental unit. In 1919 the section staffed the unit with a dental surgeon and an assistant for prophylactic work. That first service mobile dental unit was equipped with a portable dental outfit, a moving picture film on mouth hygiene, and toothbrushes and toothpaste donated by the American Red Cross.

Responding to requests for help from state health authorities, the field unit conducted dental inspections of schoolchildren and assisted local authorities in establishing school dental clinics that were to be supported through local funding. West Virginia state health authorities requested and received the service's first field visits from October

1919 to April 1920. There the unit examined the mouths of 7,059 children in forty-three communities and found a total of 16,151 decayed teeth and 1,822 missing six-year molars. The surgeon general called the West Virginia examination results "a condition of dental neglect which can be observed in many other average American communities."[17]

The passage of the War Risk Insurance law of March 3, 1919, forced the Public Health Service to conduct a hasty recruitment of dentists at the same time that it formed the mobile dental unit. The new law for care of war veterans assigned the Public Health Service the responsibility for medical and dental services. The service particularly needed specialists who could treat injuries to the jaws and teeth. To handle those oral and facial wounds, the service formed dental dispensaries in all its hospitals. Consequently, on June 9, 1919, the service commissioned its first dental officer, Dr. Ernest Eugene Buell, a graduate of the School of Dentistry of the University of Minnesota.

Buell organized the Dental Section, as it became known in the Division of Marine Hospitals and Relief, and advertised for dentists in the newspapers. By the end of Fiscal Year 1920 the Dental Section contained 100 officers, 68 "dental operators," and approximately 5,000 civilian dental examiners throughout the country. During that first year the Dental Section treated more than 17,000 patients at a cost of $1,042,856. In accordance with an executive order of April 29, 1922, the care of the veterans was transferred to the newly established Veterans' Bureau on May 1, 1922. Subsequently, the service dental officers concentrated only on the care of seamen and on public health.[18]

The very presence of dentists in the service provided a basis for promoting dental research. Consequently, although the Public Health Service conducted no dental scientific research in the decade after the war, Surgeon General Rupert Blue and his successors attempted to keep themselves informed on the course of the dental research then under way. In 1919 Blue appointed Hartzell, chairman of the National Research Council's Committee on Dental Investigations and trustee of the National Dental Association, to a new advisory board to the Public Health Service.[19]

In 1922 Hartzell initiated a campaign for the Public Health Service to form a dental corps and conduct dental research. By then president of the American Dental Association, Hartzell persuaded the associa-

Dr. Clinton Messner was
a strong advocate for
dental research in the
Public Health Service.

tion House of Delegates to support the Watson-Dyer-Newton bills
(H.R. 2764, 9291, and 9775). That legislation, which would have
established a Public Health Service dental corps for public health
work and research, did not become law. Nevertheless, the ADA effort
marked the earliest known lobbying in the twentieth century for the
Public Health Service to assume dental science research.[20]

The Public Health Service received its strongest advocate yet for
dental research when the surgeon general assigned Dr. Clinton T.
Messner as chief of dental services on May 1, 1923. Born in Oxford,
Indiana, Messner attended Indiana University and graduated from the
Indiana Dental College in 1908. After practicing dentistry in Oxford,
he moved to Portland, Oregon, in 1910 to teach in a dental school
until 1913 when he returned to Oxford and private practice. He
served in the army during World War I and left the service as a
lieutenant colonel. Messner then entered the Public Health Service

and took his first assignment in St. Louis, Missouri, until 1921 when he was transferred to Washington, D.C.[21]

Regarded by his colleagues as kindly, congenial, and dedicated to his work, Messner supervised dental treatment in the field hospitals throughout the nation, reviewed all published dental literature, and kept an indexed dental library accessible for personnel in the Dental Section. On July 6, 1927, Messner issued a strong plea to the surgeon general to establish an independent dental section that could coordinate dental health activities and conduct research. Observing that the "most prevalent disease of mankind is dental caries," he said

> the whole field of dental disease is open. As yet only the surfaces have been scratched, and the man and Service that attacks this problem successfully will perhaps render more real service to each individual than could be possible in any other manner.

Well informed on the status of dental research, Messner recognized that the Public Health Service's Hygienic Laboratory was equipped especially to search for disease preventives that had eluded dental investigators for many years. Thus, Messner urged the surgeon general to meet with outstanding dentists such as the director of Boston's Forsyth dental research facility to discuss establishing an independent unit.[22]

The American Dental Association supplemented Messner's efforts. At an August 3, 1927, meeting Dr. Henry L. Banzhaf, president of the American Dental Association, appealed to Gen. Herbert M. Lord, director of budgets of the Treasury Department, to appropriate $40,000 for dental research. The American Dental Association wanted the federal government to spend $25,000 of the money for research at the Public Health Service and $15,000 for Bureau of Standards research. Explaining that university dental schools and the American Dental Association lacked sufficient research funding, Banzhaf reasoned that only the federal government could afford to cover the cost of necessary dental research. "The Public Health Service has thus far done practically nothing" on dental disease, Banzhaf told the budget director. Banzhaf asked Surgeon General Hugh S. Cumming to support his position.[23]

Messner and Banzhaf failed to persuade Cumming to initiate dental research in 1927. Not easily discouraged, Messner continued his appeals as other advocates joined that campaign.

Establishing Dental Research in the National Institute of Health

In 1928 Messner was somewhat more successful. He met in November with Dr. George W. McCoy, director of the Hygienic Laboratory, and other leading scientists from the Public Health Service to discuss future dental science research. Messner proposed a study of the chemical composition of enamel in normal and pathological conditions with concentration on any relationship with the development of dental caries. His plan called for dentists on duty at the marine hospitals to supply the materials for studies. The scientists agreed that the Hygienic Laboratory's Division of Chemistry should undertake the basic dental research but feared that it would be difficult to locate an appropriate scientist for basic dental science. McCoy set aside funds for some part-time dental research at the laboratory but found by 1930 "that the work has not been undertaken seriously."[24]

Meanwhile, epidemiological dental surveys began in the Division of Child Hygiene. The first, involving a permanent discoloration of children's teeth, started in 1928. In 1929 the division initiated a three-year study of dental caries in relation to diet and climate.[25] The Division of Child Hygiene continued the only known service dental research until after the establishment of the National Institute of Health.

Simultaneously, pressures for federal dental research also increased in the political arena. The 1928 United States Senate hearings on the creation of a national institute of health provided a new and influential audience for supporters of dental research in the Public Health Service. Sen. Joseph E. Ransdell, a Louisiana Democrat, sponsored legislation to increase appropriations for the Hygienic Laboratory, to rename it the National Institute of Health, and to allow it to accept donations for work to determine the cause, prevention, and cure of human diseases.

Because the Senate held those hearings before the annual meeting of the American Dental Association, the association membership could not vote for a stand on the legislation. Instead, Dr. C. Willard Camalier of Washington, D.C., a member of the association's legislative committee, and Dr. Homer C. Brown of Columbus, Ohio, chairman of the association's legislative committee, personally endorsed the bill at a Senate hearing.[26]

Camalier cited the association's interest in finding causes and cures for pyorrhea and dental caries and learning about the relation of focal infection to systemic diseases. He asked Ransdell for assurance that the legislation would allow the association to place a researcher with the new institute as it had just done at the Bureau of Standards. Ransdell replied that the spirit of the bill was "to take in every branch of science that would engage in research work relating to the problems of health." Although that Congress did not complete action on the bill, the statements of Camalier and Brown remained in the record for use when the measure was reconsidered and passed in 1930.[27]

Actually, Congress established individual parts before it created the whole National Institute of Health. Sponsored by Congressman James S. Parker, a New York Republican, the first legislation, Public Law 71-106, took effect April 9, 1930. The Parker Act coordinated public health activities in government, changed the Hygienic Laboratory Advisory Board to a National Advisory Health Council, and authorized the secretary of the treasury to form new divisions in the Hygienic Laboratory. The act also created a director of a national institute of health with the rank of Public Health Service medical director.

The National Institute of Health was established on May 26, 1930, when President Herbert Hoover signed the Ransdell legislation, S. 1171 (Public Law 251). In the act Congress directed that in "the administration and operation of this institute the Surgeon General shall select persons who show unusual aptitude in science." The new law gave the former Hygienic Laboratory $750,000 to construct and equip additional buildings and more authority to investigate human disease. The Ransdell Act authorized the new institute to set up a fellowship system and to accept donations for use in ascertaining the cause, prevention, and cure of human diseases. According to the act, the institute's facilities were to be made available to state, county, and municipal health authorities for instructional and investigational purposes. At its July meeting that year the American Dental Association endorsed the legislation and passed a resolution to call to the attention of the surgeon general the necessity of conducting dental research.[28] Despite the plea of the American Dental Association, the new institute was slow to take on dental research.

Yet the National Research Council Dental Advisory Committee

thought some national coordinated effort was necessary in dental science research. In a 1931 study that committee acknowledged that dentistry "has had little support in its research activities." The committee saw the need to coordinate dental research and recommended the establishment of a dental research bureau to guide dental research along the most productive lines and to collect information on work in progress.[29]

Fate and political pressures finally led to the inclusion of dental research in the new National Institute of Health. The American Dental Association support of the new institute and Messner's lobbying helped to change Surgeon General Cumming's mind. In late 1931 Cumming appointed five dental scientists from outside the government to advise him on establishing a constructive program of dental research. The advisors were Drs. Weston A. Price, first chairman of the American Dental Association Research Commission; Thomas B. Hartzell; Thomas J. Hill, a professor of pathology at the Western Reserve University School of Dentistry; Russell W. Bunting, a dental scientist at the University of Michigan, Ann Arbor; and Homer C. Brown, secretary of the Research Commission of the American Dental Association. The consultants identified dental caries, dental infection, and mottled enamel—a permanent discoloration of teeth—as the three most important research problems in dental science. Public Health Service officials said that as soon as they could acquire qualified personnel, the service would investigate the problems of dental caries and dental infection. Meanwhile, the new institute had already taken over the mottled enamel investigation started by the Division of Child Hygiene.[30]

Observations

The foundations for federal dental research were laid in the aftermath of World War I because of individual initiative, pragmatism, and American Dental Association efforts.

While the National Research Council and some academic scientists such as William Gies lent prestige to the concept of dental research, researchers such as Wilmer Souder and Fernando Rodriguez introduced physical and biological dental investigations into the federal government. The child hygiene unit of the Public Health Service, meanwhile, initiated a dental investigation by using epidemiology. Consequently, research offered a logical means to assist army dentists and Public Health Service physicians in alleviating dental problems of soldiers and schoolchildren.

The National Bureau of Standards dental materials research unit set a special example through its success in its first decade of operation. Moreover, the bureau's arrangement for an American Dental Association Associate program provided a model for similar cooperation in the biomedical sciences and led the American Dental Association to seek a similar fellowship in biological research in the Public Health Service.

Dental research was introduced at the Public Health Service by two circumstances: first, the existence of a dental problem identified by physicians responsible for children's health and, second, the successful lobbying of Dr. Clinton P. Messner and the American Dental Association.

CHAPTER THREE

The National Institute of Health Initiates Dental Research

The secret of science is to ask the right question.

SIR HENRY TIZARD

When the new National Institute of Health (NIH) started operation in the 1930s, the leading American dental disease scientists were conducting research at less than a dozen academic institutions. None worked for the federal government.[1]

Meanwhile, the surgeon general of the Public Health Service encountered a public health dental question in need of institute investigation, a problem that a service dentist could handle. The surgeon general thus established an NIH Dental Studies unit in 1931 with one dental scientist and one assignment. As that first dental studies scientist honed his skills, the institute's dental research broadened, and the results surprised the dental world.

That National Institute of Health early dental research thus started modestly—with one man and his probe into a turn-of-the-century mystery.

The Discolored Teeth Mystery: Episode One

Reports of a strange dental disorder coincided with the United States government's assumption of dental health responsibilities during the first two decades of the twentieth century. No one then could determine the extent or importance of that peculiar dental deformity.

The first American observers, Dr. John Eager in Italy and Dr. Frederick S. McKay in Colorado Springs, found disfiguring tooth discoloration in individuals they examined in 1901. Eager and McKay never met nor corresponded with each other, and their discoveries the same year occurred coincidentally.

While examining United States-bound Italian emigrants from areas around Naples, Eager discovered the anomaly Italians called *denti di chiaie*. The Italian philosopher and art critic Benedetto Croce had coined the phrase after noting that blackened teeth marred the beauty of the women of La Villa Chiaia, Italy's Riviera. A Marine Hospital Service physician, Eager described the teeth as "apparently strong and serviceable" but stained black or brown. He suspected that the drinking water, perhaps contaminated by volcanic materials, caused the effect if children used it during enamel formation in early childhood. Eager based his suspicion of drinking water on the fact that when Naples changed its drinking water source, "the incidence of the disease among infants has greatly diminished." In 1902 the Public Health Service, successor to the Marine Hospital Service, published the Eager observation as the service's first dental article. After that publication the service took no action on *denti di chiaie* for over a decade.[2]

About the same time, McKay, who had just graduated in 1900 from the University of Pennsylvania Dental School, found many of his first patients in Colorado Springs afflicted with permanently stained teeth. After searching the dental literature, he could find no explanation for the phenomenon. For several years the slender young dentist waged a lonely campaign to arouse his fellow dentists in the local dental society about that "brown stain." In 1908 he succeeded in attracting the interest of the famed G. V. Black and in persuading the Colorado State Dental Association to invite Black to attend the 1909 convention. Once shown the condition, Black collaborated with McKay on investigating it. Black named the discoloration "mottled enamel" and used that terminology in the articles he subsequently prepared with McKay. Black and McKay, however, disagreed on the cause. McKay insisted that an ingredient in the drinking water supply caused the stain; Black doubted that the water was at fault but encouraged McKay to have water analyses conducted wherever the disfigurement occurred.[3]

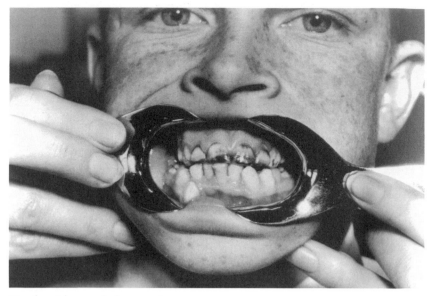

Teeth with mottled enamel.

By 1914 concern about the ugly markings had spread among the
dental community. Dr. Fernando Rodriguez, then a field dentist in
the Indian Service, described to the Panama Pacific Dental Congress
in September 1915 the extensive staining and mottled enamel among
Pima Indians on their reservation in Arizona. Like McKay and Eager,
Rodriguez found the patients' teeth "otherwise ... sound, strong,
and apparently healthy." Rodriguez also linked the dystrophy to the
drinking water.[4]

Meanwhile, in districts where Black and McKay found evidence of
the stained and mottled enamel, McKay submitted water samples for
analysis. None of the analyses provided a clue on the cause of the
disfigurement. When McKay consulted William Strieby, chairman
of the Colorado College Department of Chemistry and Metallurgy,
on the water analyses, the professor advised McKay to order sophisticated techniques such as spectroscopic tests to search for traces of rarer
elements in the water. Strieby's recommendation was difficult to
follow because most chemical laboratories then lacked such expensive
equipment.[5]

After Black's death in 1915, McKay continued the mottled enamel
work alone and published the team's results. In 1916 McKay issued

G. V. Black (left) visited Frederick McKay (right) in Colorado Springs, Colorado, in July 1909 to investigate the condition then called Colorado brown stain. Courtesy of Mrs. Frederick McKay.

an appeal for "some collateral branch of science" to investigate the problem. The subject, he said, had "passed beyond the strictly dental realm." Apparently, McKay caught the attention of Dr. F. C. Smith, a surgeon in the Public Health Service, who summarized most of the published findings on the condition in an October 1916 Public Health Service report. Smith ended his article by repeating the Strieby and McKay recommendations for future research. The service, however, did not immediately follow up on Smith's report but instead remained a passive spectator of McKay's investigations.[6]

The Mottled Enamel Puzzle Continues

Almost a decade after the Black-McKay and Smith publications, the Public Health Service returned to the mottled enamel question, thanks to McKay's dedication. McKay was a persistent man, perhaps even a driven one. He relentlessly sought to call professional and scientific attention to the disfiguring condition and visited every town and hamlet that had notified him of the mysterious affliction. By 1925 McKay still clung to his conviction that drinking water caused the staining. Occasionally he observed that the affected children did not suffer from tooth decay in the areas where staining was prevalent; to the contrary, although brown, the crevices appeared to be free of decay. But McKay's primary interest in the 1920s centered on the ugly mottling, not tooth decay.[7]

In 1925 McKay's campaign evoked enough interest at the National Research Council to cause the Division of Medical Sciences to set up a special committee to investigate the condition. That action resulted in the council's encouragement of state geological survey investigations of surface waters and subsoil geography in disease belts.[8]

Meanwhile, McKay's successful practice and association with Dr. William D. Tracy in New York City helped expedite McKay's investigation of mottled enamel reports. Such availability brought McKay to Oakley, Idaho, in 1925, three days before a town vote on changing its water supply. After unsuccessfully seeking Public Health Service help in dealing with mottled enamel in their community, Oakley officials apparently learned of McKay's interest from the surgeon general's reply. The Oakley Women's Civic League was campaigning in a bond issue election to change the city water supply in hopes of eliminating a strange stain on the teeth of Oakley children. The league members blamed the town water for the discoloration because a survey they had conducted showed that the only children with the problem were those who used city water after the source was changed in 1908. McKay examined the teeth of Oakley schoolchildren and found that every one of the native youngsters using the city water had the disfiguring stain but that children living outside the city limits and using well water showed no evidence of the mottled enamel. McKay persuaded the voters to change the water supply and then helped Oakley select the new source, which was based on his examination of students with normal teeth. Oakley became the first town in the United States to change its water supply to eliminate a dental defect.[9]

On his return to New York McKay took the mottled enamel situation up with the United States Chamber of Commerce. McKay was dissatisfied with the water analyses, which he regarded as superficial and inconclusive. The chamber, he learned, had already asked the Public Health Service to investigate domestic water supplies to determine the cause of the affliction. Chamber officials then arranged for McKay to meet with Dr. Taliaferro Clark, chief of Child Hygiene Investigations of the Public Health Service, in December 1925. In that meeting Clark advised McKay to request the surgeon general's cooperation in an investigation of the mottled enamel.[10]

The following month McKay formally requested the Public Health Service to analyze the water supplies of communities in the nine states where mottled enamel disfigured the teeth of schoolchildren. Harry F. Ferguson, chief sanitary engineer of the Illinois State Department of Public Health; J. W. Bugbee, city chemist for Providence, Rhode Island; and Robert H. Lockwood, editor of *Water Works Engineering*, supported McKay's request for an investigation by the Public Health Service. All thought that the Public Health Service "would be the best organization . . . to make . . . the investigation" because of the nationwide scope of the disease. Indeed, since its founding in 1887 the service's Hygienic Laboratory had been conducting bacteriological research into domestic water supplies. In 1913 the Hygienic Laboratory had established a laboratory in Cincinnati devoted exclusively to the study of streams used for water supplies, an operation that one assistant surgeon general called "one of the best investments not only of the Public Health Service but of the Nation."[11]

Hygienic Laboratory administrators offered minimal cooperation. Dr. George W. McCoy, chief of the Hygienic Laboratory, agreed to conduct a chemical analysis of the water but declined to undertake "a much fuller study" without some special provision. His advisors disagreed on how to handle the matter. Dr. Carl Voegtlin, chief of the Pharmacology Division of the Hygienic Laboratory, suggested that the waters "be examined for their content in heavy metals" and that some of the discolored teeth be subjected to a chemical analysis.

William Mansfield Clark, chief of the laboratory's Division of Chemistry, found McKay's articles unconvincing because McKay ignored the nutritional aspects. Admitting that he knew little about the mottled enamel, Clark nevertheless recognized the importance of fluoride to the formation and maintenance of enamel and even cited a 1925 publication of experiments by E. V. McCollum and colleagues that produced "faulty dentition in white rats" after adding fluoride to their diets. Consequently, Clark proposed studying first the food supply and mode of living of the affected children. If such studies proved unsatisfactory, then he recommended "both the food-supply and the water-supply should be investigated for deficiencies in elements peculiarly necessary to the formation of enamel. . . ."[12]

In March 1926 McKay received firmer support for the water analysis from Dr. Grover A. Kempf, Taliaferro Clark's successor as director of the service's Child Hygiene Investigations. Coincidentally, when McKay was seeking more help from the child hygiene unit, Kempf was on special assignment in New Mexico where he saw for himself the mottled enamel on the teeth of New Mexico's children. Understanding McKay's concerns, Kempf advised the surgeon general that "in my opinion the condition of mottled enamel is worthy of investigation by the Service."[13]

The surgeon general accepted Kempf's recommendation but did not order the kind of sophisticated test McKay wanted. In April 1927 McKay, Kempf, and William Mansfield Clark met in Washington, D.C., to select an area for water testing. Clark was skeptical because recent Geological Survey water analyses in three affected areas in Arizona had shown nothing unusual. The three agreed upon testing samples from the hot spring that had formerly supplied Oakley, Idaho, with water until McKay and the women's group persuaded the town to change to a different source. For unknown reasons the chemist did not follow his own advice of the previous year to investigate enamel-sustaining elements in the water. Instead, Clark conducted a routine test to determine conformation with existing standards—an examination that did not include measurement of the "elements peculiarly necessary to the formation of enamel." Clark found nothing of importance in the test results.[14] The Hygienic Laboratory, accustomed to testing for bacteria, may not have had the proper equipment in 1927 to test for rare earths. Yet such testing could have been done at other government laboratories with appropriate equipment, such as those at the National Bureau of Standards.

Although the Oakley water test provided no answer, McKay had won Kempf's interest. That relationship led the Public Health Service into its first genuine investigation on mottled enamel. The two men carried on an extensive correspondence on the subject and formed a common bond in the loneliness they felt as they pursued the cause of this strange condition. Both tried but failed to stir the American dental community to help by sending examples of defective teeth. "It is very difficult to arouse any interest among dentists in general on this situation," McKay complained, and he offered to assist Kempf as a special investigator of the anomaly in the field for the Child Hygiene Investigations unit.

Consequently, in 1928 Kempf took McKay with him to Bauxite, Arkansas, to respond to a formal request for a mottled enamel study by the Arkansas state health officer. McKay and Kempf found the brown-stained teeth in almost every one of the five hundred children they examined in Bauxite, a mining company town owned by a subsidiary of the Aluminum Company of America. Yet in the town of Benton, only five miles away, the children's teeth had a normal appearance. McKay and Kempf published their findings in a *Public Health Report* in November 1930 and noted that the Hygienic Laboratory water analysis shed no light on the cause.[15]

McKay's and Kempf's paper reached the office of H. V. Churchill, chief chemist of the Aluminum Company of America. Then combating rumors that aluminum cookware was poisonous, Churchill thought that stories about the teeth staining in Bauxite might exacerbate his company's problems. After obtaining samples of the Bauxite water, Churchill instructed A. W. Petrey, head of the laboratory's testing division, to look for traces of very rare elements in the water or substances not normally tested in water analyses. Petrey's subsequent spectrographic study of the Bauxite water revealed the unusual amount of 13.7 parts per million (ppm) of fluoride, a compound of fluorine, the lightest and most active gas of the family of halogen elements and one widely distributed in nature. In response to McKay's suggestion, Churchill then acquired water samples from other areas plagued with the mottled enamel condition. Oakley's former water source yielded 6 ppm and Colorado Springs' source 2 ppm of fluoride. Churchill stressed that "no precise correlation" had been established between the fluoride content of the water and the mottled enamel but that the severity of the dental defect appeared to coincide with the fluoride concentration in the water supplies. On January 20, 1931, Churchill informed McKay of his appraisal.[16]

Nevertheless, under existing techniques the accuracy of fluoride measurements in drinking water was questionable. "Quantitative estimation of fluorine is fraught with difficulty," Churchill said. He thought that the analytical chemistry methods then used tended to give low results and urged fellow water chemists to give attention to the control of fluoride concentration in drinking water.

On March 21, 1931, Churchill reported the findings to the American Chemical Society. When he published his results in September, he asked two questions:

- What physiological effects may be produced by these fluorides?

- What can water chemistry contribute to the concentration control of fluorides?

By coincidence other scientific evidence that year confirmed the correlation between fluoride and mottled enamel. Disturbed by the mottled enamel on the teeth of children in their town of St. David's, Arizona, three agricultural scientists, Margaret Cammack Smith, her husband Howard, and Edith M. Lantz, launched their own investigation of the problem. In June 1931 the trio published results showing that a diet including fluoride induced mottled enamel in the teeth of experimental animals. Finding the combination of the Churchill report and the Smiths and Lantz announcement compelling proof that fluoride in the water caused the dental defect, McKay urged the Public Health Service to save money and drop any plans for further field surveys. But by that time the Public Health Service's new National Institute of Health had initiated its own inquiry into the mottled enamel question.[17]

The National Institute of Health and the Mottled Enamel Investigation

Because of the persistence of two men and the American Dental Association, the National Institute of Health acquired both a dental scientist and a dental research project in 1931. McKay had pressed the association to support mottled enamel research, but because the Great Depression limited its funding, the association's Research Commission urged the Public Health Service to assume that responsibility. The influence of Dr. Clinton T. Messner, a member of the ADA Research Commission and the Public Health Service's senior dental officer, resulted in the assignment of thirty-eight-year-old Dr. Henry Trendley Dean as the institute's first dental scientist to conduct the institute's initial dental survey, the investigation of mottled enamel in the United States.[18]

Dean's background and scientific bent undoubtedly persuaded Messner to choose him for the institute position. The Winstanley Park, Illinois, native was educated in the St. Louis, Missouri, area and received his dental degree from St. Louis University School of Dentistry in 1916. During World War I Dean served as a captain in the Army Dental Corps and had a private practice before and after the war in Wood River, Illinois.

Major changes occurred in Dean's life in 1921 when he married Ruth Martha McEvoy and joined the Public Health Service. Possibly in those early days at the U.S. Marine Hospital in St. Louis, Missouri, Dean met Messner, when both served there in 1921. While Messner transferred permanently to Washington, D.C., Dean moved around the country to work in other U.S. Marine Hospitals in Boston, New York, and eventually the Presidio in San Francisco. From 1924 to 1925 Dean also studied at Boston University. By 1929 his propensity for dental research led Dean to deliver a scholarly paper analyzing fifty cases of fractures of the mandible at the annual meeting of the American Dental Association. In 1930 Dean achieved the rank of dental surgeon in the Public Health Service. Having demonstrated

Dr. H. Trendley Dean at his desk in the NIH Division of Infectious Diseases in the early 1940s. Behind him is a world map on which he marked the reported incidence of mottled enamel. Courtesy of Mrs. H. Trendley Dean.

both an interest and capability in research, Dean was a logical choice for a Public Health Service dental science position that the surgeon general had been seeking to fill.[19]

Before starting work at the new institute, Dean met with McKay because of the latter's familiarity with the mottled enamel question. Dean's lengthy friendship with the New York City dentist evolved from that April 1931 meeting about Dean's plans to conduct additional field work in the West on mottled enamel. Dean was about to apply to the mottled enamel investigation the growing science of epidemiology, the study of the causes and control of epidemic diseases by collecting information on mass effects. He needed McKay's advice, and the older man was altogether willing to serve as a mentor to the cautious, conservative Public Health Service dental scientist. After that initial discussion with McKay, Dean returned to his post in San Francisco but prepared for his future research by reviewing all the literature on the subject at the University of California.[20] Several months passed, however, before Dean started on the trail of the subject McKay had pursued for some thirty years.

After undergoing Public Health Service officer training, Dean started his career as an institute dental scientist in the latter half of 1931. In August the surgeon general ordered Dean to travel to Washington, D.C., and on September 12, 1931, officially assigned him as the first dental officer to the National Institute of Health. In his new position in the institute's Division of Pathology and Bacteriology, Dean took orders from Messner as well as from Dr. George W. McCoy, director of the National Institute of Health. At the same time Dean maintained a regular correspondence with McKay on the mottled enamel investigation.[21]

In planning his first assignment, the mottled enamel investigation, Dean set out to answer certain questions. The most important of these included:

- Was fluoride the sole cause of mottled enamel or were other substances involved?

- How many people were using water supplies with too much fluoride?

- Where were the communities in the United States with excessive fluoride in drinking water?

- How much fluoride in the water caused the defect?

- How could the excessive fluoride be eliminated from water supplies?

- How much would it cost to remove fluoride from water?[22]

Dean's first task was to locate the nation's mottled enamel communities and to establish the cause of the dystrophy. In 1931 Dr. Claude Hudson, an institute chemist, regarded the available evidence as insufficient to establish fluoride as the cause of mottled enamel. While Dean used Hudson's appraisal for official correspondence, he nevertheless referred to the dysfunction as "fluorosis" and considered fluoride at amounts above 1 ppm the most likely cause of the condition in 1931.[23]

At the start of the assignment mottled enamel had been identified in sixty-seven counties in thirteen states, and "more were suspected" by Dean. To find additional areas, Dean sent letters and questionnaires to state dental societies and health officials across the nation. McKay also kept Dean informed of his latest word on the subject. When state health authorities requested a mottled enamel investigation, Dean complied with what he called his "shoe leather surveys" to examine children's teeth, collect water samples, and confer with state health officials and local dentists.

After only four months of work on the project Dean detected a link between the mottled enamel and dental caries and recommended the continuation of the work because of that potential. Several earlier reports, including those of Eager, McKay, Black, and Rodriguez, had suggested such a possibility. Moreover, in 1928, after conducting the first scientific study of dental caries in an endemic mottled enamel area, Dr. Russell W. Bunting and his University of Michigan team had noted that some "principle in the drinking water . . . either inhibits the activity of dental caries or protects the teeth from injury." Aware of that background information, Dean in his first annual report on February 6, 1932, observed:

> Mottled enamel bears an important relationship to dental caries. Although those teeth erupt showing the most defective calcification known histologically, nevertheless these same individuals in an endemic area show a lower incidence of caries than individuals in some nearby non-endemic area. Consequently, *the study of mottled enamel may disclose some lead applicable to the vastly more important problem, dental caries.*[24]

The cautious and lone institute dental scientist, however, took several years before elaborating on that thesis.

Meanwhile, in 1933 Dean published his first results. His surveys added seventy-four counties and twenty-four states to the definitely identified mottled enamel areas and twenty-five counties in nine states to places that were suspect and required confirmation. Dean's studies indicated that the damage occurred when the child was exposed during calcification of the permanent teeth, about six years before their eruption.[25] Dean's work proved that the stained and mottled enamel condition was a national problem.

New Deal legislation offered some help to mottled enamel communities. When President Franklin D. Roosevelt took command, he began instituting reforms to counter the Great Depression. The National Recovery Act (NRA), the basis for much of the Roosevelt program, provided for financing the installation of new or altered water supplies of certain communities. In 1933 the American Dental Association membership urged Roosevelt to use the NRA to give priority consideration to resolving the mottled enamel problem. In recommending a reply for Roosevelt, Dean advised:

- Communities installing new water supplies should be aware of the mottled enamel situation, especially in the Southwest, eastern South Dakota, north central Illinois, and the Atlantic Coastal Plain along the Atlantic Seaboard; and

- The Public Health Service should cooperate, if requested, with the Public Works Administration to offer data to communities wishing to install new water supplies under the National Recovery Act to avoid mottled enamel effects.[26]

Dean worked quickly to apprise the nation's health officers and water supply departments about the mottled enamel. But he had to find a way to determine the precise amount of fluoride in the water. Until methods could be developed that accurately measured the fluoride, it would be impossible to set a safe level of fluoride in drinking water.

Dean relied on Dr. Elias Elvove, a senior chemist in the Division of Chemistry, National Institute of Health, to refine a fluoride measuring technique. A native of Russia with doctorates in pharmacy and chemistry from George Washington University, Elvove started his Public Health Service career in 1907 as a chemist for the Hygienic Laboratory. By the 1930s the rotund, balding chemist had a reputation as a scientist with a "desire for detail and accuracy in anything done." In 1933 the meticulous Elvove developed for Dean a colorimetric method that could be completed in only eighteen hours. Elvove's convenient chemical process used a zirconium-alizarin reagent to show colors identifying such elements as fluoride to an accuracy of 0.1 ppm fluoride in water. Elvove's procedure allowed Dean to compare the amount of fluoride in a community's supply with the severity of the mottled enamel and thus to determine a safe

Dr. Elias Elvove developed a method for the determination of the fluoride content of water as well as the method for removal of fluoride from water.

minimum amount of fluoride in a community's water supply. Two years later the American Public Health Association accepted Elvove's technique as its official procedure for measuring fluoride in water.[27]

As Dean continued his search, he found fluorosis both varied and prevalent, especially in the western part of the nation. By 1934 Dean had classified the mottled enamel into seven degrees of severity from questionable to severe. (Four years later he dropped a "moderately severe" classification and included most such cases in the "severe" category.) But after surveying the mottled enamel condition in Texas, Dean found it so widespread that he could not categorize the condition in that state. "The Panhandle-West Texas region constitutes the largest mottled-enamel area in the United States," he reported in 1935. Dean considered the situation "an acute and urgent public health problem." After another year of traveling, Dean had located a total of 335 endemic mottled enamel areas in twenty-five states with 86 percent of the troubled communities west of the Mississippi River.[28]

Using Elvove's colorimetric technique, Dean acquired enough evidence by 1936 to arrive at 1 ppm fluoride as a safe level in drinking water in average climates. The dental scientist's correlations showed virtually no evidence of the disorder with 1.0 ppm and below of fluoride in drinking water. Dean estimated that possibly 10 percent of all users would get the very mildest form of fluorosis, one of no cosmetic significance, after continuous use of water with 1 ppm fluoride.[29] That determination of a safe level marked another milestone in Dean's investigation of the mottled enamel problem.

Other than changing the water supply, Dean then needed a method to remove fluoride from drinking water. Again he turned to Elvove for help. In 1936 the inventive chemist devised a technique "efficient on a laboratory scale" for removing fluoride from water. The United States Patent Service later issued a patent for Elvove's method, "Removal of Fluorides from Drinking Water."

By the mid-1930s Dean needed more research help, especially an individual who could work full time on the effects of fluoride on humans. Previously he had relied on animal studies performed by the institute's section on nutrition. In July 1936 Dean hired Dr. Frank McClure, a shy bachelor from the Midwest who had published his doctoral dissertation on "The Toxic Effects of Fluoride" after receiving his degree from the University of Illinois. McClure was working in animal nutrition for the Pennsylvania State College Agricultural Experiment Station and had published two other papers on fluoride metabolism when Dean summoned him to Washington. Joining the institute as an assistant pharmacologist, McClure was assigned the task of determining how the body handled fluoride. McClure's role was essential for assessing toxicity of fluoride on humans.[30]

A young dentist also from the Midwest, Dr. Francis Arnold was the next addition to Dean's staff. Dean found Arnold through a friend, Dr. Thomas Hill, professor of pathology at the Western Reserve Dental School. A protégé and former student of Hill, Arnold was born in Orville, Ohio. Called "Pokey" by everyone who knew him, Arnold first learned dentistry as a teenage dental assistant in Orville. After Arnold graduated from the Western Reserve Dental School in 1934, Hill encouraged him to go into the Public Health Service and first recommended Arnold to Messner, the dental services chief. Messner thought that the young dentist should gain some clinical experience before going into research and therefore assigned him to the clinic at the Cleveland Public Health Service Marine Hospital. Arnold, however, preferred research to practice and with Hill's guidance finished his first dental scientific research at the hospital in the evenings. By the time Dean needed another dental researcher, Arnold was available. In September 1937 Arnold reported for work at the National Institute of Health where he soon fulfilled Hill's prediction that he would develop "into a capable research worker."[31] Consequently, by the late 1930s Dean had a research team of Elvove, McClure, Arnold, and occasionally McKay to tackle the fluorosis question.

By then the mottled enamel issue had attracted worldwide attention. Mottled enamel belts had appeared in Italy, England, China, Japan, North Africa, and Argentina, and because fluoride was used industrially, European scientists also were investigating the effects of fluoride on humans. In addition, McClure learned that agricultural experiment stations in the United States were also reporting the condition in farm animals.[32]

Meanwhile, Dean and his team's work on mottled enamel produced some significant changes in the United States during the 1930s. One of the most important was the influence on water analysis in the nation. "It took years to get water chemists to break out of the routine of analysis common to that period," Dean reminisced when he observed that the states had turned to testing ground water as a routine process because of the mottled enamel studies. His surveys and identification of disease belts also led to installation of new water supplies across the nation in the late 1930s and an accumulation of knowledge on fluoride water chemistry. In the health field the mottled enamel work produced the National Institute of Health's introduction of a new medical term, "endemic hypoplasia," to describe mottled enamel, which Dean considered a unique hypoplasia. Whereas "endemic" referred to something identified with a particular area, "hypoplasia" meant "defective or incomplete formation." But the most far-reaching effect of the mottled enamel studies emerged when Dean changed the emphasis of investigations to the link between fluorosis and dental caries.[33]

Confirming a Theory

In 1937 the National Institute of Health started to focus on the fluoride-dental caries link noted earlier by Dean. That fall two of

Dean's colleagues published their theory that fluoride inhibited tooth decay. Drs. Henry Klein and Carroll Palmer of the institute's Division of Public Health Methods suggested that Indian children they had examined showed a lower than normal incidence of tooth decay because the youngsters had been drinking water containing fluoride. Subsequently, Dean consulted McKay on the caries-fluorosis connection. By then a close friend and frequent guest at the Dean dinner table, McKay had noted as early as 1916 that mottled enamel victims had a lower percentage of carious teeth than children had in nonmottled enamel areas.

Beginning in October 1937, Dean sought to verify if, indeed, fluoridated water produced such a benefit by comparing the incidence of tooth decay of towns with and without fluoridated water. Dean's studies were aided by the refinement of the Public Health Service quantitative processes, advances in epidemiology, and a twenty-six state dental survey during 1933-1934 of American elementary schoolchildren sponsored by the American Dental Association. As a result of that effort, Dean found that some children exposed to 2.5 ppm fluoride in water had little or no mottled enamel and were free of caries. He concluded that the water produced some immunity to dental caries with or without causing mottled enamel.[34]

Supported by the historic evidence and statistics he obtained through state health departments, Dean in 1938 proposed a project to confirm the beneficial powers of fluoridated water. He recommended an epidemiological-chemical study to determine whether dental caries might be reduced through a sufficient but nontoxic amount of fluoride in drinking water supplies. Whereas others had suggested the connection between fluoride and dental caries prevention, Dean provided the first solid statistical correlation between the amount of fluoride in drinking water and the incidence of dental caries.[35]

Reaching beyond the dental and public health communities, Dean's publication stirred press interest, including that of William Randolph Hearst. Sensing a good story, the newspaper magnate assigned reporters to interview both Dean and McKay.[36]

Following Dean's lead, Dr. Gerald J. Cox of the Mellon Institute recommended adding fluoride to public drinking water to reduce dental caries. Dean, the cautious scientist, thought more investigations were necessary before attempting such an undertaking.[37] Thus, Dean's paper, "Endemic Fluorosis and Its Relation to Dental Caries," launched a new era in dentistry by inaugurating studies on the effectiveness and safety of fluoridated water.

To follow up on his proposed studies, Dean assembled a team that included Arnold, Elvove, McClure, and Dr. Philip Jay, a dental scientist at the University of Michigan. In 1939 the group found additional proof of fluoride's dental caries control in surveys of four Illinois towns. A specialist in saliva bacteria, Jay evaluated the decay-associated organism *L. acidophilus* in the children's saliva by using an index he had developed to correlate the *L. acidophilus* count with the prevalence of tooth decay. Jay found some correlations. In Galesburg with 1.6 ppm fluoride approximately 35 percent of the children aged twelve through fourteen had no decay; in Quincy with less than 0.2 ppm fluoride 14 percent were free of dental caries, and the Quincy bacteriological count of *L. acidophilus* was 3.4 times that of the Galesburg group. The studies of Monmouth and Macomb produced similar results.[38]

In subsequent investigations of twenty-one cities Dean looked for a balance in the amount of fluoride in drinking water to avoid fluorosis and yet curb tooth decay. He also wanted to verify that fluoride alone, and not other factors in a variety of circumstances, limited dental caries. With Jay, Arnold, and Elvove, Dean directed surveys in Illinois, Indiana, Ohio, and Colorado. The team found that the 3,150 children aged twelve through fourteen examined in cities with fluoride-free water had nearly three times as many cavities as the 2,250 youngsters in cities with an excess of 1.0 ppm fluoride in water supplies. Moreover, the researchers detected no correlation between the incidence of caries and any other factor, such as the amount of sunshine, gross differences in diet, or hardness of the water. By 1942 Dean concluded that there was little advantage to using more than 1.0 ppm fluoride in a water supply to reduce caries. At the 1.0 ppm level the complicating factor of fluorosis could be eliminated while the reduction of dental caries could be effective.[39]

With the 1.0 ppm fluoride level established, Dean sought to use that finding to improve the public's dental health. In September 1942 he met with Public Health Service scientists and engineers at the service's Cincinnati, Ohio, stream pollution laboratory to discuss conducting a study of artificially added fluoride in a public drinking water supply to control tooth decay. An active supporter of Dean's proposal, Dr. W. J. Pelton, accompanied Dean to that meeting.

Pelton was chief dental consultant in the Dental Public Health Section of the Division of Domestic Quarantine. The engineers agreed that it was technically and economically feasible to conduct a demonstration project over a period of ten to twelve years at a cost of between $7,000 and $8,000 per year.

While Dean expected to use such a project for practical application, he also realized that the service had to prove that no harm would come from adding fluoride to community water supplies. "Probably the first objection that we will encounter is the cry that fluorine is a poison," Dean predicted. (Dean then used the terms "fluorine" and "fluorination" when referring to addition of fluoride to water.) He considered it necessary, therefore, to study areas with long exposure to fluoride ingestion to determine whether any cumulative systemic effects appeared in residents.[40] But first Dean had to obtain the approval of higher service authorities to design an artificial water fluorination study.

Origins of the Grand Rapids Project

At a meeting in Washington in November 1942 Dean and Pelton persuaded Assistant Surgeon General J. W. Mountin to allow preliminary planning for an artificial water fluorination trial. Dean and Pelton divided tasks: Dean was to arrange for studies of human physical effects from long-term exposure to fluoride, and Pelton was to locate a community that would allow the addition of fluoride to its water supply. Dean and another service officer also agreed to design an artificial fluorination program with water engineers.[41]

News of Dean's studies and the prospect of artificial water fluorination initially evoked mixed reactions in the United States and Canada. Dr. Harold Hodge, an eminent dental scientist at the University of Rochester, withheld his approval at first. On the other hand, Canadian authorities decided to arrange a fluorination trial, and a New York state legislator from Newburgh wanted to introduce legislation to make fluoride treatment mandatory for New York water supplies. Encouraged by a subsequent proposal published in Dr. David Ast's master's thesis, the New York State Department of Health chose Newburgh and Kingston for an artificial fluorination study. Arrangements for the Canadian and New York experiments proceeded concurrently with similar planning by the United States Public Health Service.[42]

Meanwhile, to satisfy Assistant Surgeon General Mountin and his own scruples on determining the effects of long-term exposure to fluoride in water, Dean and service dental and medical officers surveyed over three hundred families in Bartlett and Cameron, Texas, in 1943. Bartlett residents had used water with 8.0 ppm fluoride since 1901; the control city, Cameron, had 0.4 ppm fluoride in its water since 1895. The team found no dangerous side effects from those surveys, which became part of a long-term study.[43]

McClure also conducted analytical studies on the effects of fluorine on the bone structures of adolescent males and armed forces selectees. McClure's studies revealed no ill effects on humans using drinking water with 1.0 ppm fluoride.[44] The Texas and McClure studies obviously cleared the path for the artificial fluorination project proposed by Dean.

In the meantime Pelton found Michigan state health authorities especially receptive to a water fluorination treatment program. No legal obstacles appeared because the state's laws empowered the state health department with supervising all water supplies treatment, control, and personnel. Ray Faust of the Michigan State Health Department Engineering Department recommended four cities for the project, including Grand Rapids with a population over 160,000 and Muskegon with over 47,500 people. Both towns obtained their water from Lake Michigan. Drs. W. R. Davis and C. R. Taylor, director and assistant director, respectively, of the Michigan State Health Department Dental Division, and Faust agreed to discuss the project with dentists and water engineers in the cities under consideration without making any commitments.[45]

Michigan, indeed, seemed an appropriate choice. The University of Michigan had been conducting basic research into dental caries since the 1920s, a factor that undoubtedly encouraged the state health authorities to seek the project. Taylor, friendly with Arnold, wanted to bring the University of Michigan into the project.[46]

In July 1944 Dean and Arnold chose Grand Rapids for the fluorination because of its large and stable school population and its use of almost fluoride-free water since 1912. They selected nearby Muskegon as the control with fluoride-free water. By then Bunting and Jay of the University of Michigan were also participating in the arrangements. Because Dean thought that the federal government could not afford the cost of the fluoride and feed equipment for adding the fluoride to the water supply, Michigan officials assured him that the W. K. Kellogg Foundation, a supporter of pilot health projects, would pay for those items.[47]

Michigan officials, Jay, and Dean and his colleagues from the Public Health Service laid the foundation for the project by meeting with the city commission, city manager, superintendent of schools, and representatives of the medical and dental professions. On August 2 the commissioner of the Michigan Department of Health, Dr. William DeKleine, wired Dean: "Grand Rapids City Commission voted to approve fluorine study." Grand Rapids residents learned about the fluorination through the local newspaper, the Michigan radio network, and the Detroit Free Press.

As the school year opened, prefluorination examinations started. In September the Michigan Department of Health, the University of Michigan School of Dentistry, and the United States Public Health Service examiners took saliva samples for bacterial counts from five hundred Grand Rapids schoolchildren from twelve to fourteen years of age.[48]

Ultimately, the Public Health Service assumed financial responsibility for the entire Grand Rapids project. In January 1945 W. L. Harris, chief chemist of the city of Grand Rapids, supervised the first addition of fluoride to Grand Rapids water. He notified Arnold and Jay: "Sodium fluoride application to the local water supply started 4:00 p.m., Thursday, January 25." With that act Grand Rapids became the first city in the world to deliberately introduce fluoride into its water supply.[49]

Other Early Dental Research in the Public Health Service

While the mottled enamel problem and fluorination emerged as the most spectacular parts of the service's dental investigations during the 1930s, a broad foundation of dental research was prepared at the National Institute of Health during those years. Oral investigations unconnected with fluoride, however, were frequently spread among various components of the Public Health Service and, while probably known to Dean, were not necessarily under his or the institute's jurisdiction. Some of those studies inevitably meshed with Dean's work on mottled enamel and dental caries; most set a precedent for the scope of future oral research. The preponderance of such work during the first few years of service dental research was, however, epidemiological.

One of Dean's earliest epidemiological studies, an analysis of radium dial painters' alveolar bone changes, involved collaboration with the service's Office of Industrial Hygiene and Sanitation. Begun in 1929, the service's investigation of the hazards of radium dial painting ended with the 1933 publication that included findings by two other scientists and Dean.[50] The inclusion of Dean, a dentist, in the service's famous radium dial painting investigation constituted recognition of the role of the dental scientist in oral cancer research.

The Division of Child Hygiene, on the other hand, continued to produce independent epidemiological dental studies of children after Dean's work began at the National Institute of Health. The division prepared several surveys of the prevalence of dental caries among various groups of children. A study published in 1934, for instance, discussed the relationship of dental caries to climate, customs, and diet.[51]

Concurrent with those other analyses, Dean, Dental Chief Messner, and other service dentists participated in national dental surveys. In the early 1930s service authorities cooperated with the American Dental Association on two major nationwide dental health surveys to determine national dental needs. Because the association lacked sufficient funds to conduct both studies, the service assumed prime responsibility for polling state departments and institutions, and the association provided dental examiners for schoolchildren in twenty-six states. The service, however, agreed to assist in the latter survey. To carry out those obligations, the service transferred Dean to the Division of Scientific Research from 1933 to 1935 to work with Dr. F. C. Cady and Messner on assessing state dental activities.[52]

The dental health activities survey covered 1928 to 1933 to allow the surveyors to compare effects of the Depression on dental activities of the institutions studied. After visiting state health, education, and welfare departments, the team found uneven treatment of dental health in the states. Five states had discontinued dental programs before 1933 because of insufficient funds. Yet fifteen states included a dental member on either a state board of health or advisory health council, twelve had a dental unit in the state department of health, and seven state health departments employed a full-time dentist.[53]

That study provided a basis for comparison later when the service wanted to assess the effects of the Social Security Act of 1935 on dental health activities. When Cady conducted a follow-up survey of state dental health activities in 1938, he revealed that Titles V and VI appropriations helped to increase the number of state dental divisions or subdivisions to thirty-five. Because of the earlier work, the service analysis found that "a revolutionary change" occurred in the nation's dental public health.[54]

The service encountered mixed results, however, with the other part of the American Dental Association proposal. The association's examination of schoolchildren was the most extensive dental survey of its kind ever conducted in the United States up to that time and represented a bold step. For that effort local dentists, hygienists, and teachers in twenty-six states examined and reported on approximately 1.5 million children in 1933 and 1934. The Public Health Service provided examination forms and persuaded the Rockefeller Foundation of New York to pay for half of the Census Bureau tabulation of data. "I simply haven't a dime" to pay for the tabulations, L. R. Thompson, assistant surgeon general and chief of the Scientific Research Division, complained to a Rockefeller Foundation officer. Fortunately, the foundation provided $15,000 for completion of the survey, and the Public Health Service published the data.[55]

Service dental analysts found a troubling methodological problem with the association survey, however. The examiners were not uniform in training nor in recording data. For example, 60 percent said that they did not count pits or fissures in teeth as dental caries. "Their exclusion," the service dentists said, "has necessarily an effect on the caries rate." Messner and his colleagues concluded that the survey gave only an approximation of the oral conditions of a large cross section of the nation's elementary school population. After Messner, Dean, Cady, and Dr. W. M. Gafafer reviewed the completed examination forms and questioned examiners, they decided that the service would assume "no responsibility for the accuracy and completeness of the examinations."[56]

Published in 1936, the study showed that "a large majority" of the 1.5 million children examined had one or more dental defects. Examiners found one or more carious teeth in 71 percent of the twelve- to fourteen-year-old youngsters.[57] Although imperfect, the survey provided the Public Health Service with the first overall picture of juvenile dental health in the United States. The twenty-six-state work was a difficult undertaking that was not duplicated for several decades, but it demonstrated that such a census was both possible and valuable.

Despite the initial criticism of the association effort, other scientists later drew important conclusions from its data. In his initial paper linking fluorosis to control of tooth decay, Dean used the survey's results, including another analyst's observation that the study showed dental caries rates varied by geographical region.[58]

An expansion in service dental research occurred during the latter half of the 1930s because of increased funding and pressure from Messner, Dean, and Cady. Additional appropriations from Title VI of the Social Security Act in Section 603(a) allowed the institute to extend dental research. Consequently, the Public Health Service initiated clinical and laboratory biological research principally in dental caries and to a lesser extent in periodontal diseases and the relation of localized infection in the mouth to other diseases of the body.[59]

While such change was under way, tragedy struck in 1936 with the sudden death of Messner, who had consistently fought for dental research in the service. His colleagues had expected Messner to assume the presidency of the American Dental Association. Instead, Dr. George B. Winter, who was elected to that office, pledged to lead the association in a campaign to carry out Messner's wishes to advance dentistry and dental research in the Public Health Service. In November 1936, honoring that promise, association officials launched the first of several attempts to obtain service cooperation with the National Bureau of Standards/American Dental Association dental materials research. Because of a Public Health Service economy program, service leaders rejected that initial association proposal.[60]

Messner's absence from the scene did not, however, interfere with the growth of dental research, especially caries investigations. Instead, Dean and Cady continued to push for more institute dental projects, and the American Dental Association, the Public Health Service, and later the Army Dental Corps increasingly supported several kinds of studies of tooth decay after Messner's death. In 1937 NIH dental caries research benefited when the Roosevelt administration reorganization of the institute gave some additional autonomy to dental studies. Dean's Dental Hygiene Unit moved to the new Division of Infectious Diseases, and Cady, who had worked with Dean on the nationwide surveys, headed the new Dental Public Health Section within the Division of Domestic Quarantine.

Under the reorganization Dean coordinated the research. Those activities, however, were spread among four divisions in the Public Health Service: the Marine Hospital Division, the Division of Domestic Quarantine, the Division of Infectious Diseases, and the Division of Public Health Methods.[61] The researchers fell under the jurisdiction of four different chiefs but also reported to Dean, who monitored and fought for the research projects although he held no titled administrative position within the institute.

The small size of the National Institute of Health combined with what old-timers recalled as a spirit of camaraderie undoubtedly minimized administrative obstacles to carrying out the dental research mission. It was common, one scientist remembered, for the director of the institute to eat lunch with everyone, from the newest to the oldest workers. Thus, the expansion of dental research in the institute in the late 1930s resulted from Dean's adept handling and the receptive attitudes of Dr. Thomas Parran, the new surgeon general, and Dr. L. R. Thompson, the new director of the institute in 1937.[62]

By September 1937 dentists and scientists in the service were conducting basic research in four laboratory projects on dental caries, eight field studies on dental caries problems, and three tests on proposals for the control of dental caries.[63] Outstanding contributions of the late 1930s included Dean's own analysis on fluoride as a deterrent of tooth decay and confirming surveys and studies produced in the Division of Public Health Methods.

In 1937 and 1938 scientists in the Child Hygiene Investigations unit in the Division of Public Health Methods developed a dental index and nomenclature to evaluate dental health in populations. Devised by Klein, Palmer, and Dr. John W. Knutson, the DMF Index, as the guide was called, represented "Decayed," "Missing," or "Filled" teeth; in addition, "tooth mortality" was included for extracted teeth or teeth requiring removal. Klein and Palmer used the index in their 1937 analysis of dental caries in American Indian children and with Knutson in a 1938 study of Hagerstown, Maryland, elementary schoolchildren. Use of the index in the Hagerstown examinations enabled the analysts to determine that 71.5 percent of the 4,416 children from six to fifteen years old had dental caries histories, a finding similar to that of the 1933-1934 American Dental Association survey. The DMF Index became a standard epidemiological tool and proved especially useful in assessing the dental health of young population groups.[64]

Caries research commanded priority attention from the American Dental Association in the late 1930s when its Research Commission established an advisory committee on dental caries research. By 1938 the committee authorized publication of abstracts of dental caries research findings by 148 researchers from around the world, including Arnold, Dean, Klein, and Knutson of the institute.[65]

In 1942 "Pokey" Arnold, Dean's young dental researcher, also published a significant, unique report. As pointed out in the 1920s by a National Research Council advisory group, dental science lacked sufficient appropriate laboratory animals. Scientists used rats in the 1930s for dental caries studies but could not duplicate the human dental caries process in rats because that rodent developed decay only from a coarse ground cereal diet instead of the finer grained food ingested by humans. In 1938 researchers imported hamsters into the United States to study leprosy. Aware of the need for a more suitable laboratory animal for dental decay experiments, Arnold decided to try the Syrian hamster, which had molar teeth resembling those of humans. After developing dental caries in Syrian hamsters by feeding them human diets, he introduced the Syrian hamster to the dental research community through the 1942 publication. Many years later an American Council on Education study on dental research cited that discovery as an example of how use of laboratory animals facilitated the study of dental diseases.[66]

Trench Mouth Research and the First Dental Fellowship at the National Institute of Health[67]

Both the American Dental Association and World War II led the National Institute of Health to assume trench mouth research. Despite the identification of the disease in the nineteenth century, dentists and scientists knew little about it and did not even know whether it was communicable. Known also as Vincent's angina, the disease included infections of the mucous membranes of the mouth and throat. The name "trench mouth" resulted from the disease's appearance in World War I soldiers in trenches.

The earliest research on trench mouth at the institute started under the first American Dental Association Fellowship there. Anxious to establish a biological research fellowship similar to the physical research arrangement at the Bureau of Standards, association leaders negotiated with the surgeon general's office for two years before working out an agreement on May 9, 1941. Association officials wanted their researcher to concentrate on dental caries, a field already covered by the institute. Ultimately, the association agreed to support bacteriological research into trench mouth, a disease that had attracted far fewer investigators than dental decay. Under the terms, the National Institute of Health accepted the sum of $5,000 "as a conditional gift for establishment of a fellowship for study, investigation and research in dental diseases."[68]

On September 15, 1941, Dr. Edward G. Hampp entered into active duty as the first American Dental Association research associate at the National Institute of Health. With D.D.S. and M.S. degrees from Washington University in St. Louis, Missouri, Hampp already had carried out research in bacteriology at Washington University, the University of Rochester, and the University of Michigan Medical School. Hampp initiated the long-term bacteriological research into trench mouth by seeking a satisfactory cultural method for isolating the bacteria associated with the disease.

Dean rapidly accepted Hampp into the fold of dental scientists and even took special measures to retain him a few months after Hampp started work. After the United States' entry into World War II when it appeared that Hampp was likely to be drafted, Dean persuaded National Institute of Health Director Rolla Dyer, also Dean's former division chief, to commission Hampp so that the association fellow could continue the trench mouth research. Hampp subsequently received his commission as an assistant dental surgeon in the Public Health Service Reserve Corps on March 7, 1942. The association, meanwhile, continued to pay the $5,000 per year for the research.[69]

The United States' entry into the war led to a rise in the incidence of trench mouth and a need for government expansion of research on the affliction. The army, navy, and dentists in the Public Health Service subsequently conducted clinical and epidemiological studies on trench mouth while Hampp continued his bacteriological investigation. In May 1942 Dean prepared forms for a study of the disease because he found that there was an "urgent need for a thorough epidemiological inquiry at this time in the hope that adequate measures for its control may be developed."[70]

Subsequently, Dean supervised dental officers sent to coast guard and service hospitals to study the disease and find a cure. During 1943 the disease prevalence was 73.1 cases per one thousand coast guardsmen and 94.9 cases per one thousand Maritime Service personnel admitted to the Sheepshead Bay, New York, dental clinic of the Public Health Service Hospital. By October 1944 Dean and Dr. D. E. Singleton, Jr., of the institute, announced a simple, successful treatment for the disease resulting from clinical work at that dental clinic. They brought about rapid recovery by immediate scaling to remove tartar from the teeth and under the gums and by brushing several times a day.[71]

In 1945 the Public Health Service studied the question of communicability and the effectiveness of the new antibiotic, penicillin, on the infection at a Manhattan Beach, New York, facility. The rapid turnover at Manhattan Beach, however, made studies difficult, and just before the war ended in 1945, Dean moved the study on the communicable aspect to the Coast Guard Training Station at Atlantic City, New Jersey.[72]

Lacking the answers he sought on trench mouth, Dean nevertheless displayed a sense of humor about the scientific predicament. On October 19, 1945, he instructed the service dentist in Atlantic City:

> As to whether or not Vincent's is communicable and [in view of] the widespread kissing on the Boardwalk on V-J day and night, [I] thought it might be of interest to check for our own cur[i]osity.[73]

With the war over, however, Dean concentrated once again on the connection of fluoride with the prevention of tooth decay. Hampp, meanwhile, continued his bacteriological research on trench mouth into the postwar era.

Reflections

When historians review dental history, they will find a sudden rise in scientific dental research during the first half of the twentieth century. Of course, the most spectacular achievement in that period was the epidemiological affirmation that the very substance inducing an ugly tooth deformity also inhibited tooth decay.

The histories of American dentistry and government scientific research provide some insight into why that landmark occurred in the United States in a modest federal facility. As previously mentioned, certain groups of dentists in the United States successfully pushed to make dentistry more than a mechanical trade by encouraging scientific research. McKay, Black, Messner, and Dean—all instrumental in work leading to the fluoride-caries link—were products of such an atmosphere. In addition, the Public Health Service and Hygienic Laboratory and its successor, the National Institute of Health, adopted and refined the relatively new science of epidemiology, which was essential for establishing the fluoride-caries connection. The multidisciplinary nature of NIH was also an important factor. Without the development of the fluoride measuring technique by the chemist, Elvove, the epidemiological successes would have been difficult, if not impossible, to achieve.

When the Public Health Service and National Institute of Health took the mottled enamel case as the first dental assignment, such a project was feasible within the institute's operation. The assumption of that task complied with Public Health Service law and with past service policies of tackling unusual, puzzling diseases. Because the preponderance of evidence pointed to the water supply as the cause of mottled enamel, the 1912 Public Health Service law made the service the most logical investigator; that act authorized the service to probe human diseases or conditions related to sanitation, sewage, and pollution from navigable streams and lakes of the United States. In the past the Hygienic Laboratory scientists, predecessors of the National Institute of Health researchers, had achieved their greatest successes in identifying causes of diseases limited to certain groups or areas, such as Dr. Joseph Goldberger's epidemiological finding that linked diet to pellagra. Mottled enamel fell into a similar category that suggested resolution by epidemiological studies.

The retention of the mottled enamel project also was bolstered by

Dean's reasoning that the fluorosis studies might produce a clue to the prevention of dental caries, the nation's most prevalent dental disease. When Dean's hypothesis materialized in 1938, that accomplishment resulted from the cooperation and hard work of a number of scientists within and outside the federal government. Moreover, the identification of fluoride as a dental decay preventive confirmed the effectiveness of and potential for dental research in the multidisciplinary National Institute of Health. The institute, however, needed more resources to broaden its oral studies.

The next chapter deals with those efforts to expand National Institute of Health investigations by establishing a dental research institute.

CHAPTER FOUR

Birth of the National Institute of Dental Research

Necessity is the mother of invention.

RICHARD FRANCK

The proposal for a federal dental research institute emerged from circumstances that ranged from the nature of twentieth century science to the dedication of a Washington, D.C., dentist. As Dean's work had already shown, the trend toward collaboration and team research in science demonstrated the efficacy of the institute structure. Moreover, the evolution of large-scale science, expensive instrumentation, and research specialization not only prepared the way for a proliferation of changes but also required funding that only governments and the most well-endowed institutions could afford. It was no longer possible for a scientist to learn everything in a discipline because discoveries after World War I doubled scientific knowledge.[1] Moreover, the New Deal and the trends in place during World War II influenced legislation enlarging the federal government's role in health matters.

Early Dental Legislation and Public Health Service Reorganization

Federal biomedical research received a boost in 1936 with the appointment of Dr. Thomas Parran as surgeon general of the Public Health Service. Having studied under Dr. Joseph Kinyoun, the Hygienic Laboratory's first chief, Parran promoted the growth of NIH. Friendly with President Franklin D. Roosevelt, Parran had easy access to the White House. In response to Roosevelt's request for a consolidation of federal health activities, Parran began studying such a reorganization as early as 1932.[2]

In 1937 the federal government created a model for biomedical research bodies targeting specific disease categories with the formation of the National Cancer Institute (NCI). Legislation creating the National Cancer Institute made the funding of basic research easier for Congress to support because it combined such work with a mission the public could understand. Congress gave the National Cancer Institute the authority to issue grants-in-aid for scientists and institutions outside the government and fellowships for promising investigators. The philosophy behind the grants-in-aid aimed at sponsoring inquiries into fundamental questions of nature that could supply more knowledge about cancer but also promote medical science in general. The researcher could pick the topic, applied or basic. When the program proved successful in attracting congressional appropriations, it set an example for other federal health research structures.[3]

Subsequently, Parran's opportunity to reorganize the Public Health Service finally materialized in 1939 when the Federal Security Agency was established. That year Congress transferred the Public Health Service, which included the National Institute of Health, from the Treasury Department to the newly established Federal Security Agency. Along with that action Parran considered structural changes in the Public Health Service. By then Dean was advising the surgeon general on dental research, and the surgeon general thus favored enhancing the NIH mission, including dental research.

Encouraged by major government reorganization under Roosevelt's social reforms, a colleague of Dean's made the first known proposal for a dental research institute in 1939. Dr. Ardzroony (Arthur) Packchanian, a protozoologist in the Division of Infectious Diseases where Dean also worked, proposed a "National Institute of Dental Research" in a plan for expanding and reorganizing the Public Health Service.[4] While not immediately implemented, several of Packchanian's ideas were later supported by Surgeon General Parran.

While Packchanian directed his recommendations to his government superiors, Dr. C. Willard Camalier, a local Washington, D.C., dentist, concentrated initially on Congress to elevate dental research in the Public Health Service. Prominent in national and local dental circles, Camalier had previously supported federal dental research when he testified at a 1928 congressional hearing in favor of a National Institute of Health. Dean's accomplishments impressed Camalier, who served as president of the American Dental Association in 1937 and 1938 and was instrumental in D.C. Dental Society activities. Camalier was also friendly with Sen. James E. Murray, a Democrat from Montana, and through Murray initiated a campaign in 1940 to promote dental research in the National Institute of Health.[5]

In 1940 Murray introduced the first legislation to establish a separate dental research program within the Public Health Service. His background contained no hint that he would become a future champion of federal support of dentistry. Born in 1876 on an Ontario, Canada, farm, he completed his education through the bachelor's degree in Canada and then studied law at New York University. After becoming a naturalized citizen in 1900, Murray chose Butte, Montana, as his home. There he practiced law, engaged in banking, and entered into Democratic party politics. Montana voters first elected Murray to the United States Senate to replace Sen. Thomas J. Walsh, who died in 1933. Upon his entry into the Senate, Murray was assigned to the Committee on Education and Labor, which had responsibility over the Public Health Service legislation. As a member of that committee, Murray learned about the health needs of the country and became a consistent advocate of federal support of dental research.[6]

Murray's eight-year effort started with his introduction of S. 3607, which provided $75,000 for the first year and subsequent annual increases to that amount of $10,000 for dental research. Although Dean supported Murray's efforts, he thought that if Congress supplied the institute with sufficient funds, then the Murray bill would be unnecessary. Only the Senate passed that bill.

Murray tried again in 1941. This time a House of Representatives subcommittee of the Committee on Interstate and Foreign Commerce held a hearing on the Murray legislation. Dr. Warren F. Draper, acting surgeon general; Watson B. Miller, acting administrator of the Federal Security Agency; and several American Dental Association witnesses supported the measure. They explained that research offered the best solution for easing dental disease, the most prevalent affliction in the nation and the major physical reason for rejection in the military draft.

Supporters of Public Health Service dental research encountered opposition at a July 1941 hearing on the bill held by a subcommittee of the Committee on Interstate and Foreign Commerce. Some of the congressmen found the bill weak because of its failure to limit expenditures, its appropriation of money for research instead of repair, and its concentrating the work in the federal government instead of in individual states or universities. Speculating on the use of potential research funding, Congressman Oscar Youngdahl, a Republican from Minnesota, preferred giving the money to the University of Minnesota instead of the Public Health Service. With such a hostile reception the Murray bill failed to gain House approval.[7]

Meanwhile, legislation on the Public Health Service reorganization fostered not only administrative conflicts but also elevation of dental research. The 1943 legislation set a potential precedent for divisiveness within the Public Health Service dental community that aroused objections by Surgeon General Parran, who wanted to increase NIH dental research. Despite the surgeon general's opposition, the American Dental Association Committee on Legislation successfully persuaded Congress to provide for a dental division in the Public Health Service. The association had wanted a separate dental corps, but the legislation passed by Congress, Public Law 184 of November 1943, only established the dental division under the surgeon general without specifying its purpose. The act also divided the service into four parts: Office of the Surgeon General, Bureau of Medical Services, Bureau of State Services, and National Institute of Health. In December 1943 Parran appointed Dr. William T. Wright, Jr., chief of dental work in the Marine Hospital Division of the service, as chief of the Division of Dentistry with the rank of rear admiral. Wright became the first dentist in the service to be promoted to that high rank. It was unclear whether the new division would mesh with the National Institute of Health dental research unit or would compete with Dean's staff.

Following the legislation establishing the Division of Dentistry, government legislative writers for the House of Representatives omitted the statute establishing the dental division in a proposed recodification of the law in 1944. That attempt angered American Dental Association officials. "Dentistry will not be pleased with this arrangement," Dr. Sterling Mead, the association's legislative committee chairman, told Sen. Lister Hill, a supporter of public health legislation.[8]

Congress compromised on the dental organization issue raised by Mead. On July 1, 1944, the Public Health Reorganization Act took effect as Public Law 410. The new law established the position of chief dental officer at the level of an assistant surgeon general in the Public Health Service but made no mention of the Division of Dentistry. It provided for grade, pay, and allowances equivalent to that of brigadier general for assistant surgeon generals. The act retained the four major departments established in Public Law 184. Under this measure the National Cancer Institute, which had been independent since 1937, became part of the National Institute of Health.

The new law upgraded the National Institute of Health dental research effort by allowing the surgeon general to reorganize or abolish divisions with the approval of the Federal Security Agency administrator. Section 301 of the law expanded the surgeon general's research authority and prepared the legal ground for research grants that could be applied to dental investigations. In 1945, as a direct result of that law, the surgeon general appointed H. Trendley Dean as the first director of the Dental Research Section, Division of Physiology of the National Institute of Health.[9]

Dental Research Section of the Experimental Biology and Medicine Institute, National Institute of Health, 1946. (L to R standing) Dr. Edwin Short, Dr. H. Trendley Dean, Dr. Frank McClure, Dr. Francis Arnold. (L to R kneeling) Dr. Stanley Ruzika, William Poole, Bertha Blue, Dr. David Scott.

Effects of World War II on the Campaign for Expanded Dental Research

National health policy changed as a result of World War II. The wartime experiences of leading government scientists aided the American Dental Association campaign for a larger government role in dental research by revolutionizing science and the relationship between government and science. The success of the Office of Scientific Research and Development, the wartime overseer for government science, brought about wide acceptance of a broad federal role in support of research in the nation's universities. The Manhattan Project to develop an atomic bomb proved the effectiveness of targeted and collaborative large-scale research by the federal government, the universities, and private industry. Those wartime developments and the advice of scientific leaders such as Vannevar Bush, who served as science czar for the White House, supported a more active role by government in science after the war.

In tune with the physical scientists, Surgeon General Parran affirmed the scientific progress made during the war through coordinated research, extensive grants-in-aid to research institutions, and "intimate collaboration similarly with our major Allies." Parran called for a continuation and expansion of government support for research in the postwar period by establishing research institutes like the National Cancer Institute that would deal with similar problems in the field of dentistry.[10]

The greatest single influence for a federal dental research institute was the recognition that the military preparedness of the United States depended on eradicating the dental deficiencies of recruits. The Public Health Service's first study of the military draft revealed the initial negative impact of dental disease on the physical fitness of American manpower. In that analysis Dr. Henry Klein reported that 20.9 percent of two million selectees could not meet Selective Service dental requirements. Also concerned about dental problems, the Army Medical Department initiated in 1940 a long-term study of the cause and prevention of dental caries.[11]

At the time of the Pearl Harbor attack that brought the United States into World War II, the category named "dental defects" led the physical reasons for rejection of recruits. Inductees needed six opposing teeth in each jaw; 8.8 percent could not qualify. President

Franklin D. Roosevelt was so concerned about the number of rejections that he decided to try a physical rehabilitation program to meet the war's manpower needs. Consequently, the Selective Service created a dental advisory committee of dental leaders living near Washington, D.C., to work on remedying dental defects. As chief dental officer of the Selective Service, Lt. Comdr. C. Raymond Wells of the Dental Corps of the United States Naval Reserve administered the dental program. The Selective Service tried a short pilot program that used civilian dentists in Maryland and Virginia. The pilot showed that dental rehabilitation could make more draftees eligible for service and prompted a change in policy.

Because of this surprising shortage of manpower to fight the war, the federal government lowered its dental requirements for service and corrected dental problems after induction. On March 15, 1942, the War Department changed its dental requirements so that recruits needed only enough teeth in the lower jaw for a partial denture; a full denture became permissible for the upper jaw. To induct more men, the Selective Service had to lower its dental requirements a second time. On October 15, 1942, the War Department accepted recruits who could be fitted with full dentures in both upper and lower jaws; the navy adopted the same policy on February 1, 1943. The problem led the navy to establish a dental research unit in 1943 under the Bureau of Medicine and Surgery. By lowering the dental requirements, the Selective Service rejected only .05 percent by 1944 for dental defects that were beyond rehabilitation.[12]

In an attempt to remedy the dental defects of recruits, the Army and Navy Dental Corps undertook "the greatest dental rehabilitation program that has ever been faced by this Nation," according to Wells, who became president of the American Dental Association in 1943. During the war the armed forces inducted twenty thousand dentists to carry on the rehabilitation and repair of battle-incurred dental injuries. The recruiting of the twenty thousand removed more than one-fourth of the practicing civilian dentists in the United States from public access and thus left the civilians with a shortage of dentists.[13]

Consequently, Surgeon General Parran predicted that after the war there would be only enough dentists to serve 25 percent of the nation's population. Dental disease was already rampant; with a postwar shortage of dentists the situation would become worse. In the

Soldier receiving dental examination during World War II. Courtesy of the National Archives.

eyes of Parran and the association officers, the best solutions were to conduct research to develop means of prevention and control of dental diseases, establish coordinated dental health education, and provide adequate dental care. Both the surgeon general and the association officers thought it especially important to concentrate on prevention by improving the dental health of the country's children. The World War II manpower experience enhanced the analyses of Parran and the association.[14]

In 1944 a Senate subcommittee investigated servicemen's health deficiencies, including dental problems, as a first step in health planning for the nation's future. Two influential senators sat in on the hearings held by the Subcommittee on Health of the Senate Committee on Education and Labor: Sen. Claude Pepper, a Democrat from

Florida and chairman of the Subcommittee on Health, and Senator Murray, who was by then the second ranking Democrat in seniority on the Senate Committee on Education and Labor in 1945. The senators learned about the impact of dental disease on America's conduct of the war and on America's population through this subcommittee's inquiry.[15]

"We were shocked to find the appalling extent of dental disease and dental neglect among our young men of military age. . . . All this set our subcommittee to exploring the subject further," Senator Pepper recalled a few months later. Subsequently, Pepper and Murray supported the establishment of a separate institute for dental research within the National Institute of Health.[16]

Legislation to Establish a National Institute of Dental Research

In 1944 the American Dental Association's legislative committee prepared a new proposal: a bill to establish a dental research institute in the National Institute of Health. The committee consulted with other groups as well as with government agencies before turning over its work to Senator Murray, who had assumed the more influential position as chairman of the Senate Committee on Education and Labor. In response to the request of Camalier, Murray introduced the association's bill as S. 190.

The legislation required the surgeon general to direct the new institute with the assistance of a national advisory dental research council. The council, with the surgeon general as chairman, would consist of six members distinguished in dental and scientific fields, with at least four holding dental degrees. The bill stipulated that the institute should:

- conduct and aid research on the cause, prevention, diagnostic methods, and treatment of dental ailments;

- coordinate dental research between the institute and outside institutions and researchers;

- provide fellowships in the institute;

- issue grants-in-aid to universities and other outside institutions;

- secure expert advice on dental diseases and conditions for the institute from consultants anywhere in the world; and

- cooperate with state health units to prevent and control dental problems.[17]

The measure also proposed authorization of $1 million for a building and equipment for the institute and up to $730,000 annually to carry out the institute's program. When he introduced the bill on January 20, 1945, Murray predicted that dental research "would be greatly increased." Agreeing with Murray's sentiments, Pepper presided over the hearings for the new legislation.[18]

Both witnesses and senators indicated that the war experience influenced their support of a federal dental research institute. In opening the hearings, Pepper cited the 1944 testimony on the dental rehabilitation of Selective Service registrants for the war service. Dr. Sumter S. Arnim, chairman of the Committee of Research and Graduate Study, School of Dentistry, Medical College of Virginia, explained that "it has required a national emergency in the form of war to focus the spotlight of attention on this most common of all ailments, dental disease." [19]

The American Dental Association organization of support also helped to create a consensus among professional groups. When Pepper convened hearings on the bill in July 1945, every major national American dental organization and the leaders of the Public Health Service supported the measure. Close to seventy organizations and individuals prominent in dentistry overwhelmingly supported the establishment of a federal dental research institute.

The only dissent came from The Committee of Physicians for the Improvement of Medical Care. While the committee agreed that dental care in the United States was insufficient, the committee's members considered the establishment of a separate institute and building as unsound. The committee stressed that dental care should not be studied in a vacuum and that the money for dental research should go to the most competent and effective men.[20]

Advised by Dean, Surgeon General Parran strongly supported the bill. He cited urgently needed research, including epidemiological studies of dental caries and periodontal diseases and studies in oral bacteriology. Describing what the Public Health Service was already doing, Parran remarked that the service had at that time no special means of preventing dental caries except for "the suggestion from current studies" that a small amount of fluorine in the water supply could reduce by one-half the amount of dental caries among school-children. Research, Parran said, was the first base of a national dental health program that should also encompass prevention, dental care and treatment, and public dental education. Pointing out that the dental research institute bill closely followed the features of the National Cancer Institute Act, Parran visualized the dental research institute functioning in exactly the same way as the NCI had been operating. Thus, he explained, "Our experience in the successful administration of research programs through our National Institute of Health leads to a general endorsement of the administrative provisions of S. 190." [21]

Dr. Sterling G. Mead, president-elect of the American Dental Association, stressed the need for dental research to help solve the problems of dental health. Although "all" accredited dental schools in the country and the federal government were engaged in research, the combined research was inadequate, he said, because of limited personnel, facilities, and funds. Pointing out the unsatisfactory state of dental health in the United States, Mead observed that "only a pittance has been spent for dental research by public and private agencies as compared to vast sums spent for less universal and less destructive diseases." The subcommittee's investigator later reported that the largest sum spent for dental research, presumably in the last fiscal year, was $50,000 by the National Institute of Health. [22]

When asked by Pepper if the dental research institute legislation might be combined with other research efforts, Mead explained why the dentists needed their own central institution. He recalled the problems the dentists encountered in correcting inequalities in dentistry in the armed services because initially dentists did not run the dental groups. "Physicians are interested in medicine; dentists are interested in dentistry. Each group has to fight for itself. . . . That is the reason we are so insistent upon an advisory council," Mead asserted. [23]

Arnim from the University of Virginia told the subcommittee there were far too few individuals trained to carry on dental research but that a national dental research institute could stimulate graduate research training programs in the dental schools. He predicted that such an institute would have the means to support the kind of research that might, for example, prevent tooth decay.[24]

Spokesmen from other groups suggested a variety of changes for the legislation, but the most significant proposals were those affecting minority grants, extramural support, attention to children, and preventive research. Dr. Russell A. Dixon, dean of the Howard University College of Dentistry and representative for the National Dental Association, the organization of black dentists, recommended that provisions be made so that black institutions receive grants-in-aid and encouragement for research training and that the advisory council include black representation.

Dr. Francis J. Brown from the American Council on Education wanted assurance that the legislation would stimulate research in educational institutions rather than centralize it in the federal government by distributing at least 50 percent of the research funding among educational institutions. Representing the dental subsection of the American Association for the Advancement of Science, Dr. Paul C. Kitchin wanted a minimum of half of the research funding to go to laboratories and institutions already conducting dental research. Kitchin, Surgeon General Parran, and American Dental Association spokesmen also thought that the public health portion of the dental program should be centered on children and prevention.[25]

In the spring of 1946 the Senate Committee on Education and Labor issued a favorable report for S. 190. The report stressed the prevalence of dental disease in the population and the shocking necessity of eliminating virtually all dental standards in order to enlist enough men to fight for the United States in World War II. The committee agreed that coordinated basic research on dental disease "must be launched if we are to raise the deplorably low level of dental health which prevails throughout the Nation." After passing the bill in June 1946, the Senate sent the measure to the House of Representatives in July.

In that busy postwar year Congress promoted the new policy expanding health research, but both houses only succeeded in passing the National Mental Health Act. Because of the limited time remaining in the current session, the House Committee on Interstate and Foreign Commerce postponed consideration of the dental research legislation until the next Congress. Proponents of the research institute, who had expected passage that year, thus prepared for another round of lobbying.[26]

Legislative Lull and Increased Support for Dental Research

Despite the setback in attempts to establish a federal dental research institute, the Public Health Service moved to increase support of dental research during the immediate postwar period. When Surgeon General Parran created the Research Grants Office in the National Institute of Health, he included dental awards along with medical fellowships and grants as part of the unit's responsibilities. The new office formed the Dental Studies Section to judge applications for the training and research stipends. Dean served as the section's executive secretary, but other members were nongovernment experts.[27]

Because of the new NIH extramural dental allocations the American College of Dentists Research Committee discontinued its own grants-in-aid program. That organization had initiated such aid in 1940, but committee members decided that the new federal arrangement made their assistance unnecessary.[28]

The results of the first few years of the NIH extramural dental program, however, confirmed previous estimations about the paucity of dental scientists and research in the nation. From January 1, 1946, to October 31, 1947, the National Institute of Health awarded 234 research training fellowships, but only 4 went to dentists. Between January 1, 1946, and August 31, 1947, the institute sponsored just twenty-four dental research projects, conducted by only fourteen of the forty undergraduate dental schools, a graduate school, and a state agricultural college. The cost for the twenty-four projects amounted to $135,607, or close to 1.6 percent of the total of $8,696,537 awarded to all institute extramural research projects during that period. Although all the dental schools were notified of the new program, twenty-one of the forty undergraduate dental schools in the United States did not even apply for a research grant. Despite the American Dental Association's requirement that dental schools con-

In 1946, Dr. Grant Van Huysen (left), at Indiana University School of Dentistry, conducted fluoride studies on the solubility of powdered enamel, research which was sponsored by NIH. Courtesy of Dr. Marjorie L. Swartz, Indiana University School of Dentistry.

duct research, Dean reported that "so far as is known, little or no research is being conducted" in many of the dental schools not applying for research grants.[29]

The lull in the push for a dental research institute allowed federal officials time to consider some modification of the legislation. One of the more important concerns involved the proposed national advisory dental research council. In 1946 Rear Adm. A. G. Lyle of the United States Navy Dental Corps called Dean's attention to the lack of ex-officio members representing the army and navy on the proposed council, although the National Institute of Health National Advisory Health Council included such representation. The National Advisory Cancer Council, upon which the dental council was modeled, contained no such ex-officio members. Dean suggested to Assistant Surgeon General W. T. Wright, Jr., that such expansion of the council deserved consideration.[30]

The pause in the legislative campaign also gave the White House time to develop a national health policy. After the Senate passed Murray's first bill for a dental research institute, no one, not even President Harry S. Truman's staff, knew how the president felt about the prospective agency because he expressed no opinion on that legislation. Indeed, Truman sought advice on the future of the federal government's role in health matters. While Congress was considering legislation to establish a federal dental research institute, in October 1946 Truman directed John R. Steelman, chairman of the President's Scientific Research Board, to study the problems of science and public policy.[31]

Steelman's researchers consulted the American Dental Association, the National Research Council, the National Health Council, and private philanthropic foundations for the fifth volume of the report, "The Nation's Medical Research," issued in 1947. Based on that consultation, Steelman reported that dental disease and several other classes of illness were among the more important conditions deserving attention but low in the number of research projects in 1947; dental and oral diseases placed ninth in importance in a ranking of one to ten based on the number of 1947 federal medical research projects. Steelman found that the small amount of federally sponsored work on dental disease reflected "the general neglect of dental research, and the need for training investigators in this field." Finally, he recommended that the federal government assume the leadership and support of a national effort to continue and expand medical research and that the government direct increased research efforts to dental and mental diseases prevalent in the general population.[32]

Legislation Establishing the National Institute of Dental Research

By the time the Steelman report was issued, Democrats and Republicans in both houses of Congress had introduced legislation to establish a federal dental research institute. In 1947 and 1948 congressmen considered six bills on the subject simultaneously with legislation to set up a national heart research institute under the National Institute of Health. In 1947 Murray filed a bill with bipartisan cosponsors that

resembled the one previously passed by the Senate. The others joining Murray were Senators Pepper, also a Democrat; Robert Taft,
Republican of Ohio; George Aiken, Republican of Vermont; and
Wayne Morse, Republican of Oregon. Their measure differed from
the earlier one by increasing appropriations to $2 million for the
institute's building and equipment. Responding to the urgings of the
Arkansas dental association, Congressman Oren Harris, a Democrat
of Arkansas, proposed a companion bill to the Senate's. A Republican
representative from Ohio, Dr. Walter Brehm, a dentist and member
of the American Dental Association, introduced one bill in 1947 and
two others in 1948. All the House bills except one of Brehm's 1948
measures resembled the Senate's.[33]

Again the American Dental Association mobilized its membership
to push the legislation through Congress. The Senate committee
reported favorably on the bill without holding another hearing but
ran into trouble on the Senate floor. Sen. Kenneth S. Wherry of
Nebraska, the Republican Whip, objected when the bill was first
called for consideration, but pressure from the nation's dentists forced
him to explain that action just before the Senate vote on July 24,
1947:

> Since then I have had telephone calls from all over the country inquir-
> ing why I object to it. I objected on behalf of another Senator. I had no
> personal objection to the passage of this particular piece of legislation.
> The Senate subsequently passed the measure and the very next day
> sent it to the House Committee on Interstate and Foreign Com-
> merce.[34]

Like the Senate hearings of 1945 the House hearing on March 11,
1948, included a parade of witnesses urging passage of any of three
bills to establish a federal dental research institute. Surgeon General
Parran, about to retire, pressed for approval and brought Dean to the
hearing. Dean described the scope of research his small staff of
twenty-three, including nine full-time professional investigators, was
conducting on a budget of $150,000. "We have no large dental
research center comparable to our medical centers. The dental research section of the National Institute of Health is one of the largest
of its kind in the world," Parran told the committee.[35]

As in the 1945 Senate hearings, the 70,000-member American
Dental Association provided the greatest number of supporting wit-

nesses. The International Association for Dental Research and the American Association of Dental Schools also sent spokesmen. Although repeating much of the testimony given in the 1945 Senate hearings, institute advocates supported their contentions with data from the Steelman and Dean reports on the dearth of dental research and investigators.[36]

The bill passed by the Senate encountered obstacles during the winter of 1948. While Marcus Collins, acting administrator of the Federal Security Agency, backed up Parran's views, James E. Webb, director of the Bureau of the Budget, opposed the legislation. Acknowledging the need for a dental health program as part of the president's proposed national health plan, Webb thought that the legislation would create a duplication of effort within the Public Health Service. He considered the establishment of separate institutes for research in particular diseases as administratively unsound and counter to the integration of a balanced public health program. Therefore, Webb concluded that enactment of any of the legislation under consideration "cannot be regarded as being in accord with the program of the President." [37]

To meet Webb's objections, Parran, who wanted the dental institute established, recommended certain changes in the bill. He suggested that the committee recast the legislation as amendments to the basic Public Health Service Act and that dental and medical research be combined in the same building. Dr. Harold Hillenbrand, the American Dental Association secretary, agreed to the amending of the Public Health Service Act because the changes were largely statutory in nature. But he and Dr. Carl Flagstad, the association's legislative chairman, opposed Parran's building proposal because, as Hillenbrand explained, "The dental profession has always had to struggle for funds which it can expend on its own problems." [38]

In May 1948 pressure mounted for a dental research institute. First, at the National Health Assembly, sponsored by the Federal Security Agency, the dental health section recommended increased federal support of dental research as part of the ten-year health goals set at the meeting. Then, on May 19 Dr. H. B. Washburn, American Dental Association president, and Camalier, at that time an assistant secretary in charge of the association's Washington office, met with Truman. At that White House meeting Washburn and Camalier obtained Truman's agreement to increased federal support of dental research.[39]

On May 27 Brehm introduced H.R. 6726, which incorporated Parran's but not the association's recommendations. The House Committee on Interstate and Foreign Commerce issued a favorable report on that measure and called the bill representative of the best thought of the committee on how to provide a sound legislative foundation for a dental research program. The committee cited dental caries, dental pyorrhea, and dental malocclusion as the three most important dental problems that the legislation would affect.

Brehm's bill contained some other significant changes. It omitted all reference to appropriations for a building, equipment, and research support because a special rule was necessary to insert such a provision. The House committee also enlarged the advisory council to four ex-officio members and twelve appointed members, only six of whom would need to have technical or professional training. Of the six, four would be dentists. Committee members considered the combination of laymen and technical experts superior legislatively and politically to the smaller council previously proposed. The advisory council provision also complied with the 1946 navy request, which was relayed to Congress. The Brehm bill, which conformed structurally with the National Cancer Act, passed the House on June 8.[40]

As passed by the House, H.R. 6726 upset NIH dental researchers because it did not provide any appropriations for a building or research. They wanted the new surgeon general, Dr. Leonard Scheele, to be apprised of this problem and hoped that a revised bill would include money for planning a building. Subsequently, the Senate granted some of those wishes. After making technical changes, the Senate restored the $2 million authorization for the planning, erection, and equipment of buildings and facilities for the institute. The Senate passed the revised bill on June 12. When the amended measure reached the House floor two days later, Brehm led floor discussion toward passage. After Congressman Errett P. Scrivner of Kansas objected to the sum for a building, Brehm retorted, "We cannot conduct dental research out in a pasture field or in a pup tent." The House then agreed to the Senate amendments.[41]

Truman's appointees also supported the legislation. Federal Security Administrator Oscar Ewing urged Bureau of the Budget Director Webb to approve the bill. The president received requests for approval from Elmer B. Staats, assistant director for legislative reference in the Bureau of the Budget, and Dr. Bruce D. Forsyth, Truman's

President Harry S. Truman signing the bill establishing the National Institute of Dental Research on June 24, 1948. Also present are (from left): Dr. C. Willard Camalier, director, Washington office of the ADA; Congressman Walter E. Brehm (Ohio), author of the bill; Dr. H. B. Washburn, president, ADA; Dr. Bruce D. Forsyth, chief dental officer, PHS; Dr. Carl O. Flagstad, chairman, ADA Committee on Legislation; Dr. Daniel F. Lynch, past-president of the District of Columbia Dental Society; and Dr. H. Trendley Dean, dental director of the National Institutes of Health.

personal dentist and by then assistant surgeon general and chief, Division of Dentistry. On June 24, 1948, President Truman signed H.R. 6726. Transformed into Public Law 755, the law was named the "National Dental Research Act." [42]

Establishing the National Institute of Dental Research

Public Law 755 entrusted the National Institute of Dental Research (NIDR) with national leadership in dental research. Under the act the Institute's most important responsibilities included the following:

- conducting and fostering research on the cause, prevention, methods of diagnosis, and treatment of dental diseases and conditions;

- promoting coordination of institute research with that of other agencies, organizations, and individuals;

- obtaining expert consultants from the United States and abroad;

- cooperating with state health agencies in prevention and control of dental diseases and conditions; and

- providing training and instruction within and outside the institute on "matters relating to the diagnosis, prevention, and treatment of dental diseases and conditions."

The act also authorized the National Advisory Dental Research Council (NADRC), composed of experts and lay members, to review dental research programs, collect and disseminate dental studies, and approve support of promising dental research and training applications. Under the new law both the Institute and NADRC could accept gifts or donations to support the Institute's mission.

In writing the legislation, however, Congress left several administrative issues unanswered. For instance, the act's language did not limit dental research in the service or NIH to the Institute. Officials in the Public Health Service had to resolve such questions.

The surgeon general's task was complicated by a blurring of dental research responsibilities among the various units of the Public Health Service. Since the 1920s Public Health Service dentists, both within and outside of the National Institute of Health, had carried out some dental research and experimentation. The Grand Rapids project and fluoridation and defluoridation experiments were such examples.[43] Of the two hundred PHS dental officers in 1948, only 5 percent engaged in full-time research; but others intermittently participated in some of the fluoridation field studies. Most of the other dental officers in the service practiced in the field at service hospitals or on Indian reservations.[44] How would such work be divided?

After the president signed the Dental Research Act, Dr. Rolla E. Dyer, director of the newly named National Institutes of Health

(NIH), wasted little time in commenting on the limits of the dental research institute. Dyer asserted that the National Institute of Dental Research was an integral part of the National Institutes of Health that should be located on the grounds of the institutes. In July 1948 Dyer, previously Dean's chief when both served in the Division of Infectious Diseases, advised Surgeon General Scheele that the new institute's operational research activities should be separated from the service's treatment and control programs. Dyer expected the chiefs of the new institute and the service's Division of Dentistry to coordinate their activities. Yet he wanted the chief dental officer to retain responsibility for the dental research institute's appropriations by including such funding within an overall service dental budget. Dyer proposed allocating dental research funding through the Division of Dentistry to the NIH. Scheele followed Dyer's recommendations.[45]

Several months later the surgeon general tried to resolve the assignment of responsibilities by placing a Division of Dental Public Health (DDPH) under the newly established Bureau of State Services in the Public Health Service. Most of the division's activities involved traditional public health duties, such as treating wards of the government. Nevertheless, the surgeon general gave the division responsibility for conducting "basic internal research" through field studies on care and prevention of dental diseases and conditions and allocated five division employees to the Grand Rapids project. The division also assumed control of defluoridation projects.[46] Thus, the Division of Dental Public Health, the National Institute of Dental Research, and the state of Michigan jointly operated the Grand Rapids program. While the principals in such an activity worked easily together in the 1940s, it remained to be seen whether such a bureaucratic arrangement could function as smoothly in the future.

Major questions immediately confronted the future staff of the new institute before the Dental Research Section was converted into the National Institute of Dental Research. What goals should the Institute seek? Did the dental researchers prefer to work in the new National Institutes of Health clinical setup or did they want a separate building? What did they think Congress visualized as their main mission? If the Institute director wished to hire promising scientists, how could he attract and keep them without adequate equipment and facilities?[47]

On July 20, 1948, Dr. Bruce Forsyth, by then chief dental officer of the Public Health Service, met with his staff to decide the future course of the new National Institute of Dental Research. As one participant explained, the separate institution would put dental research in a better position for recognition so that it would not be "just a tail on a dog someplace [sic] on fifth deck." They agreed that Congress established the Institute to curb or eliminate dental caries, then the most prevalent dental disease. As some in the group saw the situation, clinical investigations into dental caries prevention had run the gamut; therefore, the logical approach to wipe out tooth decay was through fundamental research, the weakest point in existing dental research. Others worried that clinical work might prevent others from pursuing basic investigations, but one staff member feared that certain scientists would use the Institute as an easy means of obtaining work in NIH medical research. Yet the group declined to reject clinical research entirely. "If you need clinical facilities, the clinical hospital is there," observed one of the dentists, referring to the future clinical center to be built at NIH. Finally the group, which included Dean and Arnold, unanimously decided that they wanted a separate building to concentrate on basic research.[48]

Despite the dental scientists' wish and the inclusion in the act of a provision for a separate building, two obstacles prevented any immediate start on a dental research institute structure. The first occurred on August 6 when Dean's conference with Dr. Jack Masur, medical director of the National Institutes of Health, concluded with Masur's attempt to house the new institute in the future clinical center. The other obstruction involved congressional omission of the dental research building appropriations from the budget for the next fiscal year, scheduled to end in 1950.[49]

The nucleus of less than a dozen investigators continued to operate under the Dental Research Section's chief, Dean, until September 13 when the surgeon general issued General Circular Number 49, Organization Number 16, establishing officially the National Institute of Dental Research. Through additional orders the surgeon general transferred the dental intramural research projects and dental scientists to the new facility.[50]

On September 16 Scheele appointed Dean as director under Personnel Orders Number 203. A logical choice for the Institute's first director, Dean retained a jovial but businesslike manner—answering telephone calls with "Dean here"—and gave priority to enhancing the Institute's scientific research. Dean's colleagues at NIH observed that the conservative new director made "quite a concession to allow a woman to come into the lab" when he hired Rachel Harris, a chemist, in 1948. As one scientist explained the policy, Dean followed NIH tradition and set a precedent for his successors in attempting to attract the most promising scientists "and then let them do what they felt was important." Moreover, Dean governed democratically by concealing his own opinions while soliciting the views of his professional staff on the mission and future operations of NIDR.[51]

By October 1948 the Institute staff numbered twenty-seven, including seventeen civil service personnel, eight PHS commissioned officers, and an ADA Research Fellow and his laboratory technician. Several months later W. P. Dearing, acting surgeon general, approved Arnold as the new institute's associate director with responsibilities for both laboratory and clinical research.[52]

In organizing the new institute, Dean could build on a group already recognized for accomplishments in dental research. Nine of the Section's dental scientists, including the American Dental Association Fellow, had submitted twenty scholarly articles for publication during the fiscal year that ended June 30, 1948.

A significant accomplishment by Dr. David B. Scott was among those contributions. In 1947 the promising young dental scientist helped develop a method to obtain the first detailed views of tooth surfaces under the electron microscope. Scott had joined the Dental Research Section in 1944 and was part of a new generation of dental scientists combining the study of dentistry with that of science. A graduate of Brown University, he had received his dental degree from the Baltimore College of Dental Surgery, University of Maryland, and afterwards a master's degree in science from the University of Rochester. At NIH Scott had collaborated with Dr. Ralph W. G. Wyckoff of the Experimental Biology and Medicine Institute to produce the first micrographs, by optical and electron-microscopic methods, of details showing changes occurring with age and characteristics of early signs of dental decay.[53]

When the National Dental Research Act took effect, the Dental Research Section was focusing on epidemiological and laboratory studies on the causes and control of dental caries, and Hampp, the ADA Fellow, was continuing his bacteriological investigation into trench mouth. The group's most well-known work was, of course, the Grand Rapids fluoridation experiment.[54]

While Dean was committed to completing the Grand Rapids project, he also wanted to expand internally the scientific role of the Institute. The Dental Research Section had contained five units: Electron Microscope Studies, Ulcerative Stomatitis, Grand Rapids Low-Fluorination Study, Biochemistry, and Epidemiology and Bacteriology. At first Dean contemplated organizing the Institute by the three fields of dental caries, periodontal diseases, and clinical research. Later, however, he decided to follow the National Institute of Health example of organizing the Institute according to basic discipline for laboratory research and according to disease for clinical research, all of which fell under Arnold's supervision.

The Institute's first structure thus conformed to NIH tradition. Under laboratory research Dean established oral bacteriology, pathology and histology, and oral and biological chemistry sections. For clinical research he formed sections for dental and periodontal diseases, dental equipment and materials, and growth and development. Dean thought that periodontal research was equally important to caries investigations and had been neglected for too long. Otherwise, he indicated, dental caries control would only save teeth for exposure to periodontal diseases. Recognizing the importance of his own specialty of epidemiology, Dean created a separate section for epidemiology and biometry.[55] (See Appendices for NIDR organizational charts.)

Also anxious to use the Institute to promote dental research in the nation, Dean proposed a program with three objectives: (1) to expand training of dental researchers, (2) to encourage all the country's forty dental schools and certain graduate schools to expand dental research through research grants-in-aid, and (3) to establish some small research studies in universities coordinated and administered by NIDR. To accomplish those goals, Dean needed help from people and institutions outside the Public Health Service.[56]

In establishing a National Advisory Dental Research Council, Congress provided Dean with just the kind of support he sought. The composition of the first council, which held its first meeting on January 10, 1949, was impressive. The regular council members included four faculty members from university dental schools, staff members of the Colorado Department of Public Health and the American Dental Association, the vice-president of the University of

The first meeting of the National Advisory Dental Research Council, January 10, 1949.

Chicago, the president of the University of Texas, the dean of the University of Michigan's School of Public Health, the president of the National Congress of Parents and Teachers, a magazine editor, and the social services director of a New York City hospital. That council also contained ex-officio members from the Army and Navy Dental Corps and the Veterans Administration.[57]

Appointed executive officer of the council, Dean steered the council toward taking immediate action on encouraging dental research. For many years millions had been spent on conquering and controlling diseases of interest to physicians, but until then virtually nothing had been spent on dental research, Dean said. He estimated that less than $1 million of the $0.9 billion the American people spent on dentistry went into dental research. Moreover, Dean wanted the dental community to encourage more young dental graduates to take graduate training in the basic sciences for research. He presented as an example the National Institutes of Health postdoctoral fellowship program, which supported only 11 dentists but 188 physicians out of the 86,000 dentists and 200,000 physicians in the nation.

Proposing solutions, Dean urged the council to act immediately by voting to support grants-in-aid recommended by the Dental Study Section. The council responded by approving eleven research grants totalling $62,498 in January and thirty-four additional projects amounting to $200,000 at meetings in June and November 1949. But the council deferred the question of traineeships that first year.[58]

Meanwhile, the NIH leadership took steps to promote training of dental researchers. To assist in judging applications for dental and other research fellowships, the National Institutes of Health Research Fellowship Specialty Board enlarged its membership so that Dean could form a separate board from the Institute. Dean chose Dr. Robert Stephan, a dental scientist who had joined the Dental Research Section in 1946, as a board member to represent the Institute. In June 1949 Dean created a Dental Research Specialty Board on Fellowships with Arnold as the chairman. Later that year Dr. Poul Pedersen, a dentist and an anthropologist from Copenhagen, Denmark, became the first special research fellow at the Institute. For the fiscal year ending in 1950, NIDR awarded fourteen research fellowships worth $34,415.[59]

In the Institute's first years unforeseen events, including the Korean War and its financial consequences, dashed hopes for a separate building and prevented the funding of expanded dental research. The 81st Congress repealed the $750,000 ceiling for Institute appropriations in 1950 under Public Law 692. Despite protestations of the American Dental Association spokesmen, subsequent budgets for dental research did not fulfill the need. The Institute building appropriations never reappeared in the budgets submitted to Congress for the duration of the Korean conflict. Moreover, the $221,000 funding for dental research grants, approved in 1950 for the 1951 fiscal year, also remained at that level for the rest of the war. By 1953 the Institute needed $564,000 for what scientists thought were worthwhile extramural dental research projects, but the Truman administration refused to allocate more than the 1951 ceiling.

Dental research fellowships met the same fate. By 1950 the Institute wanted $130,000 for dental research fellowships but only received $50,000 for the 1951 fiscal year. The Institute was able to award only eleven fellowships with the $50,000 for the 1954 fiscal year, down from the fourteen it granted the first full fiscal year of its operation.[60]

After only slightly more than a year of existence the dental research institute staff outgrew its space. In 1950 Dean and Arnold had to move part of the staff to the Public Health Service Hospital in Stapleton, Staten Island, New York, and to the Eastman Dental Dispensary in Rochester, New York, until more room could be made available in Bethesda.[61]

Despite the administrative disappointments, at midcentury the scientific and dental communities regarded the Institute and Dean with respect for their accomplishments. By then the professional staff was publishing in a variety of scholarly journals, including the *Journal of Bacteriology*, the *Annual Review of Biochemistry*, and the *Journal of Dental Research*. The American Water Works Association and the Washington Academy of Sciences had recognized Institute achievements through awards for caries prevention and laboratory work to Dean and the Institute's American Dental Association associate. Dean was serving on major national dental research committees, including that of the National Research Council of the National Academy of Sciences and the Committee on Research of the American College of Dentists.[62] Thus, by 1950 NIDR was solidly in place.

Commentary

As the legislative history indicated, the relationship of dental health to national security played a major role in the establishment of the National Institute of Dental Research. World War II revealed that dental problems made the difference between insufficient and adequate manpower to fight in the United States armed forces. More than any other argument, the significance of dental health in World War II influenced the legislators supporting the creation of the Institute.

The wartime scientific experiences and the recommendations for increased federal support of health research also contributed to a favorable political atmosphere. But the credit for using such information to persuade politicians to form the Institute went to the American Dental Association with its lobbying and organizational assets.

The legislators, however, left the implementation of the Dental Research Act to the scientific leadership. At first most scientists favored concentrating on basic investigations on tooth decay, but Dean, who testified at the hearings for the Institute's establishment, recognized the importance of broadening the research.

Nevertheless, some of the early administrative decisions raised the potential for future conflicts. Following the advice of the director of the National Institutes of Health, the surgeon general gave some research responsibilities to the new Division of Dental Public Health. Although DDPH and NIDR staffs then worked well together, would such a division of research be confusing later?

Meanwhile, like their backers at the American Dental Association, most dental scientists in the new institute wanted housing exclusively for Institute research. Because of the medical domination of NIH they feared that intramural research might not expand unless the Institute possessed its own building.

Yet the Institute had already demonstrated its value to society through earlier accomplishments, barely mentioned in the testimony supporting its formation. As a new agency within NIH, the Institute still faced the completion of a major project: determining the role of fluoridation in preventing dental decay.

CHAPTER FIVE

Fluoridation: Success and Controversy

Truth revealed through science has been
challenged and stubbornly resisted again
and again throughout history.

DR. H. TRENDLEY DEAN

Of all the projects undertaken by the National Institute of Dental Research and its predecessor, the Dental Research Section, fluoridation drew the most publicity and the most controversy. Working in the midst of challenges to their scientific principles, those dental investigators introduced fluoridation to the world.

Grand Rapids Project Begins, 1945-1948

In 1945 the world's initial artificial fluoridation projects began in the United States and Canada. The first, the Grand Rapids, Michigan, trial, was the flagship of the Public Health Service fluoridation program. As previously mentioned, Dean selected Grand Rapids as the city to receive artificial fluoridation and fluoride-free Muskegon as the control community. The test was to last fifteen years.

To provide a basis for comparison, Michigan state dentists had to examine the teeth of all Muskegon and Grand Rapids schoolchildren before fluoridation could affect their teeth. Some of those examinations had been completed in September 1944, and the remainder were to be finished by the following spring.

101

But World War II restrictions almost prevented the completion of those essential examinations in the winter of 1945. Ironically, the problem was not the gasoline rationing imposed under wartime conditions but the shortage of automobiles in, of all places, Michigan, famous for its automobile plants. Michigan officials found themselves without cars for traveling between Grand Rapids and Muskegon to examine the schoolchildren's teeth. "We are having pressure put on us to conserve travel in any way possible and yet render essential service," Dr. William Davis, director of the Michigan Bureau of Public Health Dentistry, remarked shortly after the Grand Rapids-Muskegon fluoridation started. National officials came to the rescue. With the help of Arnold, Dean's right-hand man in the Dental Research Section, the researchers managed to obtain the cars they needed to shuttle examiners back and forth between the two cities.[1]

Arnold especially wanted the Grand Rapids project to proceed smoothly because of his convictions about fluoridation. He was so convinced about the benefits and safety of fluoride treatment that he gave fluoride tablets on a daily basis to his own children before his home community installed fluoridation. Years later Arnold attributed his children's caries-free teeth to their early ingestion of fluoride.[2]

In spring 1945 the scientists selected approximately one-third of the thirty-two thousand Grand Rapids and eight thousand Muskegon students they had examined for the study. They completed the first year's work by July 1945. The sponsors hoped that the program would provide answers to several scientific and technical questions:

- What were the effects of the artificially fluoridated water on deciduous or baby teeth and permanent teeth?

- Would bacteriological and chemical studies of saliva specimens from the Grand Rapids students show how fluoride protected teeth from decay?

- How smoothly would the technical aspects of artificial addition of fluoride to water work?

- Was artificially fluoridated water as effective as naturally fluoridated water in inhibiting dental decay?

For the latter question the investigators used as the standard for comparison a 1945 survey of schoolchildren in Aurora, Illinois, which had naturally fluoridated water close to the ideal 1 ppm.[3]

Dean enlarged his staff and the scope of dental research to cover as many aspects as possible of the Michigan fluoridation project. Between 1945 and 1948 his investigators included the following:

- Dr. Isadore Zipkin, a biochemist, who joined with McClure to investigate the effects of fluoride on teeth and the processes of dental erosion;

- Dr. Scott, who used the electron microscope to study sodium fluoride's action on human enamel;

- Dr. Robert M. Stephan, who studied local factors and bacteria involved in the development of cavities;

- Drs. H. B. McCauley and Robert C. Likins, dental scientists who specialized in the project's epidemiological and physiological surveys;

- Dr. Arnold, who concentrated on trying to find the link between fluorides and the inhibition of dental caries; and

- Dr. McClure, who measured the amounts of fluoride in human enamel and dentin from fluoridated and nonfluoridated waters.

Moreover, in 1946 NIH research grants supported nongovernment scientists conducting research on the effects of fluoride on bone development.[4]

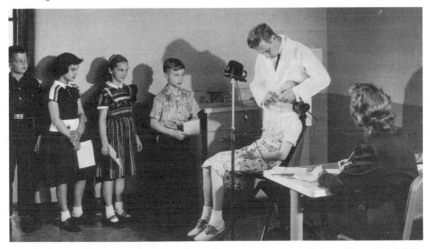

Dr. Robert Likins conducting dental exams on Grand Rapids schoolchildren.

By 1946 there were several fluoridation trials to compare with that at Grand Rapids. In addition to the Brantford, Ontario, and New-burgh-Kingston, New York, tests, the Wisconsin State Health Department had started one in Sheboygan; Michigan had initiated another in Midland; and the University of Chicago's Zoller Clinic had mounted an extensive fluoridation study in Evanston, Illinois. The Public Health Service provided financial support for the Evanston project, which some officials considered one of the most elaborate conducted. F. J. Maier, sanitary engineer with the Dental Public Health Section, State Relations Division, U.S. Public Health Service, visited the Wisconsin and Michigan filtration plants with W. L. Harris, the Grand Rapids plant chemist, in 1946 and found all three carefully monitoring the fluoridation operations. Otherwise, scientists managing the various fluoridation projects operated independently but kept each other informed of their progress.[5] The very isolation of each fluoridation program assured the integrity of any comparison of results of all the projects.

While the Grand Rapids project ran uneventfully during its first three years, the results also proved initially unremarkable. Dental examiners found no significant improvement in the rates of decay in the teeth of the Grand Rapids children by the middle of 1948, but then the youngsters expected to reap the greatest benefits of fluoridation—those receiving fluoridated water from birth—had yet to enroll in schools.[6]

Topical Application Question of 1948

A potential obstacle to the integrity of the Grand Rapids project arose in 1948. Dr. Fred Wertheimer, director of the Bureau of Public Health Dentistry of the Michigan Department of Health, wondered whether topical applications of sodium fluoride to the teeth of Grand Rapids and Muskegon children might invalidate the results of the project. "For some time now we have been 'groaning in spirits and wrestling with prayer' . . . to clarify our thinking in regard to the topical application of sodium fluoride," Wertheimer remarked in January.[7]

Topical fluoride application involved coating teeth with a fluoride solution to prevent cavities. Scientists started investigating such a

Grand Rapids schoolchildren providing saliva samples.

Dr. Philip Jay (left) and Dr. Francis Arnold counting colonies of bacteria in cultures made from the saliva of schoolchildren during the Grand Rapids study.

method after Dean called for studies of a link between fluoride and reduced dental caries. In those first years of the fluoridation movement dental scientists sought alternate ways to introduce fluoride products because at least one-third of the United States population did not use communal water supplies and thus could benefit only if children could receive safe amounts of fluoride through other means. As early as 1940 a scientific team, including Drs. J. F. Volker, Harold C. Hodge, H. J. Wilson, and S. N. Voorhis, determined that fluoride in liquid underwent a chemical reaction when combined with powdered enamel. Led by Volker of the University of Rochester, the group suggested that coating teeth with a solution including fluoride might help prevent decay. In 1941 Dr. Basil Bibby, a dental scientist at Tufts College Dental School, started experimenting with a 2 percent solution of sodium fluoride applied to the teeth of adolescents. One year later Dr. V. D. Cheyne of Indiana University reported that his topical applications of a fluoride solution resulted in a 50 percent reduction of new dental decay in a treated group in comparison to another untreated group of children of the same age.[8]

Working with three Minnesota communities in 1942, Dr. John Knutson at the Minnesota State Department of Health and Dr. Wallace Armstrong of the University of Minnesota produced the most comprehensive study on topical fluoride application yet done in the United States. After painting the teeth of their young subjects seven to fifteen times on one side of the mouth over an eight-week period, Knutson and Armstrong found a 40 percent reduction in dental caries on the treated sides one year after their coating started. Successive studies by Knutson and Armstrong and researchers at the Forsyth Dental Center in Boston (formerly the Forsyth Dental Infirmary) proved so persuasive that favorable publicity on the treatment swept the nation.[9]

Even President Truman commended the work. "I'm mighty glad to hear that progress is being made. I've been very interested in sodium fluorine since the Public Health Service first revealed its amazing qualities," Truman told an American Dental Association delegation in 1948. *Everyman's Almanac* for that year also gave an entire column to the subject.[10]

As a result of these favorable findings, the Public Health Service planned a program combining demonstrations and publicity for the states to introduce the new procedure into common use. After receiving expressions of overwhelming support for topical fluoride application to the teeth of the nation's schoolchildren, Congress allocated $1 million for such a project in the 1949 fiscal year.[11]

Thus Wertheimer worried that a sufficient number of topical fluoride applications by Grand Rapids and Muskegon dentists might distort future results of the Grand Rapids-Muskegon study. To avert that danger, he met with Grand Rapids dentists to dissuade them from treating young patients with the topical fluoride, for the youngsters were already receiving the fluoridated water. Muskegon, however, bothered Wertheimer. Already some residents there thought that their children were serving as subjects of an experiment without any resulting benefits. Wertheimer did not know what to do about Muskegon where reportedly three or four dentists were already giving topical fluoride treatments.[12]

Dean and Arnold in Washington and Dr. Philip Jay at the University of Michigan thought, however, that topical fluoride applications would have little effect on the project because too few children were receiving the treatments. Wertheimer agreed. Moreover, Dean observed that proof was lacking to show that topical applications for children already drinking fluoridated water would provide additional resistance to dental caries. Of course, from the scientific point of view, Dean recognized that ideal conditions would not include topical application of fluoride solutions until this study ended, but he realized that such a prohibition was impractical under the existing circumstances. As Arnold explained, "It would not be right to withhold topical applications of fluoride from children" in either city.[13]

The Public Health Service continued to promote topical fluoride. Knutson, the service's first dental officer to earn a doctorate in public health and by 1948 the chief of the PHS State Services Dental Public Health Section, led the topical fluoride campaign. As Dean and the others predicted, the promotion did not affect the Grand Rapids-Muskegon project, which instead became subject to pressures from other quarters.[14]

Pressure for Public Health Service Endorsement of Fluoridation, 1946-1950

Ardent fluoridation proponents in Wisconsin, however, gave the Public Health Service dental scientists a major battle during the first five years of the Grand Rapids-Muskegon project. From 1943 to

1945 the Wisconsin State Dental Society examined appropriate literature and the state's communities with naturally fluoridated water
to determine the impact of fluoridated water on dental health. In
1945 the study committee's results led the state society to recommend
the addition of 1 ppm fluoride to public water supplies. After finish-
ing a similar survey, eight physicians of the Wisconsin State Board of
Health arrived at the same conclusion that year. Sheboygan, which
added fluoride to its water supply in 1946, provided the subjects for a
state dental study that by 1948 showed a 28 percent decline in decayed or extracted baby teeth and an 18 percent reduction in decayed,
missing, or filled permanent teeth.

Anxious to institute fluoridation statewide, Wisconsin officials
wanted the blessing of the Public Health Service for mass fluoridation. Conservative scientists from the University of Wisconsin and
some Madison politicians disagreed with the fluoridation proponents
over instituting fluoridation in Madison in 1946 and 1947. The
opposition wanted more proof of the safety and value of fluoridation.
While the forces supporting fluoridation in Madison won, Wisconsin fluoridation advocates pressed the Public Health Service to recommend mass fluoridation for the general public in order to persuade the
rest of the state to fluoridate.[15]

But Dean withheld such approval because Grand Rapids results
were inconclusive. In response to those 1948 pressures, Dean refused
to make a definite statement on the effectiveness of fluoridation in
controlling dental caries "until the results of the present experimental
studies are completed." He did not expect conclusive results until the
next five to seven years, but in 1949 the NIDR director stopped
rejecting fluoridation as premature when the subject came up at
professional society meetings.[16]

By the summer of 1949 Dean predicted that "a beneficial result
may eventually result, but the study must continue for perhaps ten
years before the procedure can be evaluated definitively." At the 1949
meeting of the American Water Works Association Dean and the
association acknowledged that additional research was necessary to
determine safe, effective levels of fluoride according to climatological
variations. Thus, areas with high mean annual temperatures might
require less than 1 ppm fluoride because inhabitants drank more
water; the reverse would apply for communities with colder than
average mean temperatures.[17]

Dean also exercised caution on recommending fluoridation because his staff was continuing research on the human safety of fluoridation. Although no evidence associated any unusual illnesses or death rates with naturally fluoridated drinking water supplies, McClure and his colleagues were still conducting batteries of tests on the physiological effects of fluoridated water.

In 1950, after studying the 1949 dental examinations, Dean, Arnold, Jay, and Knutson found a marked reduction in dental decay in the youngest subjects in Grand Rapids. Nevertheless, they wanted more time to determine the effects of fluoride on students nine years of age and older.[18]

Dr. Francis A. Bull, director of Dental Health for the Wisconsin State Board of Health, led pressure for federal endorsement of fluoridation. He thought that by 1949 the Sheboygan, Wisconsin, and Brantford, Ontario, surveys already had proved the efficacy of fluoridation in preventing dental decay. After forty months the Brantford study showed a 22 percent reduction in new decay rates for permanent teeth. "The evidence is sufficiently conclusive," Bull pleaded, adding that the nation's dentists could only handle less than one-third of all dental caries cases. Acknowledging that federal government officials based their resistance on scientific skepticism over uncompleted experiments, Bull argued that "The history of public health is filled with examples of great harm done to the public because skepticism was maintained long after it had ceased to be scientific or logical." In May 1950 Bull and other state dental health directors converged on Washington, D.C., and in a show of unanimity urged Dean, by then director of the National Institute of Dental Research, and Dr. Bruce Forsyth, chief dental officer of the Public Health Service, to endorse mass fluoridation.[19]

In June 1950 the Public Health Service changed its policy on mass fluoridation. Citing new evidence from the Grand Rapids project, Forsyth issued a preliminary statement in late May that communities wishing to fluoridate water supplies by scientific procedures should be "strongly encouraged" to proceed. Pressure for a stronger federal announcement followed on June 8 when the state and territorial dental directors unanimously approved a positive resolution. The dental directors recommended fluoridation in areas where local and medical professionals approved such a program and where the community could adhere to standards set by the state health authorities.

On the following day Forsyth announced:

> Preliminary data indicate a lowered amount of dental decay following
> fluoridation of the public water supply.... In order to utilize this
> preventive at the earliest possible moment, therefore, fluoridation of
> public water supply as a procedure for the partial control of dental
> caries can be encouraged subject to the approval of the state and local
> health authorities and the dental and medical profession.[20]

Forsyth's acquiescence placed the Public Health Service in an awk-
ward position. The chief dental officer's tentative endorsement not
only preceded the acquisition of definitive results of the Grand Rapids
study but also appeared prior to the completion of some of the
Institute's physiological and epidemiological examinations of fluoride's effects. Although changing community water supplies in the
United States depended on local or state laws, this preliminary recommendation complicated the politics by the broad statement leaving decision making to local authorities without taking into account
climatological, geographical, and economic considerations.

Considerably more cautious than Forsyth, Dean later in June gave
his most positive appraisal yet of fluoridation. In his annual report for
the National Institute of Dental Research the director stated:

> Dental investigators of the Public Health Service are attempting to
> assess the value of supplementing communal water supplies with
> fluorides as a caries control measure. These studies were begun in
> 1945, and although it is far too early to draw any unqualified conclu-
> sions, preliminary results in Grand Rapids, Mich., are sufficiently
> encouraging to indicate that this may prove to be one of the most
> feasible methods for controlling caries on a mass basis.[21]

The die was cast. Would the Public Health Service's approval of
mass fluoridation promote fluoridation or would it stir up dissent?

Beginning of Fluoridation Conflicts: Challenges to Science, 1950-1952

For a brief period euphoria reigned in the fluoridation movement.
In 1950 the American Dental Association, the American Public
Health Association, and the Association of State and Territorial

Health Officers joined the chorus of approval for fluoridation of community water supplies. That year the number of communities instituting fluoridation doubled from forty-nine in 1949 to one hundred, giving almost 1.6 million people access to fluoridated drinking water in the United States. Surgeon General Leonard Scheele told Public Health Service personnel in the field that sodium fluoride added to public water supplies "will substantially reduce dental decay in children, and the reduction is greatest when fluoride water is used continuously from birth." [22]

Simultaneously, trouble was stirring in the hinterlands. In his history of the nationwide fluoridation battles, Donald McNeil called the midcentury a turning point at which the fluoridation wars became political. In 1950 the town gadfly and two allies in Stevens Point, Wisconsin, managed to bring the fluoridation question to a referendum and then persuaded the voters to reject fluoridation. McNeil found that the Stevens Point case introduced the first organized opposition to fluoridation in the United States. Because in many places in the nation ordinances or referendums were necessary to alter the public water supplies, fluoridation became subject to political pressures. Taking advantage of such a situation, the victorious fluoridation opponents spread their message elsewhere in the nation with claims that fluoridation was highly poisonous. [23]

The poison argument struck at the heart of the problem the Institute scientists had to face in the years following. The use of fluoride powder in high concentrations to kill rodents gave antifluoridationists a provocative argument. Yet fluoride appeared in trace amounts in nature, in numerous drinking water supplies throughout the world, and in common foods; no one had shown that those minute quantities were harmful to humans except for mottled enamel of teeth from water with more than 1.5 ppm fluoride, depending on the climate. [24]

Nevertheless, it was the mission of the Institute, as an agent of the Public Health Service, to assure the safety for public use of any recommended procedure, such as fluoridation. As Dean had earlier recognized, scientists had to overcome a history of political resistance to tampering with water supplies. The release of recommendations made before the NIH completion of studies on fluoridation's effectiveness and safety compounded the federal government's effort to persuade a scientifically unsophisticated public that fluoridated water helped to prevent dental caries and yet was safe for human consumption.

The situation was complicated further by challenges from some scientists, health care professionals, and intellectuals. Several years later Arnold recalled that in 1950 he had regarded the government's endorsement as premature but, like his colleagues, had not anticipated the degree of adverse reaction that followed. The unleashing of such opposition compelled the scientists of the National Institute of Dental Research and their colleagues in other institutes to exceed the ordinary to prove the safety of fluoridation; they had to answer to charges widely publicized by the opposition.[25]

In 1950 Dean and his colleagues encountered the first scientific assertion against fluoridation. Word leaked out from a closed 1950 meeting of Texas officials that a University of Texas scientist had observed that a concentration of 1 ppm fluoride in drinking water accelerated the development of tumors in laboratory mice. To check on the rumor, Dean and Dr. H. B. Andervont, chief of the biology section of the National Cancer Institute, visited the scientist's laboratory. Dean and Andervont found the experiment to be faulty: the samples were too small to meet any statistically valid test; the particular species of mice used was known to vary in susceptibility to tumors; the fluorine concentration in the water was only 0.4 ppm, and the animals' feed, Purina Dog Chow, contained such a high amount of fluorine, up to 45 ppm, that it obliterated any effects of fluoridated water. Alfred Taylor, the investigator with a doctorate in biochemistry, indicated that he would not publish his findings because he was unable to confirm those results in a second experiment.

Dean and Andervont were especially upset about the incident because the story had been widely circulated informally and thus was not open to a public review. "From our point of view this is regrettable, since we cannot publicly refute a claim that has never been made publicly and the psychological damage done is great," complained Dr. Norman Topping, associate director of the NIH. Dr. Edward Taylor, director of dental health of the Texas State Department of Health, apologized for the incident and promised to issue a refutation to the hypothesis that fluorine was connected with breast cancer. Nevertheless, opponents of fluoridation and Alfred Taylor himself used his results in arguments against fluoridation.[26]

Rising Support for Fluoridation, 1951-1952

On the other side of the controversy, public health dental officers mobilized to counter the unfavorable publicity about fluoridation. Tackling the issue presented a major problem because the conflict pitted antagonists using politics and misleading scientific declarations against government scientists accustomed to nonpolitical and objective scientific work. "There are 16,000 community water supplies in this country that we would all like to see fluoridated," Knutson, then chief of the PHS Division of Dental Public Health, told a 1951 meeting of public health dental officers.[27]

Although public health dentists did not come close to meeting the goal proposed by Knutson that year, the fluoridation campaign continued to flourish. Surgeon General Scheele announced on April 24, 1951, that the Public Health Service's scientific studies had reached the point where he could give an unqualified endorsement to mass fluoridation of public waters as a means of reducing dental decay by two-thirds. The National Research Council of the National Academy of Sciences recommended that any community with a sufficient number of children and a fluoride-free or low-fluoride water supply "consider the practicability and economic feasibility of adjusting the concentration to optimal levels" in accord with climate. Further, the chairman of the American Medical Association announced that its council on pharmacy and chemistry and council on foods and nutrition considered 1 ppm fluoridation of community water supplies safe. Those positive pronouncements accompanied the largest gain yet in communities instituting fluoridation. During that year over 3.5 million of the nation's inhabitants received fluoridated drinking water for the first time.[28]

In addition, Drs. A. L. Russell, an epidemiologist, and Elvove of the Institute published a significant finding that year. Their survey of Colorado Springs, with naturally fluoridated water, showed that residents through the age of forty-four had about 60 percent fewer decayed teeth and had lost only about one-fourth as many teeth as adults of comparable ages who had drunk fluoride-free water. That study produced the first comprehensive evidence that the beneficial dental effects of fluoridated water continued into adulthood.[29]

Ironically, the initial successes of the fluoridation movement contributed to a considerable limitation of the Grand Rapids study.

While major health-related organizations followed the Public Health Service acclamation favoring fluoridation of public water supplies, Wertheimer, Michigan's guardian angel of the Grand Rapids project, had doubts about the wisdom of the service's public endorsement of fluoridation. Yes, the militant proponents would rejoice, but now what would happen to the Grand Rapids project? Wertheimer predicted that Muskegon people would soon agitate for fluoridation there. "I can't very well ask my friends over there to block attempts at fluoridation in the future," he complained. If Muskegon started fluoridation, the control city in the project would be lost. Wertheimer's premonition materialized in July 1951 when Muskegon officials instituted fluoridation after completion of the annual dental examinations for the Grand Rapids project.[30]

The fluoridation achievements of the United States also attracted attention abroad. In 1952 the United Kingdom Ministry of Health dispatched a mission to the United States to examine the fluoridation programs. The English group was so favorably impressed that it urged the Minister of Health to start fluoridation trials in the United Kingdom, and a fluoridation campaign there soon followed.[31]

Yet in the United States those same successes met with a mixed reception in Congress. The controversy over fluoridation prevented Congress from actively promoting fluoridation. The Truman administration favored supporting local efforts to implement fluoridation, but in the early 1950s Congress rejected requests from the Institute and from the American Dental Association to appropriate funds to aid state and local fluoridation projects.[32]

Delaney Committee Hearings of 1952

In 1952 the Grand Rapids program, fluoridation, and the scientific research associated with the process came under congressional scrutiny. Congressman James J. Delaney, a Democrat from New York, presided over a House of Representatives committee investigation of fluoridation that took up the last seven sessions of two years of hearings on chemicals in foods and cosmetics. The committee hearings commanded nationwide attention and were reported on the front pages of Washington, D.C., newspapers. Although the committee confined testimony to expert witnesses, Dean and his Institute colleagues testified at length "amid hostile questioning from" Vincent K. Kleinfeld, committee counsel, and Congressman A. L. Miller, a Republican from Nebraska. Kleinfeld grilled Knutson and Dean as if they were on trial. With eleven proponents and seven opponents testifying, the preponderance favored fluoridation.

Among the negative witnesses, Alfred Taylor of the University of Texas presented the results of the laboratory experiments previously examined by Dean and Andervont but made no mention of the feed with high amounts of fluoride and the erroneous statistics. Some twenty Texas cities were delaying fluoridation because of his studies, Taylor said. Based on his findings, Taylor advised the Delaney committee that "a city should wait until we have had time and other laboratories have had time to investigate this further." The National Institutes of Health countered his statement by submitting Dean's and Andervont's report questioning the validity of Taylor's work.[33]

As the committee learned, the mainstream organizations, such as the American Dental Association, the Association of State and Territorial Health Officers, and the National Academy of Sciences, supported fluoridation. Nevertheless, some of the scientific testimony by federal government witnesses appeared as potentially damaging to the fluoridation movement because the Public Health Service had endorsed the process before completion of some important field work. For instance, Knutson reported that National Cancer Institute comparative studies of cancer mortality incidence consistently showed that death rates were slightly higher in fluoride-free cities than in communities with naturally fluoridated water. Yet when questioned about the effects of artificially fluoridated water, Knutson had to respond that insufficient time had elapsed to study cancer prevalence with controlled fluoridation.[34]

The Institute's case might have been stronger if Frank McClure had appeared as a witness, but McClure, who had spent more time than anyone in the Institute studying the physiological effects of fluoride, was sick during the hearings and unable to testify. In addition to his studies on the effects of fluoridated water on World War II recruits, McClure also had published by 1952 his findings on the amounts of fluorine in foods and its presence and that of other trace elements in the metabolism. Instead, the committee accepted a written statement from McClure on his research and gave only a little time to Isadore Zipkin, a biochemist working with McClure, to discuss McClure's work.[35]

Apparently, during the last three sessions the testimony converted one of the committee members, Miller, the Nebraska Republican, from a fluoridation supporter to a foe. A physician and state health director for Nebraska from 1941 to 1942, Miller had introduced legislation in June 1951 authorizing the fluoridation of Washington, D.C., drinking water. Miller changed his mind after hearing conflicting testimony on the safety of fluoridation, especially after the February 26 opposition by Margaret Cammack Smith and Howard V. Smith, the husband-and-wife team that in 1931 discovered that fluoride caused mottled enamel in the teeth of laboratory animals. Although both opposed fluoridation, Margaret Smith spoke in favor of topical application of fluoride to the teeth of children. The Smiths argued that even a small amount of fluoride in water induced mottled enamel. When the Smiths finished speaking, Miller said, "In the last few days we have had some testimony from experts in the field . . . some of their findings have disturbed me a little bit. I am sort of between and betwixt as to what we should advocate."[36]

Miller later explained that he had only introduced the District of Columbia legislation to stimulate discussion of the fluoridation question, and he criticized the District of Columbia officials for not weighing fluoridation carefully before approving it. Like some other opponents of fluoridated drinking water, Miller approved of topical applications of fluoride to the teeth of young children.[37] Consequently, as a result of the Delaney hearings, the antifluoridation movement gained a friend in Congress.

Although the Delaney committee decided not to recommend federal legislation on fluoridation, it issued a cautious majority report that Miller signed. The committee advised communities to exercise conservatism in deciding whether or not to add fluoride to drinking waters. In addition, the committee differed from the traditional definition of medication by calling fluoridation "mass medication." In contrast, the official Public Health Service statement described fluoridation as a simulation of a natural phenomenon and noted that fluoridation did not qualify as a medicine because it was not a treatment or cure for any disease. In their report committee members urged the continuation of research to determine the long-range effects of fluoridation on the chronically ill and aged. As revealed in his supplemental statement, Miller regarded fluoridation as still in an experimental stage and asserted that the reaction to natural fluoridation was different from that to raw fluoride added to water.[38]

Aftermath of the Delaney Hearings, 1952-1953

At first the Delaney committee hearings seemed to have little effect on the momentum for fluoridation in the nation. The number of people receiving fluoridated drinking water jumped from over 5 million in 1951 to almost 13.9 million in 1952. On the other hand, the number of communities discontinuing fluoridation also increased from two, serving 29,450 individuals in 1951, to seven that shut off fluoridated water to 204,125 in 1952. Arguing primarily on scientific grounds to a nonscientific electorate, fluoridation proponents also lost the largest referendum yet in Seattle, Washington, by two to one in March 1952. Fluoridation advocates considered the Seattle defeat a major blow to the fluoridation campaign.[39]

In the long run, the Delaney committee hearings helped to mobilize both sides of the fluoridation issue. The hearings, combined with a somewhat more conservative mood prevailing in the country, provided a focus for the opponents of fluoridation and political extremism. Disparate groups combined to fight fluoridation. The Cold War, growing in intensity since 1947, produced some who considered fluoridation a Communist plot to poison American citizens. Libertarians viewed fluoridation as a deprivation of their civil rights. Health-foods followers opposed any additive, such as fluoride, to drinking water. Adherents to faith-healing religions usually objected to fluoridation, although the Christian Scientist leaders declined to take a stand and instead left the decision to local churches. Certain individuals in the vitamin and health-food industries also worked against fluoridation, apparently for commercial reasons. Chiropractors, some dentists and physicians, and a few scientists also played leading roles in the antifluoridation movement that grew after the Delaney hearings.[40]

Some even claimed that fluoridation was started to benefit Federal Security Agency Administrator Oscar Ewing and his law firm, which had represented the Aluminum Company of America (ALCOA) in New York City. The antifluoridationists alleged that ALCOA paid

Ewing's law firm $750,000 per year and sold fluoride as a byproduct for community water supplies. Both Ewing and ALCOA denied the allegations. Rebuffing the charges in an affidavit, Ewing noted that he had retired from his New York law firm in 1947 before assuming his government post and had no further financial interest in it. ALCOA's general counsel supplemented Ewing's statement by retorting that the annual retainer for Ewing's firm was "never within shooting distance" of the alleged $750,000 and that the company did not promote water fluoridation nor even deal much in sodium fluoride.[41]

In October 1952 the American Public Health Association, however, strengthened its profluoridation stand by awarding the prestigious Lasker Award in medical research to Dean and McKay "for their pioneering studies which have opened a new vista in disease control." [42]

Before Truman left the presidency, several attempts were made to promote fluoridation of community water supplies. Realizing the difficulties of conveying the scientific complexities of the argument to the public, some proponents sought various means to appeal to voters in communities holding referendums on fluoridation. The American Dental Association issued a primer on "How to Obtain Fluoridation for Your Community through a Citizen's Committee." Dean and his colleagues in the National Institute of Dental Research and the Division of Dental Public Health gave talks around the country. While Dean recognized that scientific investigations of objections to fluoridation were necessary, he also believed that "the weight of scientific evidence is far overbalanced in the direction of the proponents of fluoridation." [43]

In 1953, with the major part of the fluoridation mission under way, Dean retired from government service. He continued to speak out in favor of fluoridation before congressional hearings and at public meetings in his new capacity as the secretary of the American Dental Association Council on Dental Research.[44]

Fluoridation Policy in the First Eisenhower Administration

The fluoridation issue posed a persistent dilemma for the federal government. Opposition to the process had increased by the time

Dwight D. Eisenhower assumed the nation's presidency in January 1953. The following month when Oveta Culp Hobby became federal security administrator, Public Health Service Surgeon General Scheele vowed to continue supporting fluoridation, including its promotion and research for technical and safety purposes. Scheele analyzed the fluoridation problem for Hobby. In Scheele's view, the chances of harm from the service's recommended levels of fluorides in water were so remote that there was no valid reason for any community to withhold fluoridation. The surgeon general recognized a similarity between past acrimonious, lengthy debates over water purification and the more recent disputes about fluoridation: both combined a mixture of legal, religious, and medical issues. He concluded that the government's task in coping with the opposition was complicated:

> Considerations advanced by quacks, sincere but uninformed people, and well qualified people are so intertwined that real and spurious issues become indistinguishable in the public mind. *We are in such a situation now, and expect no clean cut resolution in the near future.*[45]

Alerted to the controversy, Hobby needed to develop a policy to answer "a relatively large number of letters" protesting fluoridation that she received upon assuming office. She heeded some of Scheele's counsel by citing the Public Health Service's work affirming the safety and dental benefits of fluoridation. Yet Hobby and the Eisenhower administration remained neutral in local contests over fluoridation. She referred some correspondents to an American Association for the Advancement of Science publication on fluoridation. Even when a profluoridation group asked for assistance and information for use in a referendum campaign, Hobby suggested that the group consult the local state health officer.[46]

At the political level the Eisenhower administration policy changed the strategy initiated in the Truman administration. Knutson, who previously had openly urged states and local communities to institute fluoridation, modified his position in 1954 when testifying as the chief dental officer of the Public Health Service before a congressional hearing. "We believe that they [local communities] are entirely competent to make such decisions and that Federal intervention, either to require or to prohibit fluoridation, would not be justifiable," Knutson concluded.[47]

The approach toward fluoridation differed somewhat at the Institute during the Eisenhower years. Arnold, who succeeded Dean as Institute director, adhered to his predecessor's policies and philosophies on fluoridation. He, however, saw a positive side to the antifluoridationists: their allegations forced the Institute to broaden its research to investigate their accusations. While overseeing that research expansion, Arnold, nevertheless, countered fluoridation opponents by allowing proponents to use his personal endorsement in a 1956 community fluoridation campaign.[48]

Eisenhower gave limited support to fluoridation with a message commemorating National Children's Dental Health Week. He declared:

> It is fitting to note the recent development of measures, including the fluoridation of water supplies to prevent tooth decay in the early years of growth. I invite the attention of the public to the study of programs in this field and I urge all citizens to cooperate in such measures as will lead to the improved dental health of our children and youth.[49]

Fluoridation Hearings, 1954

During the Eisenhower administration years the Institute produced such a solid case for fluoridation that Congress rejected attempts to kill the procedure. The most serious challenge arose in 1954 when Congressman Roy Wier, a Democrat from Minnesota, introduced a bill that prohibited water fluoridation in the United States. During three days of hearings presided over by Congressman John Wolverton, a Republican from West Virginia, the House Committee on Interstate and Foreign Commerce heard a variety of witnesses, including fluoridation opponents with little or no technical or scientific qualifications pertinent to the issue. Opposition witnesses called fluoridation unconstitutional, a form of socialized medicine, compulsory medication, and a poisoning of the population. Among the opponents testifying was Vincent Kleinfeld, the Delaney committee's chief counsel, who appeared on behalf of several groups opposing fluoridation. To support his position, Kleinfeld summarized Delaney committee testimony for the Wolverton committee.[50]

By 1954 the National Institute of Dental Research scientists had accrued more definitive information on fluoridation to present to the committee than the Institute had developed for the 1952 Delaney hearings. The scientists relayed to the Wolverton committee the latest results of the Grand Rapids and other studies.

Almost ten years old, the Grand Rapids project showed favorable results on the prevention of dental caries and on safety. Researchers had conducted mortality studies on Grand Rapids and Muskegon in response to allegations by Congressman Miller, formerly of the Delaney committee, that Grand Rapids had a higher death rate after the introduction of fluoridation. The Institute studies disproved Miller's assertions with mortality charts. The Republican congressman from Grand Rapids, Gerald Ford, urged the committee not to recommend legislation that would take away such a benefit from his hometown.[51]

Additional evidence from a 1953 update of a Texas study enabled the National Institute of Dental Research scientists to testify on long-range effects of fluoridated water. Ten years earlier Dean and a team of National Institute of Health physicians, dentists, and scientists had conducted complete physical examinations of the inhabitants of fluoride-free Cameron, Texas, and of Bartlett, Texas, where the water supply had contained 8 ppm fluoride since 1901. They studied the two communities to determine whether drinking water with excessive fluoride produced any harmful physical effects other than mottled enamel on humans. With that exception, the NIH team had found nothing adverse in the physical conditions of Bartlett residents in 1943. Supervised by Dr. Nicholas Leone, chief of the Institute's Medical Investigations, the 1953 head-to-toe examinations reaffirmed the 1943 findings. Actually, the physicians discovered that the fluoride-free community of Cameron exhibited a higher incidence of cardiovascular disease than that of Bartlett.[52]

The Institute and outside scientists also presented the Wolverton committee with results of microscopic and chemical analyses of bone and soft tissues of drinkers of 8 ppm fluoridated water. Again, the researchers found no detectable structural changes and no functional impairments.[53]

Dr. Isadore Zipkin, by then a senior scientist at the Institute, investigated kidney excretion because of concern over the effects of fluoridated water on people with kidney disease. Zipkin told the committee that even in people with severe kidney and heart disease, the kidney still was so efficient that it continued to excrete halogens, the family of elements to which fluorine belonged.[54]

The government testimony against the Wier bill was overwhelming. In addition to the evidence presented by Institute scientists, Chief Dental Officer Knutson, and Dean, as a spokesman for the American Dental Association, several members of the Eisenhower cabinet informed the committee of their opposition to the bill. Secretaries of the Departments of the Army, the Interior, and Health, Education and Welfare registered disapproval of the Wier measure along with the chiefs of thirty-three state health departments, including the head of the department in Wier's home state of Minnesota. With the congressional session drawing to a close, the House took no action on the Wier bill. Nevertheless, the publication of the hearings with a variety of antifluoridation testimony provided the opponents of fluoridation with a handy reference for future use.[55]

Expansion and Polarization of Fluoridation Views, Mid-1950s

The scientific case for fluoridation grew stronger by the mid-1950s and gained some important scientific support. After seeing the results of the Newburgh, New York, fluoridation experiment in 1954, Margaret and Howard Smith, the Arizona scientists who had opposed fluoridation at the Delaney hearings, reversed themselves. The completion of the tenth year of the Grand Rapids-Muskegon study showed what Arnold, Dean, Jay, and Knutson termed "a striking reduction" in dental decay in both baby and permanent teeth. There was even evidence of less decay for persons whose teeth had already formed or erupted before they started consuming fluoridated water. NIDR publicized these results widely. From 1954 to 1955 the New York City Board of Health conducted a detailed study and recommended water fluoridation for the city. Institute Director Arnold supplied the positive Grand Rapids results and his strong endorsement to the city's fluoridation proponents and allowed the campaigners to use his letter "for the sake of . . . the children of New York."[56] Resistance in New York, however, stalled fluoridation for the nation's largest city for a decade.

The year 1954 also included a significant legal milestone in fluoridation history. In December the U.S. Supreme Court issued its first ruling upholding a community's right to fluoridate its water supply. In that case the Court sustained a Louisiana court ruling on the right of Shreveport to fluoridate its water supply.[57]

Fluoridation expanded, but opposition to the process increased during the first term of the Eisenhower administration. By 1954 over 22 million people were receiving fluoridated water in the United States, but the number discontinuing fluoridation increased dramatically from 256,399 in 1953 to 1.4 million in 1954. The rise in terminations indicated that the antifluoridation movement had gained influence in the nation.[58]

While isolated groups had formed earlier to oppose fluoridation in Massachusetts, California, and Washington, a national antifluoridation effort emerged in the mid-1950s under the leadership of Dr. George Waldbott, a Detroit allergist, and his wife. In 1955 the Waldbotts initiated a bimonthly newsletter, the *National Fluoridation News*, that disseminated antifluoridation information. Subsequently, the Waldbotts joined forces with other opponents and organized national letter-writing campaigns to Congress. Later Waldbott collaborated with Dr. Frederick Exner, a Seattle radiologist, on an antifluoridation book, *The American Fluoridation Experiment: The Subornation of Science.*[59]

The opposition to fluoridation vexed and surprised scientists who had carried out the fluoridation research. In a humorous observation, Arnold suggested that pamphlet printers were behind the antifluoridation campaign because they needed such a clientele to reverse their lack of business.[60]

The controversy was also responsible for the introduction of social science research techniques into dentistry. In the 1950s social scientists had become interested in the question of why voters rejected fluoridation. Early investigators traced the cause to "free floating anxiety," but others later attributed the opposition to a variety of circumstances, including "antiscientific" attitudes. The Division of Dental Public Health of the Public Health Service funded some of those first examinations of decision making on fluoridation.[61]

In the 1950s social scientists surveyed several communities to elicit reasons for distrust of fluoridation. In an early analysis of the antifluoridation sentiment, Bernard and Judith Maussner reported in a 1955 issue of *Scientific American* that increasing anti-intellectualism, distrust of scientists, and fear of conspiracy fed the growth of resistance to fluoridation in the nation. Harvard University anthropologists found that communities instituting fluoridation were wealthier, better educated, and populated with larger numbers of children under fifteen years of age than communities rejecting fluoridation. The Harvard group also learned that a larger proportion of individuals over sixty-five were more skeptical about fluoridation than those under that age.[62]

The opposition to fluoridation and the impossibility of installing fluoridation everywhere also led the dental science community to seek alternate means of bringing fluoride's benefits to the public. By 1955 the Institute and Public Health Service research indicated that only topical applications of fluoride could serve as a dental decay preventive when fluoridated water was unavailable. At that time Surgeon General Scheele recommended against the use of fluorides in vitamin tablets and food because there was no way of regulating intake and there was insufficient data on the safety and effectiveness of fluoride ingested in these forms. Research was still under way on fluorides in toothpaste and mouthwashes, the two other potential aids. Nevertheless, water fluoridation, estimated at a cost of ten cents per capita annually, remained the surgeon general's preference for curtailing dental caries.[63]

In 1958 a World Health Organization expert committee announced its support of fluoridation. By then scientists in a wide variety of fields had published almost three thousand research articles since 1938 on the biological effects of fluoride. In analyses of those works the committee asserted that there was no evidence that 1 ppm fluoride in drinking water impaired the general health. The committee concluded that controlled fluoridation "is a practicable and effective public health measure."[64]

Completion of the Grand Rapids Study, 1960-1961

Institute scientists reached a landmark in 1960 when they completed the fifteenth year of the Grand Rapids study. Looking back on the annual examinations, Dr. David B. Scott remembered the experience as "one of the biggest thrills in my life." The only Institute scientist to participate in the entire series, Scott marveled at the change he witnessed when he examined the initial group of kindergarteners and first graders reared entirely with fluoridation. "You didn't have to have a microscope ... to sense that you were seeing something totally different. ... It was obvious that there was an immense change in this generation of teeth," Scott recalled.[65]

Indeed, the study satisfied most of its original objectives. Artificial fluoridation displayed the same effects as natural fluoridation. The trial demonstrated that 1 ppm fluoride in drinking water safely controlled development of dental caries. Compared with the decay prevalence of children drinking fluoride-free water, the Grand Rapids dental caries rate was from 50 to 63 percent lower for children aged twelve to fourteen years and 48 to 50 percent lower for those fifteen and sixteen years old. Moreover, none of the 1,031 children examined showed any significant cosmetic damage to their teeth. Only 4 of the 1,031 children aged twelve to sixteen years old had mild fluorosis, which, according to Dean's classification, was a visible white coloration of the enamel.[66]

Water engineers also gained valuable information from the experience. While the water treatment equipment consistently worked well, the operators found that sodium silicofluoride was just as effective as sodium fluoride in producing the desired fluoride level and less costly. In 1958, therefore, Grand Rapids started using sodium silicofluoride to fluoridate its water supply. The results, similar to the other fluoridation studies in New York and Canada, fulfilled the expectations of the sponsors and gave fluoridation proponents strong proof for future use.[67]

By 1960 at least seventeen countries had joined the United States and Canada in introducing fluoridation to some of their communities. The Fédération Dentaire Internationale, representing forty-five countries, voted in favor of resolutions affirming the safety of fluoridation and urging all countries to give serious consideration to using fluorides to control dental decay. In the United States over 41 million people were drinking fluoridated water by the end of 1960 while fluoridation was discontinued from 1950 to 1960 for 2.5 million.[68]

That same year an important supplemental development occurred when the American Dental Association Council on Dental Therapeutics officially recognized Crest toothpaste, a dentifrice with fluoride, as "an effective decay reducing agent." The association's approval was its first granted to a fluoride dentifrice.[69]

(L to R) Dr. Francis Arnold, director, NIDR; W. L. Harris, superintendent, Grand Rapids Water Filtration Plant; Dr. Fred Wertheimer, chief of the Public Health Dentistry Section, Michigan Department of Health; and Dr. Philip Jay, professor of dentistry, School of Dentistry, University of Michigan, examine a chart illustrating the impact of the fluoridation of drinking water on children's teeth.

Government Takes the Offensive on Fluoridation, 1960-1970

Despite overwhelming scientific justification for fluoridation, proponents appeared to be losing against antifluoridationists in referendums in the United States. The November 1960 elections that elevated John F. Kennedy to the nation's presidency brought disappointment to the advocates of fluoridation. While forty thousand voters approved the institution of fluoridation, almost 1 million rejected fluoridation in referendums. Distressed about the growing sentiment against fluoridation, members of the Institute's National Advisory Dental Research Council urged the surgeon general to consult with the American Dental Association to reappraise the situation and to allow the Public Health Service to work with medical councils and societies to develop a long-range campaign to support fluoridation.[70]

Subsequently, the Kennedy and Johnson administrations actively promoted local fluoridation and started to fight back in an organized campaign against antifluoridation accusations. The Public Health Service dropped the policy of neutrality in fluoridation campaigns, but the antifluoridationists had gained such a foothold that the task of countering their charges was difficult. The PHS Institute and Division of Dental Public Health and Resources and the American Dental Association promoted fluoridation and combated the accusations leveled against the process. The Institute increased its public relations effort by publicizing its fluoridation research results through exhibits, radio, and television. Moreover, when Institute Director Arnold learned of a local attempt to start fluoridation, he wrote letters of support, as he did in 1963 in the case of Fredonia, New York. To respond to antifluoridation statements, the Division of Dental Public Health and Resources started issuing fluoridation memorandums on the scientific and medical facts.

Others rallied to the fluoridation cause. The American Dental Association, which had consistently publicized the benefits of fluoridation, produced a film, "One in a Million," in 1963 for wide dissemination to promote the process. In a 1966 address Dr. Luther Terry, vice-president of the University of Pennsylvania and surgeon general during the resurgence of federal support, called fluoridation "one of the four great mass preventive health measures of history" along with pasteurization of milk, purification of water, and immunization against diseases.[71]

All the presidents in the 1960s—John F. Kennedy, Lyndon B. Johnson, and Richard M. Nixon—praised fluoridation as, in Nixon's words, "a highly effective method for the prevention of tooth decay." The three leaders urged citizens to support, as Johnson expressed it, "the encouragement and adoption of such preventive measures as fluoridation of community water supplies to reduce painful and costly tooth decay among our children."[72]

Fluoridation Research After 1960

Meanwhile, the National Institute of Dental Research continued research on all aspects of fluoridation. Considerably more was at stake than refuting the claims of fluoridation opponents. Although by the 1960s the mainstream scientific community had accepted fluoridation as safe and effective in curbing dental decay, scientists still had much to learn about the mechanisms involved in its effectiveness. After over twenty years of research, scientists still did not know how fluoride worked to prevent dental caries. How did the fluoride ion combine with elements of the tooth structure to create more resistance to decay? Moreover, no one could explain why, when drinking water was fluoridated, some people had more cavities than others.

McClure and his Institute colleagues and Dr. Finn Brudevold and his associates at the Forsyth Dental Center in Boston investigated the chemical reactions between fluoride and enamel. Brudevold suggested that significant amounts of fluoride acquired beyond ten years after tooth eruption adhered to the surfaces of crystals on teeth and thus reinforced the enamel. NIDR scientists discovered in the 1960s that fluoride enhanced the perfection of crystals in tooth enamel, but they needed to determine whether the more perfect crystals provided greater resistance to tooth decay. The search thus went on for answers on the very basis of the fluoridation process.[73]

Scientists also had to determine the effectiveness of fluoridation on all kinds of individuals. How long did the decay-preventive qualities of fluoridation last? Did older people benefit? Could the mother's ingestion of fluoridated water during pregnancy increase dental caries resistance in children? The Institute supported such work by its own scientists and researchers in other institutions.

Funded in part by the Institute, an important study of the 1960s by Drs. Harold R. Englander and Donald A. Wallace of the University of Illinois boosted the importance of fluoridation by showing that eighteen- to fifty-nine-year-old residents of Aurora, Illinois, with 1.2 ppm fluoride in their drinking water, had 40 to 50 percent fewer dental cavities than their counterparts had in fluoride deficient Rockford, Illinois. Moreover, the examiners found no objectionable enamel fluorosis in any of the Aurora subjects. That study supported findings of the earlier one by Russell and Elvove in Colorado Springs but covered almost three times as many people. The Englander-Wallace work was especially significant because it demonstrated that fluoridation's benefits extended well past middle age.[74]

On the other hand, scientific teams disagreed on whether prenatal consumption of fluoridated drinking water increased a child's resistance to dental decay. In the 1960s scientists were unable to determine whether fluoride passed through the placental barrier in sufficient quantities to provide the fetus with added resistance to dental caries. Some thought that the Grand Rapids study and another of Evanston, Illinois, indicated prenatal ingestion reduced caries by 10 percent, but Dr. James Carlos's work for the New York State Department of Health on Newburgh children showed no significant difference. To resolve the issue, Drs. Herschel Horowitz and S. B. Heifetz of the Division of Dental Health conducted an extensive epidemiological study of Minneapolis children that confirmed Carlos's findings. Thus, the Food and Drug Administration banned the sale of fluoride tablets as a prenatal preventive of dental decay on the grounds that the tablets were ineffective, although the tablets did not present a health hazard to mother or fetus.[75]

In the 1960s the researchers continued to seek other means of introducing fluoride to prevent dental caries because a sizable portion of the world's population would not have access to fluoridated water supplies. The Institute supported one such study in Colombia to set a standard for maximum concentration of fluoride in salt and to compare its preventive effects with those of fluoridated water. In addition, the Institute and the PHS dental public health staff supported intramural and extramural testing of the uses of fluoride tablets and fluoridated toothpaste. The two agencies also funded research aimed at improving the method of topical fluoride application.[76]

During the Kennedy and Johnson administrations the Institute played a leading role in promoting fluoridation internationally. Its scientists collaborated on studies with the Fédération Dentaire Internationale and the World Health Organization (WHO) by supporting other countries' efforts to adopt fluoridation. Institute epidemiologists and WHO colleagues judged the dental effects on various populations of fluoride exposure and focused on the diets of groups with dental caries rates different from the norm.[77]

In 1963 Arnold and Dr. Donald Galagan, chief of the PHS Division of Dental Health and Resources, traveled to Dublin to appear as expert witnesses on fluoridation for the Irish government. Their testimony helped the government win its case. That court victory set the stage for fluoridation of water supplies throughout Ireland.[78]

Press Accusations, 1960-1979

Despite scientific advances and international acceptance of fluoridation, in the 1960s the Institute, surgeon general, and PHS dental public health officials had to contend with unexpected adversaries, some of the nation's press. Most of the nation's magazines and news-papers supported fluoridation. Thus, federal officials were surprised to read a December 7, 1963, attack in the widely respected *Saturday Review of Literature.* The *Saturday Review*'s science editor, John Lear, criticized the Public Health Service for its promotion of fluoridation at a time when New York City officials were still undecided about instituting fluoridation. Hoping to quell the issue, Galagan preferred remaining publicly silent. Unaware of Galagan's stance, J. Stewart Hunter, assistant to the surgeon general for information, protested the Lear article in a letter to Norman Cousins, the *Saturday Review* editor. Cousins responded by defending the magazine and presenting both sides in the dispute.[79]

Lear based a second attack in January 1964 on a single paper titled "Accumulation of Skeletal Fluoride and Its Implications" by authors identified by the Institute's McClure as three Canadians—a labora-tory technician, a dairy chemist, and a farm scientist—without any training or experience in fluoride studies. The Canadians claimed that fluoride was a potential health hazard because of skeletal reten-tion of fluoride. The article provoked an exchange between Institute Director Arnold and the Canadian Department of National Health and Welfare's Dental Health Division. Ultimately, Arnold con-demned the Canadian report as erroneous.[80]

As federal officials considered strategy to counter a possible third *Saturday Review* antifluoridation article, readers flooded Cousins with profluoridation mail, much of which he published. Still defending his journal, Cousins tried to shift the argument against fluoridation to his magazine's right to comment on a public matter. Again Galagan recommended silence, a policy that Dr. Luther Terry, surgeon gen-eral and a strong advocate of fluoridation, followed. In 1965 the *Saturday Review* temporarily abandoned the fluoridation battle.[81]

While the *Saturday Review* dispute caused public relations problems for the federal government, it failed to prevent the spread of fluorida-tion in the New York metropolitan area or elsewhere in the nation. On May 28, 1965, Connecticut, where many Manhattan workers lived, became the first state in the nation to mandate fluoridation of public water supply systems for communities serving more than twenty thousand people. New York City voters finally accepted fluoridation, and in September 1965 fluoridated water started flow-ing through the water supply of the nation's largest city. In 1967 the

Minnesota legislature approved a law requiring fluoridation by 1970 for some five hundred communities. Although by 1967 antifluoridationists succeeded in persuading five states to require local referendums on initiating fluoridation, there was no evidence that the *Saturday Review* affected those decisions. Instead, by 1967, of the nation's ten largest cities, only Los Angeles and Boston remained without a fluoridated water supply.[82]

Nevertheless, the public relations aspect continued to worry Institute and Division of Dental Health officials. By 1967 62.5 million of the nation's population were receiving fluoridated drinking water. Arnold, McClure, and their colleagues feared that their efforts to increase those numbers were jeopardized by antifluoridationist misuse of Food and Drug Administration regulations restricting fluoride products, such as vitamin tablets. Consequently, Institute and Division of Dental Health officials urged their Food and Drug Administration counterparts to insure that such statements would not damage fluoridation promotion. Reacting to those concerns, the Food and Drug Administration approved, with the concurrence of the Institute, a fish protein concentrate containing fluoride primarily for use in underdeveloped nations.[83]

Despite the care to avoid unfavorable publicity the Institute encountered new *Saturday Review* accusations in 1969 over the use of fluoridated water in artificial kidney machines. By that time the National Institute of Arthritis and Metabolic Diseases, responsible for research on artificial kidney development and clinical use, had insufficient information on the safest amount of fluoride in water used for hemodialysis, the process by which the artificial kidney cleansed the patient's blood. Patients undergoing hemodialysis used approximately 900 liters of water weekly—50 to 100 times the amount of fluid consumed by a healthy person. Because of this inconclusive research the National Institutes of Health reported in February 1969 that most dialysis centers were using deionized, or purified, water to insure the safety of dialysis. Such a problem, however, had no bearing on normal consumption of fluoridated water from community water supplies.[84]

Probably unaware of the Public Health Service report, Lear renewed his *Saturday Review* attacks on fluoridation. He accused the Public Health Service of failing to disseminate the results of research suggesting that excessive and possibly harmful amounts of fluoride appeared in a patient's skeletal tissue from long-term dialysis. Several columnists, including James J. Kilpatrick, sided with Lear. Dr. Joshua Lederberg of Stanford University, 1958 Nobel Prize winner in medicine, called for more research on fluoridation's effects. In the May 1969 issue the *Saturday Review* published a refutation by Dr. Frederick J. Stare and associates at the Harvard School of Public Health, the Harvard Medical School, and the Harvard School of Dental Medicine. Asking if any proof existed that fluoridated water at 1 ppm was harmful to anyone, the Harvard group responded that after twenty years of research, "The answer continues to be a clear, emphatic 'No.'" [85]

The antifluoridationist publicity had mixed influence. More than eight hundred inquiries about fluoridation overwhelmed the reduced staff of Public Health Service dental health information specialists during the first half of 1969. Almost 90 million residents in the United States were drinking fluoridated water by then. Yet 59 percent of the fluoridation referendums that year ended in victories for the opposition. Social scientists studying the fluoridation opposition searched for a common thread. "As a result, there is no consistent body of information that enables us to explain under what circumstances fluoridation is accepted or rejected or how to campaign effectively for its introduction," one concluded. But several other investigators regarded fluoridation resistance "as one instance of community conflict." [86]

The accusations persisted, and Institute scientists, who by the late 1960s were publishing almost 90 percent of their work on nonfluoridation matters, had to check out significant charges. One of the first after the 1969 *Saturday Review* incident originated in the Stanford University Department of Biological Sciences. There Edward Groth III, a doctoral candidate in biology, prepared his dissertation on "Fluoridation: Anatomy of a Controversy." The dissertation included references to articles reporting on fluorosis by NIH scientists, including Dean. While still assembling his thesis, Groth sent a letter attacking fluoridation to the editor of *Consumer Reports*, which had published a profluoridation article in its March 1969 issue. Dr. Donald Kennedy, chairman of Stanford's biological sciences department, and Dr. Paul R. Ehrlich, the noted biologist, sent a covering letter to *Consumer Reports* that described Groth as "a highly competent and responsible scientist" and urged the editor to give "careful attention" to Groth's comments. [87]

In 1974, when Groth was working as a research fellow at the California Institute of Technology, he tried to get his dissertation accepted for publication. Initially he attracted the attention of Jack Anderson, a nationally syndicated columnist who publicized Groth's antifluoridation conclusions but later admitted that he considered fluoridation safe and effective. Upon carefully reviewing the thesis Groth wanted to publish, Institute scientists found the work well-written but with some gross errors "and numerous innuendoes that give away his true feelings." In his analysis Groth attempted to use early articles by Dean to indicate that fluoridation was harmful. Groth also sought support of Dr. Lloyd Tepper, associate commissioner for science of the Food and Drug Administration, but Tepper denounced the work. The issue, however, continued to 1979 when Donald Kennedy was serving as commissioner of the Food and Drug Administration. During a state fluoridation study an antifluoridationist circulated a copy of Donald Kennedy's 1969 covering letter for Groth's statement to *Consumer Reports*. Explaining in his response that this 1969 communication primarily served as a covering letter, the commissioner proclaimed his support for optimal fluoridation of community water supplies.[88]

Budget cuts in the early 1970s reduced funding for the Public Health Service fluoridation research, public education, and technical assistance for local communities desiring to institute fluoridation. The Nixon administration impoundment of funds contributed to that situation.[89]

Scientists versus Scientists, 1974-1976

In 1974 a new antifluoridation leader, John Yiamouyiannis, joined the battle when the National Health Federation of Monrovia, California, hired him as science director. Yiamouyiannis had earned degrees in biochemistry at the Universities of Chicago and Rhode Island. Also an opponent of polio vaccination and pasteurization of milk, Yiamouyiannis conducted the federation's antifluoridation campaign by giving speeches around the world, appearing on television and radio shows, and assisting opponents in drawing up lawsuits against fluoridation. Donald McNeil found that Yiamouyiannis played a major role in defeating fluoridation in a Los Angeles referendum in 1975.[90]

National Cancer Institute scientists had to refute statements by Yiamouyiannis and a retired NCI scientist, Dean Burk. In 1975 the pair submitted to Congressman Delaney a statistical analysis, based on NCI data and published by the federation, claiming that cancer deaths in the United States were highest in fluoridated cities. Delaney brought that report to the attention of the House of Representatives. In rebuttal, NCI scientists pointed out factual errors and the neglect of important environmental and social variables. The cancer experts concluded that their data did "not support any suspicion of carcinogenic hazard associated with fluoridation." Burk and Yiamouyiannis responded with another report, which, in turn, drew additional NCI denials. The dispute lasted almost a year and abated only in February 1976 when Dr. Donald S. Frederickson, director of the National Institutes of Health, reaffirmed the findings of the National Cancer Institute.[91]

The 1976 meeting of the American Chemical Society in San Francisco provided another forum for the fluoridation opponents. Dr. Aly Mohamed of the Department of Biology, University of Missouri at Kansas City, gave a paper concluding that fluoride caused an increase in chromosomal abnormalities in bone marrow and testes cells in adult mice. The Institute sent experts to Missouri to check on the Mohamed report. The team discovered that Mohamed had based his talk on a former graduate student's master's thesis that relied on poor quality pictures. Their investigation also revealed that Mohamed's study contained statistical discrepancies, inaccuracies, a lack of objectivity, and an absence of original data to support his conclusions. One investigator found that Mohamed's assertion that "permanent genetic damage was induced by sodium fluoride is unmerited." After the Missouri visit an Institute scientist repeated Mohamed's animal experiment and obtained results showing that fluoride did not alter chromosome structure and was not mutagenic. Moreover, the results of NIH and University of Minnesota studies produced no evidence that fluoride affected human genetics. Despite the overwhelming proof against Mohamed's conclusions, the Missouri scientist continued to use those findings in public speeches against fluoridation.[92]

Administrative Changes in Federal Fluoridation Promotion, 1975-1985

Until the mid-1970s the PHS Division of Dentistry, aided by the Institute, promoted fluoridation. In June 1975 senior officials of the Department of Health, Education, and Welfare decided to transfer the Division's fluoridation and other preventive dentistry programs to the Centers for Disease Control (CDC) in Atlanta, Georgia. The actual move occurred primarily in 1976 when the Atlanta agency took over the preventive dentistry functions of consultation, technical assistance, promotion, and health education. "We anticipate renewed emphasis on preventive dentistry programs," predicted Dr. John C. Greene, special assistant for Dental Affairs in the Office of the Assistant Secretary for Health in the Department of Health, Education, and Welfare.[93] In the reorganization federal authorities apparently hoped to strengthen fluoridation promotion, for President Gerald Ford, the former congressman representing Grand Rapids, Michigan, was known as a strong advocate of fluoridation.

Although Division of Dentistry fluoridation personnel were offered their same positions in Atlanta, most of them declined to move. Some instead transferred to the Institute, which began serving as the CDC liaison for obtaining fluoridation information from Washington, D.C., area federal agencies. The Institute subsequently arranged for apprising the CDC of such matters as the National Cancer Institute studies on fluoride and cancer.[94]

While the main fluoridation promotional activities were housed in Atlanta, the Institute continued support of the process in congressional hearings. After Scott, with his thorough knowledge of the Grand Rapids work, assumed the position of Institute director in 1976, he promoted fluoridation in congressional testimony during his term of office. When the CDC did not send a witness to testify at hearings in 1977 on the fluoridation of public drinking water, the Institute coordinated a National Cancer Institute refutation of the leading opponent, Yiamouyiannis. The antifluoridationist again introduced his statistical studies with Burk and placed Mohamed's paper in the committee's record. Members of the National Cancer Institute supplied the preponderance of the rebuttals to the charges made by Yiamouyiannis, who commanded newspaper headlines with the claim that fluoridated water would kill at least five hundred thousand people. Congress took no action but continued to monitor claims after the hearings ended. Several years later the staff of the House committee responsible for those hearings indicated that it had accepted the National Cancer Institute's conclusions.[95]

The CDC fluoridation functions expanded during the term of President Jimmy Carter, who, as governor of Georgia, had signed a mandatory fluoridation bill. Carter continued his fluoridation advocacy as president by issuing strong supporting statements. Under his administration the CDC extended community and school water fluoridation throughout the nation by providing financial and technical assistance, health education, grant funds, training, and laboratory proficiency testing. The Institute continued to coordinate supplemental research and transmit results to the CDC. In 1979 the Department of Health, Education, and Welfare set a goal of providing the opportunity to fluoridate all community water supplies in the United States by 1989.[96]

Consequently, as the 1970s advanced, an increasing number of United States residents started using fluoridated water. In 1977 105 million, or 49 percent of the population, had access to fluoridated water. Of the total drinking fluoridated water 94.6 million consumed artificially added fluoride, and the remainder received fluoridated water from natural sources.[97]

Attacks on fluoridation also persisted. After he left the National Health Federation in 1979, Yiamouyiannis continued to oppose fluoridation by starting his own group, the Center for Health Action, in Delaware, Ohio. He issued a new charge that fluoridation caused premature aging and even tried suing a Public Health Service scientist who disputed his claims. Other opponents, especially in San Francisco, attempted to link acquired immunodeficiency syndrome (AIDS) to fluoridation.[98]

In 1983 the opponents won twice as many referendums as the advocates of fluoridation. In analyzing public rejection, social scientists had identified a variety of patterns underlying fluoridation opposition. Such a situation presented a dilemma for a democratic society. Sociologist Annabelle B. Motz suggested that the fluoridation issue emphasized the necessity of clarifying the role of the democratic process in a highly technological, populated society. On the other hand, McNeil, the historian, found that the resistance to fluoridation was the price of maintaining an open political system in the United States.[99]

Yet in the 1980s other changes affected fluoridation in American life. In 1981 the CDC fluoridation grant program for the states expired, and the administration of President Ronald Reagan incorporated the fluoridation aid into preventive health block grants. Emphasis on fluoridation subsequently diminished in the competition with such projects as mental health and immunization for the block grant money. Nevertheless, Public Health Service support continued. In 1983 Dr. C. Everett Koop, surgeon general, strongly backed fluoridation in public announcements as well as in a letter to the Environmental Protection Agency on a question involving fluoridation. Under Koop the Public Health Service set a goal of offering fluoridation to 95 percent of all community water systems in the United States by 1990.[100]

By 1985 the fluoridation campaign continued to gain adherents but still faced formidable obstacles. Eight states had mandatory fluoridation laws, and seventy-five national science and health organizations had endorsed fluoridation. In over thirty completed court cases through 1985, the courts consistently upheld the legality of fluoridation. Community water supplies serving 70 million, including Los Angeles, California, with almost 3 million people, still lacked fluoridation. On the positive side, more people than ever in the United States were consuming fluoridated water—54 percent of the total population with 61 percent of those using public water supplies.[101]

In Retrospect

The role of government in civilian health matters contributed to the success and the controversy surrounding mass fluoridation. Without satisfactory government testing of artificial fluoridation, implementation of mass fluoridation would have been impossible. Yet the path that led to federal endorsement and government influence also provoked opposition.

In the case of fluoridation, epidemiology rather than basic research helped to identify the inhibitor of dental caries. Of the four most important mass public health achievements, fluoridation was the only one resulting from the use of epidemiology. The basic research attempts to explain the fluoride role followed the epidemiological result. When the Grand Rapids and similar projects started, scientists knew more about fluoride's dental benefits than about how it worked to prevent dental caries.

Faced from the outset with a public relations problem, Public Health Service officials had to deal with the two-faced nature of fluoride. Like many other substances, including common ones such as water, in high concentrations fluoride was toxic; in minute quantities it inhibited dental decay and was safe. Consequently, government authorities understood the necessity of proving to the public fluoridation's efficacy and safety through sufficient testing before endorsing mass implementation.

The early success of the Grand Rapids fluoridation project presented government health administrators with a typical scientific dilemma. Given the apparent dental benefits to the recipients of fluoridation, how long could federal authorities resist demands to recommend mass fluoridation? Ten years before the end of the Grand Rapids testing Public Health Service officials gave in to pressures from their state counterparts and endorsed fluoridation.

The premature approval produced mixed results. First, how could the Public Health Service authorities refuse fluoridation's advantages to the subjects in the control group at Muskegon? Of course, the researchers complied with the wishes of the Muskegon parents. But the Muskegon control was lost to the Grand Rapids project. Nevertheless, the Grand Rapids program produced valuable information that the National Institute of Dental Research needed to uphold the safety and efficacy of the water treatment's process and benefits.

Another major consequence of federal government endorsement was a huge upsurge in communities installing fluoridation. Statistics indicated that the first substantial increase in fluoridation adoption in the United States followed the official federal recommendations for mass fluoridation. Later fluoridation polls indicated that the degree of government promotion and assistance affected the rise in community adoption of fluoridation across the nation.

On the other hand, the early approval provoked opposition to fluoridation. While Dean predicted resistance, he thought extensive testing would minimize such problems. Even Arnold, who considered the substance safe enough to give his children, recognized the political dangers of premature recommendations. But, as Arnold said later, no one anticipated the vehemence that antifluoridation unleashed.

As social scientists recognized, some of the attacks on fluoridation resulted from the very nature of the democratic system. When did government stop protecting a minority view in order to benefit a majority? Were referendums appropriate for a mass public health measure? How could a scientific decision that fluoridation was beneficial be reconciled with the political charge that fluoridation invaded the individual's private choice of what to drink?

Ironically, dental research benefited from fluoridation and the opposition. As Arnold pointed out, Institute and nongovernment scientists engaged in extensive investigations to respond to the antifluoridationists. Researchers in a variety of health fields conducted testing that disproved allegations of fluoride's involvement in cancer and other diseases. Basic research also continued into the 1980s on the mechanism by which fluoride helped to prevent dental decay and why everyone did not benefit equally from it.

By 1985 over half of the nation's population on public water supplies used fluoridation. Research on the process was continuing, and the Public Health Service was aiming for fluoridation of most of the nation's public water supplies by 1990. Only the future might reveal what those basic investigations might unearth and how the findings might affect fluoridation.

CHAPTER SIX

The Struggles For Growth in Dental Research

Nature is not a temple but a workshop in which man is the labourer.

IVAN SERGEIVICH TURGENEV

In a 1956 editorial the *Washington Post* praised Congress for funding a National Institute of Dental Research laboratory building that would facilitate the nation's dental research. To support the newspaper's position, the editor asked readers to "witness Uncle Sam's huge dental bills for the armed services." [1]

Indeed, the Institute needed the facilities and the people to carry out its mission. The legislation establishing the Institute, however, only authorized funding but did not appropriate money. Obtaining funds was another matter. Instead, backers of the Institute struggled to persuade the federal government to fulfill the authorizations provided in the 1948 law.

In the forefront of Institute support were officials of the American Dental Association, Senators James Murray, the Democrat from Montana, and Lister Hill, a Democrat from Alabama, and Congressman John Fogarty, a Democrat from Rhode Island. Already instrumental in establishing the Institute, Murray continued to champion federal dental research until he retired in 1961. Hill and Fogarty, two leading Capitol Hill advocates of federal health research, coordinated and guided Institute legislation through Congress from the 1940s through the late 1960s.

Hill was a natural champion of health research. Son of a pioneer Alabama physician and named for the famous British surgeon, Lord Joseph Lister, he took an interest in public health fostered by his family's friendships with Alabama health professionals. Hill graduated from the University of Alabama and was admitted to the bar after studying law at the University of Michigan and Columbia University. In 1923 he entered the House of Representatives where he served until his 1938 appointment to the Senate. Subsequently, Alabama voters repeatedly elected Hill to the Senate throughout the war and postwar periods. By the time he became a promoter of dental research legislation, Hill already had achieved a reputation as a supporter of federal aid to health through his cosponsorship of the Hill-Burton Act of 1946 to aid in hospital construction and of legislation establishing the Institute. In 1955 Hill assumed the chairmanship of the Subcommittee on Health of the Committee on Labor and Public Welfare, where he exerted his greatest impact on dental research funding.[2]

John Fogarty's background differed greatly from that of his Senate counterpart. His interest in health legislation arose instead during his congressional service. Reaching adulthood during the Great Depression, Fogarty attended but did not graduate from Providence College. Instead he became a bricklayer and rose to the presidency of Bricklayers Union No. 1 of Rhode Island. In 1941 Fogarty began his House of Representatives service and, except for wartime service in the U.S. Army, remained in the House. Fogarty's union background must have led him to serve on the House Department of Labor—Health, Education and Welfare subcommittee of the Committee on Appropriations, where he became an admirer of Congressman Frank Keefe, a Republican from Wisconsin. A firm supporter of the 1940s Wisconsin dental health officers' fluoridation promotion, Keefe set an example for Fogarty, who credited the Wisconsin Republican with educating him on health legislation. In 1949 Fogarty succeeded Keefe as chairman of the subcommittee responsible for the NIH budget. Fogarty's congressional colleagues subsequently nicknamed him "Mr. Public Health" for his staunch advocacy and influence exerted for federal support of health research and programs.[3]

Murray, Hill, and Fogarty and the American Dental Association called for sufficient funding as Institute administrators sought to expand dental research in the 1940s and 1950s.

To Build or Not to Build: The Dispute over a National Institute of Dental Research Laboratory

For a decade after the Institute's founding, government officials argued over whether to fund a separate dental research laboratory. The future growth of the Institute's intramural research depended on the resolution of that question because NIH lacked the space to house the Institute staff, which amounted to seventy-five by 1951.

As NIH Director Dyer and NIDR Director Dean found out before the Institute completed its first year, the law that authorized building funds did not guarantee that Congress would appropriate the money. Both had expected to go forward in planning the laboratory structure. But in 1949 the Bureau of the Budget omitted the construction funds from the proposed budget because planners thought that the dental research activities could be housed either in the future NIH Clinical Center or in space vacated by other institutes.[4]

After a groundswell of support from the American Dental Association, five senators of both parties, the surgeon general, and Dr. Bruce Forsyth, assistant surgeon general and chief dental officer, Congress allowed $100,000 for planning the building. President Truman signed the legislation on June 19, 1949.[5]

But as Wisconsin's Congressman Keefe, an Institute supporter, later observed, the planning money went "into the rat hole, so to speak." When the building blueprints were almost completed and the site chosen, the Bureau of the Budget reneged on construction funding in 1950. Even Dean's complaints about a lack of space to a sympathetic Fogarty failed because a budget deficit led Congress to postpone most building projects for 1951. Finally, the financial burden of the Korean War that started in June 1950 killed the Institute building project, at least for the duration of that national emergency. Yielding to the succession of budgetary defeats, the Public Health Service leaders modified their position in 1951 to one favoring postponing the building *"until the need for such construction becomes apparent."* [6]

Meanwhile, cramped Institute working conditions forced Dean to create what Arnold called "research colonies" of employees at the Stapleton Public Health Service Hospital in Staten Island, New York; the Eastman Dental Dispensary in Rochester, New York; and various buildings in the Washington, D.C., metropolitan area. To ease conditions for the Institute's seventy-five employees, NIDR administrators negotiated an agreement in 1951 with the NIH leadership to house personnel in Bethesda when the Clinical Center opened. By the time all the staff members had returned to Bethesda, there was insufficient room because the Institute had hired twenty-nine more people by 1955. Again Institute scientists worked in crowded quarters.[7]

Dr. Francis Arnold championed the building cause when he succeeded Dean as Institute director in 1953. A pioneer NIH dental scientist, Dean's right-hand man, and a vocal advocate for dental research, he wanted adequate facilities in order to enlarge the Institute's scientific staff. Although the Korean War had ended, only congressional friends of the American Dental Association revived the issue in government circles. The new push started in 1956 when Senator Murray and Congressman Percy Priest, a Democrat from Tennessee and chairman of the House Interstate and Foreign Commerce Committee, introduced legislation to increase the laboratory building authorization to $5 million because of rising costs. Both men were influential members of the committees responsible for disposition of the measures. Hill, one of the bill's cosponsors, vowed to "do everything in my power to win the increase."[8]

The staff of the National Institute of Dental Research in 1953, when Dr. Dean retired and Dr. Arnold became director.

The executive department disagreed. Because of a fundamental policy change, the administration of President Dwight D. Eisenhower differed from Truman's staff on the proposed building. Whereas Truman's Bureau of the Budget opposed the project for fiscal reasons, Eisenhower's Department of Health, Education and Welfare, formerly the Federal Security Agency, objected on the grounds that the building would produce an enlarged intramural research program. Instead, the administration wanted to promote research in the nation's dental schools. "If we get an institute building in Bethesda . . . [it] might actually serve to draw research manpower away from the dental schools," Dr. Lowell T. Coggeshall, a department spokesman, explained to Hill's Senate Subcommittee on Health in 1956. Surgeon General Scheele and NIH Director James Shannon supported the department's view, but Institute Director Arnold was conspicuously absent from the witness list for the Senate hearing.[9]

Actually, the department's position had distorted somewhat a National Science Foundation appraisal and recommendations on NIH support of dental research. In January 1955 Department Secretary Oveta Culp Hobby, concerned with rising costs of the Public Health Service, had asked Dr. Alan Waterman, director of the National Science Foundation, to undertake a review and evaluation of her department's medical research programs. After interviewing Arnold and some of his staff, the foundation's committee of five physicians and three doctors of philosophy had concluded that the National Institute of Dental Research

> needs better facilities and more money for its operation. However, in view of the shortage of qualified individuals to carry out research in the field of dental medicine, the primary need would seem to be for additional funds to assist in the training of much needed research and teaching staff in non-Government institutions.

Moreover, the foundation study had clearly exempted the National Institute of Dental Research from a general recommendation against a major expansion of the NIH intramural program. The committee had stipulated that its particular proposal applied to "all Institutes except those of Microbiology and of Dental Research."[10]

Officials from the American Dental Association and one of the nation's leading academic dental scientists challenged the Eisenhower administration position. Dr. Joseph Volker, dean of the Alabama

School of Dentistry and president of the International Association for Dental Research, told Hill's subcommittee that a separate Institute building "would have absolutely no effect on our present standing research center." Alabama, he added, provided more adequate dental research facilities than the federal government.[11]

Facing pressure from the nation's organized dentistry, Congress and the Eisenhower administration compromised on the issue. At first the Senate unanimously voted for the $5 million authorization, and the nation's dental groups urged the House to do the same. Subsequently, Marion B. Folsom, the new secretary of Health, Education and Welfare, and the Bureau of the Budget staff talked congressional negotiators into lowering the authorization to $4 million. Both houses accepted the lower amount. Congress then satisfied the administration's aim of expanding research in the nation's dental schools by approving $3.7 million for grants for research at dental schools and $90 million for construction and improvement of dental and medical school research facilities (Public Law 635). Because Congress had granted the increased funding for dental school research, Folsom advised Eisenhower to agree to the $4 million authorization for an Institute building. On July 19, 1956, Eisenhower signed S. 3246, which became Public Law 732, part of a package authorizing considerable construction at the National Institutes of Health.[12]

Assured of a building, NIH administrators chose a new site for the Institute building, the Glenbrook golf course, which was south of the new Clinical Center. Because the former blueprint for the building was obsolete, Congress approved $200,000 in a supplemental appropriation bill for a second planning of the laboratory.[13]

But in 1957 the Institute's housing prospects again deteriorated. Because the Eisenhower administration launched an anti-inflation economy drive, the Bureau of the Budget denied all new federal construction funds. In addition, the Institute lost 3,000 square feet that left scientists with approximately 112 square feet of working space, or 40 square feet less than the standard for National Institutes of Health principal investigators. The Institute was forced to rent space in Silver Spring, Maryland, approximately twelve miles from the Bethesda campus. The inadequate facilities prompted over two dozen employees, some of them principal investigators, to leave the Institute. Dr. Floyd W. Pillars, vice-chairman of the American Dental Association's Council on Legislation, called the situation "a de-

plorable state of affairs" and "inconsistent with the avowed policy of
the Government of encouraging basic scientific endeavor." [14]

Later that year the Eisenhower administration's concern over national security almost delayed implementation of the Institute building plan. The president wanted to concentrate on countering the
Soviet Union's advances in space technology, revealed by the October 1957 launching of an artificial satellite, Sputnik, and increased
Soviet influence in neutral countries. Consequently, in December
1957 when Dr. William R. Alstadt, president of the American Dental Association, urged Eisenhower to fund the Institute's building,
Sherman Adams, assistant to the president, wrote in reply that the
administration was not contemplating construction of dental research
facilities in the near future. Adams explained that the budget instead
had to accommodate high priority national security programs.[15]

The Adams letter provoked a division of opinion among senior
officers of the American Dental Association. Some, including Executive Secretary Dr. Harold Hillenbrand, wanted to defer lobbying for
the Institute building for at least a year because of the Adams statement. Alstadt, however, thought "that the time was right to make an
'all-out' attempt to secure this much needed building," and he was
prepared to obtain the help of his friends in the Arkansas Democratic
congressional delegation for that task.[16]

A behind-the-scenes worker in the Arkansas Democratic Party,
Alstadt was friendly with Democratic Senators J. William Fulbright
and John McClellan and Congressmen Wilbur Mills and Dr. Dale
Alford, an Arkansas ophthalmologist. With the help of the Arkansas
congressional delegation, Alstadt arranged a meeting of Hill and
Fogarty with ADA officers to discuss the Institute building appropriations.[17]

Encouraged by talks with Hill and Fogarty, ADA officials launched
an intensive effort in 1958 to press for approval of the Institute's
building appropriations. The association's Chicago headquarters issued special bulletins to members to persuade their senators and representatives to fund the Institute building. One appeal, for example,
alerted dentists with the headline, "LACK OF FACILITIES HAMPERS
DENTAL RESEARCH—A.D.A. ASKS ALL DENTISTS TO WRITE
CONGRESS." Association officers also pleaded for the appropriations
at congressional hearings that year.

With the influential Hill and Fogarty supporting the association, both houses of Congress approved the construction appropriations. The House voted for $3.7 million before its Easter recess, and the Senate passed the allocation by voice vote on June 20, 1958. The pressure for allowing the building's construction was so great that the Eisenhower administration withdrew its objections. After ten years of waiting the Institute supporters gained appropriation of the construction funds on August 1, 1958, when Eisenhower signed the legislation, which became Public Law 85-580.[18]

Construction of the dental institute building began in 1959, the centennial year of the American Dental Association. On September 21, 1960, Dr. John W. Knutson, chief dental officer of the Public Health Service, and Institute Director Arnold participated in a simple cornerstone-laying ceremony on the southwest section of the National Institutes of Health campus. But by the time it was completed, the Institute's building was already too small. The structure was designed to accommodate 200 researchers in its five floors and two basements.[19] Arnold, however, had increased Institute personnel from 180 in 1960 to 258 in 1961.[20]

On a rainy spring day in 1961 congressional and health research dignitaries, including Dr. H. Trendley Dean, the Institute's first director, gathered for the building's dedication on the Bethesda campus. For the first time since his retirement Dean met with the old-timers associated with the fluoridation successes: Dr. Frank McClure, the chief of the Institute's Laboratory of Biochemistry; Arnold, the Institute director; and Dr. Elias Elvove, the chemistry wizard by then retired. Senator James Murray, so instrumental in establishing the Institute, had died before the building was finished, and his son and trusted legislative assistant, Charles, came in his place. Abraham Ribicoff, secretary of Health, Education and Welfare, spoke of the "noble and sacred purpose—better health through research" that was represented in that ceremony. Hill, Fogarty, and other supporters of the Institute bestowed their good wishes.

It was a fitting coincidence that the dedication of the National Institute of Dental Research Building—Building 30—took place on May 26, 1961, thirty-one years to the day that the law establishing the National Institute of Health took effect. The dedication ceremonies celebrated the past, present, and future. The principal speaker, Emory Morris, president of the W. K. Kellogg Foundation, which had supported the Grand Rapids project, summed up the prevailing

(L to R) Dr. Francis A. Arnold, director, NIDR; Dr. C. Willard Camalier, assistant secretary and director of the Washington office of the ADA; Dr. John W. Knutson, chief dental officer, PHS; and Dr. Seymour Kreshover, associate director, NIDR, at the ground breaking for the dental building, April 19, 1959.

sentiments: "Let us . . . unite our dreams and our energies to make the years ahead even more rewarding in terms of improved dental health for the people." [21]

The Years Ahead: Rivalry over Dental Research in the Public Health Service

With a separate laboratory building the Institute administrators faced the 1960s with the prospect of expanding research and personnel. Yet changes within the Public Health Service in the early years of that decade raised questions about the extent of the Institute's mission.

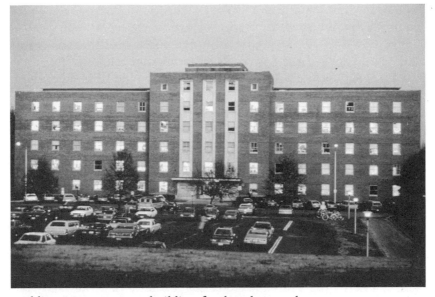

Building 30—a separate building for dental research.

After 1949, competition had developed over budgets and research between the Institute and the two Public Health Service divisions charged with dental health responsibilities, the Division of Dental Public Health and the Division of Dental Resources. The three had coped with coordination problems on appropriations because their budgets were combined into one prepared by the Institute budget officer for submission to Congress. Moreover, by direction of the surgeon general, all three agencies had assumed research tasks for fluoridation and defluoridation. The Division of Dental Public Health and the Division of Dental Resources had dealt usually with applied research, and the Institute with basic biological research, but the distinctions were sometimes blurred in their investigations.

In 1960 the House Appropriations Committee alleviated some of the budget difficulties by requiring each agency to submit a separate budget. The Institute administration expressed relief over the congressional directive, which eliminated problems Institute officers had faced in trying to coordinate budgets of the three agencies.[22]

Meanwhile, Surgeon General Leroy E. Burney tried to improve the dental research establishment when he reorganized the Public Health Service in 1960. He based his action on the findings of the Hundley

Report, an examination of the Public Health Service which, in its dental review, reflected the advice of over forty individuals prominent in medicine, dentistry, education, and public health. The consultants acknowledged the Institute's clear mission for fostering intramural and extramural basic and clinical research but differed on how to assign responsibilities. Some feared that the Institute's biological research role would be diluted if the Institute assumed the obligation for training in other kinds of research. Others recommended that the Institute be combined with the Division of Dental Public Health to handle both basic and applied research. Burney compromised by leaving the Institute intact but merging the two divisions and placing them under the Bureau of State Services. He appointed Dr. Donald Galagan, a participant in the Hundley study, as chief of the new Division of Dental Public Health and Resources.[23]

Instead of easing the differences over dental research, the reorganization intensified disagreements after the new division implemented one of the Hundley study suggestions. A dental activities planning group of the Hundley review had recommended creation of an applied research dental health center. Shortly after assuming leadership of the new division, Galagan, who had served on that planning panel, established a dental health center in San Francisco in 1961. The San Francisco center opened with a multipurpose mission: to conduct applied research in prevention and control of dental diseases; to train dental public health workers in the application of research findings; and to operate an epidemiology program on periodontal diseases, dental caries prevention, dental fluorosis, and cleft lip and palate. Galagan invited the Institute to partake in center operations, but Arnold "decided not to participate." Nevertheless, some funding for the center came from appropriations originally set aside for Arnold's Institute.[24]

Disagreement over the San Francisco center and the division's other responsibilities did not emerge immediately. In 1962 both Galagan and Dr. Seymour Kreshover, associate director of the National Institute of Dental Research, were upset about prospective usurpation of their work by nondental agencies, particularly the future National Institute of Child Health and Human Development. By 1963, however, whatever solidarity existed between the two dental agencies began to disintegrate when the Institute started losing projects, extramural grants, and money to the division. When

Galagan tried to acquire the Institute's extramural dental education research grants program in 1963, Institute administrators objected on the grounds that the proposed takeover exceeded the division's legislative authority.[25]

Arnold and Galagan also disagreed in 1963 over the responsibility for testing dental materials. Both were drawn into a jurisdictional dispute between Dr. Allen Astin, director of the National Bureau of Standards, and Dr. James Shannon, director of the National Institutes of Health, over which agency should finance such work. The disagreement upset American Dental Association officers because the association and the bureau had supported that dental materials research for over twenty-five years. At first, the ADA asked Arnold to take over the program. But when Arnold did not reply, the association administrators turned to Galagan, who agreed to establish a dental materials and technology laboratory if Surgeon General Luther L. Terry consented to such an arrangement. Hearing that the division might acquire the project, Arnold protested and persuaded Terry to reject Galagan's proposal because such activities fell within the jurisdiction of both agencies. Although the matter was resolved by leaving the dental materials unit at the bureau, in 1964 Galagan's successor, Dr. Viron Diefenbach, nevertheless convinced Terry to let the division form a dental materials research and development program at the San Francisco center. The issue remained a sore point between Kreshover, who became Institute director in 1966, and Diefenbach for the remaining years of the San Francisco center's existence.[26]

By 1966 the rivalry had sharpened. The division leadership proposed combining all Public Health Service dental activities into a dental bureau. Kreshover opposed the plan. In 1967 a loss of influence in Congress added to the dissension; Fogarty died suddenly and Hill was preparing to retire. Consequently, senators and representatives started complaining in appropriations hearings about the lack of coordination and possible duplication of effort by the Institute and division. Moreover, the Senate committee proposed legislation to integrate all dental health activities in one autonomous agency. While several members of the National Advisory Dental Research Council approved of the consolidation, they urged that the House committee counterpart retain such an organization within the National Institutes of Health.[27]

For help, the politically sensitive Shannon turned to Institute Director Kreshover, who, like the NIH director, was an articulate and eloquent spokesman for biomedical research. After the Health Manpower Act of 1968 placed the Division of Dental Health, the new name for the division, and professional biomedical education responsibilities under NIH, Shannon asked Kreshover to develop a plan to eliminate duplication and overlap of the dental activities. To comply, the Institute director formed an ad hoc advisory committee of eminent professional and academic leaders. The consultants recommended merging all dental research and educational support into a National Dental Institute. Kreshover and Shannon endorsed that proposal, but Division Director Diefenbach expressed reservations. Instead, he cautioned Dr. Robert Marston, Shannon's successor, that "no hurried steps should be taken to disengage service-related activities of the Division of Dental Health or to relocate them in the Public Health Service." [28]

NIH Director Marston attempted to foster agreement between Diefenbach and Kreshover, but the two maintained their different viewpoints. After reading the separate accounts by Diefenbach and Kreshover of the meeting with Marston, an American Dental Association official analyzed the problem: "I am not sure the two good doctors attended the same meeting." [29]

In January 1969 both Diefenbach and Hillenbrand, the association executive secretary, asked for another study of NIH dental activities. Although Marston agreed to the additional review, he delayed acting until the new Nixon administration's policies were clear. In June Marston assigned Dr. Robert E. Greenfield of the National Cancer Institute and Betty Jolliffe, a management analyst at NIH, to lead a fact-finding team that would recommend organizational options for the two agencies. [30]

Greenfield and Jolliffe found that because the Institute and division were attempting to fulfill quite different missions, projects that appeared to be duplications actually complemented one another. While the Institute's research and training responsibilities were codified in the 1948 law establishing it, the 1968 Public Health Service reorganization authorized the division to administer and support programs to prevent and control the same diseases and disorders that the Institute investigated. Greenfield and Jolliffe observed that for several years the Institute had attempted to find applications for its basic research results. They also determined that the division, with limited funds, was conducting research to assess and improve dental practitioners' techniques and to determine environmental hazards facing dentists and patients. But the extramural activities of the two agencies proved too complicated for the team to analyze in the time allowed.

In comparing the overall work, Greenfield and Jolliffe gave more favorable marks to the larger, better endowed Institute. While praising the Institute as a facility "dedicated to scientific excellence . . . and proud and protective of NIH's scientific reputation," the team evaluated the applied research supported by the division as having "limited national impact." Consequently, in providing four organizational options, the team included one abolishing the division, two combining all of the functions of the Institute with most of the division's obligations, and one merely clarifying Institute and division responsibilities. But the investigators made no recommendation and concluded instead that the complex problems of organizing dental activities ruled out a simple, satisfactory solution.[31]

After studying those findings, Dr. Roger Egeberg, assistant secretary for Health and Scientific Affairs, ordered Marston to leave the Institute and division basically as they were but to consider some modifications. In advising Marston in 1970, Kreshover and Diefenbach suggested limiting the Institute to biomedical research and research training and the division to dental service methods and activities, education, and manpower training. Both recommended that future division research would only support division responsibilities.

When Marston approved the reorganization of NIH dental activities, the Institute emerged with additional functions and the division with diminished authority. In 1971 the epidemiology and dental materials branches were phased out of the San Francisco center, and the funds and positions for those branches were diverted to the division's remaining center activities. Several center staff members, including some of the epidemiologists, moved to the Institute. The division's applied and basic oral science research and training grants were transferred to the Institute. In 1973 the Division of Dental Health was placed in the new Bureau of Health Resources Development in the Public Health Service but outside of NIH. Subsequently, other division functions were absorbed by the Institute. In 1976 the Institute assumed responsibility for social science dental research, which the division had launched in the 1950s. Thus, with the rivalry over, the National Institute of Dental Research, with an expanded mission, remained intact in the National Institutes of Health.[32]

The Institute and the Expansion of Dental Research, 1948-1966

In obtaining public support for federal funding of its research, the Institute faced a unique situation at the National Institutes of Health. Various philanthropic and voluntary organizations, such as the American Cancer Society, campaigned for the other institutes. Dental research lacked such advocates. Instead, the mainstays for dental research were the professional organizations, principally the American Dental Association, which faithfully lobbied Congress and the White House year after year. Moreover, while the association and some institutional financing contributed to noncommercial dental research, the federal establishment provided the most important source for dental science appropriations. With the consistent backing of the association and key members of Congress, including Hill, Fogarty, and Congressman Melvin Laird, a Wisconsin Republican, the Institute expanded its mission.

When the Institute started, two main avenues of research already existed: intramural, or work performed by Institute scientists, and extramural, or studies supported by NIH-administered grants to non-NIH researchers and institutions. The procedures for extramural awards, which were granted usually to individual investigators, changed when the National Advisory Dental Research Council (NADRC) was established in 1949. Following the advice of the Institute director, the NADRC decided which grants to fund and forwarded its recommendations to the surgeon general. On the other hand, the Institute leadership determined the nature of intramural research and briefed the council on significant investigations.[33]

In 1949 the Institute's intramural and extramural research programs were modest—a situation that Dean vowed to alter. With the exception of trench mouth studies, the intramural program had been concentrating on dental caries, fluorosis, and fluorides. The small extramural support covered a broader range, a trend that persisted. To improve the research picture, Dean suggested some changes. He intended to increase investigations into periodontal diseases, an area he considered neglected and worthy of major attention. Dean also wanted to broaden the scope of Institute laboratory work and to stimulate research in the nation's forty dental schools and other institutions. To accomplish the latter, Dean and Arnold, the research director, subsequently urged the nation's dental school deans to apply for research grants. In 1952 the President's Commission on the Health Needs of the Nation supplemented the Institute plea by recommending more emphasis on dental research.[34]

The Institute, however, encountered difficulties in meeting extramural financial needs. Although the extramural grants sponsored a greater variety of projects than the intramural program supported, until 1956 the Institute's intramural budget exceeded the extramural appropriations. At other NIH institutes extramural grants received more money than intramural operations. That NIDR unbalance, an anomaly at NIH, resulted from a combination of political and intellectual circumstances. Initially, the Truman Bureau of the Budget omitted the Institute appropriations from the budget for NIDR's first full year and forced NIH to transfer funds from other units to pay for intramural and extramural work. Although by 1952 Congress and the Truman administration had removed the previously set $750,000 yearly cap for Institute expenditures, that action did not alleviate money problems for several years because of the Korean War and tight budgets. After the Korean War started, Truman's budget managers placed an annual ceiling of $221,000 for dental research grants for the duration of the conflict. Operating with a stringent fiscal policy, the Eisenhower administration retained the $221,000 grants limit until 1955 despite Institute estimates calling for at least $500,000 annually. Unable to fund some of the worthy research applications during this period of lean financing, the National Advisory Dental Research Council blamed insufficient grant funding for a "suffering" dental research grants program.[35]

But the lack of research by dental schools also curtailed the extramural program. Concerned about broadening and improving extramural dental research, Arnold, Institute director in 1953, sought help from old friends. First, he asked Dean's advice. The retired director, famous for his surveys, suggested sending questionnaires to dental schools. In 1954 Arnold persuaded his former mentor and pathology professor at the Western Reserve Dental School, Dr. Thomas Hill, to serve as the first chairman of the Institute's Program Planning Committee, created by Arnold to review and advise on dental research. After reviewing the grants situation, the Hill committee determined that there were "not enough good dental research applications to be reviewed." That finding sent committee members on trips to assess the research potential in the nation's dental schools—reviews that stirred interest in dental research at several institutions Hill visited.[36]

In addition, the lid on extramural appropriations limited the number of grantees and prevented the entry of new non-Institute researchers into dental research. Those left out vented their feelings by complaining to the NADRC that an "old boy" network funneled money to a favored few, even though those recipients were usually the best qualified. Made aware of the problem, Congress increased extramural dental research appropriations to $421,000 for 1955. After that infusion of additional money and the encouragement by NIDR and the Program Planning Committee, the Institute almost doubled the awards that year in its extramural program by adding twenty-five new grantees.[37]

From 1948 through 1955 the Institute's intramural program fared better than the extramural. In 1953, when Arnold assumed the Institute leadership, 67 employees worked for the Institute in the three laboratories and two branches established by Dean in 1949; by 1955 the roster totalled 104. During that period of growth McClure headed the Laboratory of Oral and Biological Chemistry, Dr. Robert Stephan the Laboratory of Oral Bacteriology, and Dr. David B. Scott the Laboratory of Functional Morphology. In 1954 Scott's laboratory was renamed the Laboratory of Histology and Pathology. Dr. Albert L. Russell, a dentist and epidemiologist, directed the Epidemiology and Biometry Branch. The Clinical Investigations Branch was directed by Dr. Ralph S. Lloyd in 1954 and Dr. Edward Driscoll in 1955.

Intramural research appropriations increased from approximately $150,000 in 1948 to over $900,000 for the fiscal year beginning July 1, 1953. The rise in appropriations contributed to a broadening of the Institute's research. From 1948 to 1953 the Institute intramural program had emphasized studies of dental decay and fluoride. Even with less than he asked for in funding, Arnold observed that with the growth of its budget the Institute had fostered an expansion of dental research beyond the areas of dental caries and fluorides. In 1954 he established the Board of Scientific Counselors, which included eminent scientists within and outside the government, to advise on intramural program policies.[38]

During that same period the Institute intramural clinical research picture was mixed. Contrary to the expectations of Dean and Arnold, the new NIH Clinical Center started operating in 1953 without room for patients solely with dental diseases. Instead, NIH placed dental service under the jurisdiction of the Clinical Center and allowed the Institute to engage in clinical studies there only with patients already admitted for other illnesses. Under this confusing arrangement the Institute clinical research activity was separated officially from the Clinical Center's dental service group. Moreover, the Clinical Center personnel situation left the Institute with the problem of almost a 10 percent turnover in clinical staff because the combination of university employment and private practice offered young dental scientists a far more lucrative income than government pay. With the Clinical Center dental research scope limited, Institute clinicians spent most of their time measuring the systemic effects of fluorides on individuals hospitalized for nondental reasons. Any other Institute clinical work had to be performed on an outpatient basis. Consequently, the most promising intramural clinical projects during the 1950s were those conducted on sites away from Bethesda by Institute scientists collaborating with investigators from other NIH components.[39]

On the other hand, the Institute-sponsored extramural clinical work progressed in the late 1940s and the 1950s. For instance, the oldest extramural-supported clinical program started in 1949 with studies of postnatal growth of facial and head skeletal tissues at the Division of Services for Crippled Children and the Cleft Palate Center of the University of Illinois. That project developed into cooperative work in the 1950s with the Institute.[40]

By 1955 the Institute's intramural work was shifting in emphasis from applied to more basic research. Former Institute laboratory chief Stephan has suggested that such a change may have resulted in part from a shortage of qualified dental scientists and the hiring instead of more researchers trained in the pure sciences. But the move also could have been due to the policy of expanding basic research espoused earlier by Dean and followed by Arnold. In continuing that trend in 1956, Arnold recruited as his scientific research director Kreshover,

who came to the Institute with the aim of strengthening its fundamental research capability.[41]

With Arnold's encouragement and support, Kreshover built up
dental research as a basic science field at the Institute from 1956 to
1966. Under Arnold and Kreshover the Institute staff grew from 122
in 1956 to 327 in 1966, with the biggest additions occurring after the
Institute acquired its own laboratory building in 1961. In 1958 they
strengthened emphasis on microbiology by recruiting Dr. Henry
Scherp, a University of Rochester professor and coauthor of an oral
microbiology textbook, to head the Laboratory of Microbiology, a
spin-off from McClure's oral bacteriology and chemistry laboratory.
McClure's laboratory was renamed the Laboratory of Biochemistry.[42]

Politics also played an instrumental role in the growth of Institute-
supported research after the mid-1950s. To help explain Institute
work to Congress and the public, Arnold added an information officer to his staff in 1955. Although the Institute lacked the help of
citizen groups, such as the American Heart Association, the American
Dental Association remained a powerful friend. Consequently, the
Institute's research situation changed radically in 1956 because of the
intense lobbying by the association. "Write your Congressman
Now," urged the *ADA News Letter* editor in an appeal to the nation's
dentists to pressure Congress into increasing dental research funding.
In response, dentists across the nation deluged the legislators with
hundreds of telegrams and letters. Dr. Harry Lyons, president-elect of
the association, pressed Congress to appropriate $6 million for the
Institute for expenditures for the fiscal year starting July 1, 1956,
including the 230 new projects recommended for approval in the
extramural program. Both the National Science Foundation and the
National Advisory Dental Research Council added to that plea by
criticizing the inadequate funding of the Institute's research.

As a result of the lobbying, Hill's committee asked the Institute to
prepare broader dental science studies. By the time Fogarty's committee in the House and Hill's in the Senate had finished with the
Eisenhower request for $2.2 million, Congress had voted to fund
over $6 million for Institute dental activities. Approximately $3.7
million of that amount was assigned for extramural research grants,
which not only covered all that Lyons had requested but also added
enough for forty-four more investigations.[43]

Eisenhower signed the major increase, which became Public Law

635, because it reflected his administration's policy to spend more on nongovernment research than on federal studies. Consequently, grant funding rose more than six times from the $521,000 allocated during the previous year. By a lesser magnitude, appropriations also went up for the intramural program from $1.6 million in Fiscal Year 1956 to $2.3 million for Fiscal Year 1957. For the first time the Institute's extramural funding exceeded that for the intramural program, and the Institute's budget ratio between intramural and extramural funding resembled that of most of the other institutes of the National Institutes of Health. That gap became permanent and increased in subsequent years. The funding change prompted Arnold to announce that the change in funding "allowed for the first time in the history of the NIDR the development of a well-rounded and integrated Extramural Program consisting of Research Grants, Fellowships, and Training Grants." [44]

Thus extramural research expanded during the Institute's first decade, with the most dramatic leap occurring in 1957. Supported by Institute grants totalling $11 million, researchers published 730 scientific articles in professional journals between 1949 and 1959. Under Drs. F. Earle Lyman and Robert C. Likins, each of whom served as an extramural program chief for Arnold, research grants increased ten times from 30 in 1953 to 331 by 1966. Lyman reported a rise in dental school participation in extramural research from 50 percent of all schools in 1956 to 94 percent in 1959. After Likins became extramural program chief in 1962, the Institute established special sections for training and research grants. [45]

The availability of money after 1956 had aroused not only dental schools and researchers but also nondental institutions. In 1957, for instance, the Institute received ten times more requests for research grants than it had the previous year. The change resulted in more diversified investigations with 28 percent of the Institute's 1958 extramural appropriations supporting research in hospitals, local health departments, and other research settings. Basic research took about 75 percent and clinical research approximately 25 percent of the 1958 fiscal year extramural funding. By 1960 the Institute had disseminated 372 research grants to 101 institutions in thirty-six states and territories and seven foreign countries. [46]

Even with the great increase in extramural funding, no other outside institution employed as many dental research specialists as the

National Institute of Dental Research. Although the intramural staff operated on a smaller budget than the extramural program, in 1960 Arnold considered the Institute's intramural program and its forty-four principal investigators "probably the most qualified single group of dental researchers in the world." [47]

After the 1961 occupation of Building 30, the Institute's new laboratory structure, Arnold and Kreshover provided specialized sections to accommodate several scientists engaged in promising basic research. From 1961 to 1962 they established sections for enzyme chemistry; gnotobiotics, or germ-free animals; protein chemistry; and oral pharyngeal development and function, or facial and head growth. [48]

In 1964 Kreshover and Arnold expanded the Institute's clinical research, which came under the intramural program, by adding human genetics and oral medicine and surgery branches. They also persuaded NIH Director Shannon to transfer the Clinical Center Dental Department to Institute control. Under the new arrangement the Institute-administered dental clinic, the Dental Services Branch, provided an environment for and conducted research in addition to caring for patients admitted by other institutes. With this change the Institute gained a new experimental dental operating room at the Clinical Center. Arnold appointed Dr. Edward Driscoll as the new Institute clinical director. [49]

To make dental research information more widely available, the Institute administrators negotiated a contract with the American Dental Association in 1964 to establish a dental research information center. A 1962 nationwide association survey of dental schools and nonfederal institutions had demonstrated a need to clarify means for planning and funding dental research. Under the 1964 agreement's terms the association collected, stored, and disseminated a broad spectrum of data on dental research essential for designing and developing national research and graduate training programs. This service proved especially valuable for planning the Institute's intramural and clinical programs. [50]

Kreshover and Arnold extended the Institute program to include a collaborative research office in 1964. Under that system the Institute contracted out research, particularly in biomaterials studies. The new program enabled intramural scientists to collaborate with investigators in extramural institutions. Dr. Wilbur A. Trick acted as the first

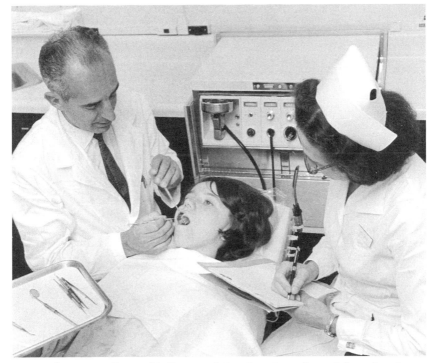

Dr. Herbert Swerdlow, chief, Dental Services Branch, and dental assistant Frances Davis work on a patient in the Dental Clinic in the NIH Clinical Center in 1967.

chief of the Collaborative Research Office. In 1966 Dr. Robert Nelsen, instrumental in developing the high-speed drill at the Bureau of Standards, took charge of the Institute's collaborative research activities.[51]

Sensing a growing inclination in Congress and at the White House to favor more directed research, Institute administrators drew up a plan in 1965 to reorganize extramural research by categories recognizable by disease or condition instead of by biomedical discipline: dental caries and hard tissue studies; periodontal diseases and soft tissue research; orofacial growth and development; and biomaterials and special field projects. The new arrangement took effect in 1966 and aimed at stimulating grant proposals that would have both program relevancy and scientific merit. Both Institute health science administrators and outside experts served as advisors on the new extramural operations. As Kreshover later explained, the purpose of the reorganization was to provide a "continuing identification and a sense of common purpose of extramural staff with intramural scientists and advisory groups in the fulfillment of the Institute's mission." [52]

Consequently, dental research and the Institute had changed markedly by the time Arnold left his post. After thirty years in dental science Arnold departed to assume the position of chief dental officer of the Public Health Service. In 1936 he had been the third person hired to conduct dental research for the National Institute of Health. When he relinquished the directorship in February 1966, over three hundred people worked at the Institute.

Policy Changes and Reorganizations, 1966-1984

In March 1966 Kreshover took over as director of the NIDR. The son of a New York City physician, Kreshover initially wanted to follow his father into medicine. But talks with several friends who were dentists led him instead to study dentistry because it presented a challenging "frontier." After obtaining his dental degree at the University of Pennsylvania in 1938, Kreshover prepared a dissertation on dental sciences as a Carnegie Fellow at Yale University, which awarded him a Ph.D. in pathology in 1942. During World War II he worked overseas in the Yale General Hospital Unit—an experience that led him to earn his M.D. in 1949 at New York University. With the three postgraduate degrees, Kreshover concentrated on dental research because of his goal of connecting dentistry, which he considered a specialty of medicine, with the biomedical sciences. From New York he went to the Medical College of Virginia to serve as chairman of the department of oral pathology and director of the dental research program. In that capacity he met Institute Director Dean, who recruited him as a consultant to the Institute's clinical sciences program. When Arnold later asked Kreshover to head the Institute's intramural program, Kreshover accepted with the intention of implementing his objective of broadening the base of dental research. [53]

During his service as director from 1966 to 1975 Kreshover continued his policy of promoting basic research in both intramural and extramural programs. To continue emphasis on fundamental research, Kreshover brought in as his intramural scientific director Dr. Richard C. Greulich, professor of oral biology and anatomy at the Schools of Medicine and Dentistry, University of California at Los Angeles (UCLA), Health Sciences Center. With his Ph.D. and training in anatomy, Greulich was the first Institute research director without a dental degree. His appointment reinforced Kreshover's determination to promote fundamental studies in the intramural program.

Kreshover's extramural chiefs, Drs. Driscoll, Robert M. Grainger, Clair Gardner, and Thomas E. Malone, also recognized the importance of bridging basic and applied research. To encourage the nation's dental schools to participate in extramural research, Kreshover visited each one during 1967. Gardner, superviser of the extramural activities for most of Kreshover's tenure, retained and strengthened the categorical nature of extramural programs but also promoted a broadening of basic dental research in the academic community.[54]

To pursue his research policy, Kreshover also had to reconcile competition among the intramural scientists and political pressures from the Lyndon B. Johnson and Richard Nixon administrations. While the researchers vied for additional support for their own specialties, most wanted to retain the basic research nature of the intramural program. Whereas the Eisenhower staff had been concerned with increasing funding for extramural rather than intramural work, congressional committees and Johnson and Nixon spokesmen increasingly called for more targeted, short-term research.[55]

Kreshover responded to such pressures by introducing more links between basic and applied research at the Institute. In 1966 he established a clinical laboratory to investigate canker sores at the U.S. Public Health Hospital in San Francisco, California, as an extension of the Institute's oral medicine and surgery branch based in Bethesda. During the first two years of the Nixon administration he created a National Caries Program to find means to eliminate dental caries.[56]

Under Kreshover and Greulich the intramural research emphasis also became more diversified as new scientific leaders replaced some of the Institute's original laboratory directors. The Institute administrators established several new units to accommodate specialties of the staff, which grew from 327 in 1966 to 398 by 1974. When McClure retired in 1966, his successor as chief of the biochemistry laboratory, Dr. Karl Piez, a protein chemist, increased emphasis on collagen studies. At the same time Dr. Marie Ussing Nylen, recognized for her achievements in electron microscopy, assumed direction of the Laboratory of Histology and Pathology after its chief, Scott, joined the faculty of the Western Reserve School of Dentistry. The experimental pathology section in Nylen's laboratory grew enough by 1970 to form a separate branch headed by Dr. Harold Fullmer. In 1973 Kreshover and Greulich converted the branch to the Laboratory of Oral Medicine led by Dr. Abner Notkins, who specialized in virus research.[57]

Meanwhile, in 1971 Kreshover appointed Scherp to head the National Caries Program and replaced him with Dr. Stephan Mergenhagen as chief of the Laboratory of Microbiology. In keeping with Mergenhagen's research emphasis on microbiology and immunology, his group was renamed the Laboratory of Microbiology and Immunology in 1972.[58]

At the same time Kreshover elevated the importance of clinical studies by establishing a separate office of clinical director. Dr. Robert W. Berliner, NIH deputy director for science, had opposed such a step because such dual leadership in other institutes' intramural programs had fared poorly. Kreshover named Driscoll as the first NIDR clinical director.[59]

The most extensive changes of the Kreshover directorship materialized with the intramural reorganization of 1973 and 1974. During 1973 Greulich pondered a realignment of the entire intramural effort to cope with diminished funding, a "coordinated and controlled reduction in position ceiling," and pressures from intramural scientists for even more splintering of the laboratories. Indeed, the NIDR staff had decreased from 409 in 1971 to 377 by 1973, and Institute appropriations had dropped from almost $47 million in 1973 to just under $45.6 million in 1974. While all agreed on the necessity of preserving a first-rate basic research program, the intramural director and research chiefs differed on how to accomplish that goal. Greulich's solution was to abolish all developmental biology programs, merge the Laboratories of Biochemistry and Biological Structure, divide Mergenhagen's laboratory into one for immunology and one for microbiology, and place certain National Caries Program scientists in the proposed laboratory for microbiology. Nylen protested the fusion of her laboratory with Piez's. Also opposed, Piez, Mergenhagen, and Dr. George Martin, leader of the connective tissue

Dr. Seymour J. Kreshover (right) consults with Dr. George Martin (left) in 1966.

section in the Laboratory of Biochemistry, recommended at the same that Kreshover and Greulich establish seven laboratories under three programs.[60]

The outcome shook so many staff members that Kreshover tried to restore morale by taking the entire Institute on a three-day retreat at the Hunt Valley Inn in the Maryland countryside. Although no one lost a job, many were displaced. In the reorganization Kreshover abolished the Human Genetics Branch, reduced Piez's biochemistry laboratory from twenty-three scientists in 1973 to eleven in 1974, and placed almost half of Nylen's scientific staff elsewhere in the Institute.

The reorganization, however, laid a foundation for future accomplishments at the Institute with the creation of new, significant research bodies. Kreshover established a Laboratory of Developmental Biology and Anomalies headed by Martin and a Neurobiology and Anesthesiology Branch under the Office of Clinical Investigations with Dr. Ronald Dubner, a specialist in pain research, as chief.[61]

Meanwhile, Greulich left the Institute at the end of 1973 to direct the President's Biomedical Research Panel. Subsequently, Kreshover persuaded Dr. Wallace D. Armstrong, a pioneer fluoride researcher, to serve as acting intramural director. Armstrong, who had come to the Institute to translate a Russian text, continued in that position after Kreshover's retirement. Armstrong's task was to preside over the new research establishment.[62]

Later, scientific achievements in the newer units eventually sustained the foresight of Kreshover's policy of broadening dental science and linking it to biology and medicine. But contrary to his fears of a shrinking staff, Kreshover saw the number of intramural research scientists increase in all laboratories before he retired in June 1975.[63]

Stability prevailed at the Institute for several years after the implementation of the 1974 reorganization. Gardner served as acting director until the end of 1975 when Dr. David B. Scott returned to the Institute on January 1, 1976, to take the position of director.

Born in Providence, Rhode Island, Scott fulfilled a childhood wish by becoming a dentist. After receiving his dental degree at the Baltimore College of Dental Surgery at the University of Maryland and a master of science degree in physiology at the University of Rochester, Scott had intended to continue with his doctoral studies. Instead, Dean, on a recruiting mission at the University of Rochester in 1944, persuaded him to join the Grand Rapids fluoridation project. In those early years of NIH dental research Scott seized the opportunity offered him by Dean to conduct research with the electron microscope. Thus, he collaborated with Dr. Ralph W. G. Wyckoff, another NIH scientist, on tooth structure studies, added that field to the basic dental research at NIH, and helped to create the Institute's Laboratory of Histology and Pathology. From 1954 to 1965 Scott, who became an international authority on calcified and mineralized tissues, headed that laboratory. Joining Case Western Reserve University in 1965, Scott served on the faculties of the dental and medical schools and from 1969 to 1976 as dean of the School of Dentistry.[64]

During the 1976 to 1981 period Scott led an Institute that had been reorganized before his return to Bethesda. Under Scott the Institute placed greater emphasis on periodontal extramural research and intramural and extramural clinical studies. To expand dental behavioral and social science research, Scott brought Dr. Lois Cohen to NIDR in 1976. A sociologist, Cohen had served in the Division of Dentistry.

In 1980 Scott established the Diagnostic Systems Branch to conduct studies of noninvasive diagnostic techniques and the Clinical Investigations and Patient Care Branch to coordinate patient treatment with Institute clinical research. Only one major change of internal leadership occurred under his directorship. When the position of intramural director became vacant, Scott appointed Nylen to direct that program in 1977. The first woman to head a laboratory at the Institute, Nylen also became the first woman at the National Institutes of Health to serve as an institute intramural director. Under Scott, Armstrong, and Nylen no drastic intramural upheavals occurred. Instead, Scott and his staff, staunch supporters of dental science studies, followed the policies that had been worked out in previous Institute administrations to strengthen dental research.[65]

After Scott retired in 1981, the Institute underwent additional realignment. To reflect changed research trends in 1982, Dr. John Goggins, acting director, replaced the biochemistry and biological structure laboratories with a Laboratory of Oral Biology and Physiology and a Mineralized Tissue Research Branch. Goggins also added a contract management section and the functions of the collaborative research office to the extramural program. During his administration the Institute planned Pain and Dry Mouth Clinics, which opened shortly after his year's leadership ended.[66]

In 1983 Dr. Harald Löe, an internationally recognized expert in periodontal research, assumed the directorship of the Institute. Löe earned his doctor of dental surgery and doctor of odontology degrees from the University of Oslo. Close association with a number of leading dental researchers in Europe and the United States had inspired Löe, a native of Steinkjer, Norway, to take up dental research. A Fulbright fellowship in the 1950s introduced him to American academic dentistry at the University of Illinois, a major academic dental research center. Löe had conducted landmark periodontal clinical studies on gingivitis, bacteria, and antimicrobials, including chlorhexidine. A past president of the International Association for Dental Research, he had received awards from over half a dozen international and American professional organizations, published over two hundred papers on various aspects of dental disease, and by 1984 had received honorary degrees from universities in five countries, including the United States, for his scientific achievements. Löe had taught in dental colleges in Norway, Denmark, Israel, and Michigan before becoming dean of the University of Connecticut School of Dental Medicine in 1974.[67]

A strong proponent of fundamental and clinical investigations, Löe started a reorganization to enhance the quality and broaden the scope of Institute research. Löe placed Dr. John D. Termine in charge of the newly organized Mineralized Tissue Research Branch in 1983. That branch became the only bone and mineralized tissue research branch in NIH and one of less than a dozen of its kind in the entire United States. Subsequently, the branch's scientists collaborated with researchers in all the other institutes of NIH. In 1984 he replaced the National Caries Program with the Epidemiology and Oral Disease Prevention Program. He also chose new assistant, associate, and deputy directors after Goggins, who served as his deputy and extramural program chief, left the Institute that year to become dean of the School of Dentistry at Marquette University in Milwaukee, Wisconsin. Löe appointed Nylen as the new extramural program chief and Notkins as the head of the intramural program.[68]

The NIDR and the Campaign to Train Dental Scientists

"Money without manpower is useless," NIDR Director Dean told a 1950 radio audience when he was recruiting scientists for the new Institute. Dean was referring to the long-time scarcity of well-trained scientists in dental research. Because they could make a much better living by practicing dentistry, young dentists generally did not prepare for research or teaching.[69]

One of the most vexing problems facing the National Institute of Dental Research from its inception was the dearth of scientists working in basic research related to dentistry. The shortage affected the Institute's intramural and extramural programs and the Institute's war against dental diseases and disorders. Moreover, the laws establishing the NIH and the Institute authorized the surgeon general, through the Institute, and the National Advisory Dental Research Council to support both research and research training.

To deal with the issue, the Institute applied two major approaches. One used the Institute as a training ground for dental scientists through Public Health Service postdoctoral fellowships and guest-worker positions, and the other provided training elsewhere through various kinds of fellowships and grants.

The American Dental Association Research Associates system launched dental research training at NIH in 1941 and continued it until 1970 when the association opened its own laboratories in its Chicago headquarters. Between 1941 and 1970 the association sponsored thirteen associates in the biological sciences. Several of the associates transferred to the Institute, and in 1988 three former associates—Drs. George Martin, John Folk, and Jack London—continued basic research there.[70]

Like the legendary Topsy, other research training at the Institute "just grew" and flourished, with fate playing a role at the beginning. The experience of one of the earliest trainees, Marie Ussing, for instance, started with a casual meeting on a Copenhagen streetcar in 1949 with Dr. Poul Pedersen. About to go to the Institute as a visiting scientist, Pedersen invited Ussing, only two years out of dental college, to help him conduct research in the United States. Accepting the offer, Ussing traveled to Bethesda where she found herself as a volunteer researcher helped by Pedersen, who bought her lunches. Almost three months later Dr. Harry Kaplan, a kindly Washington, D.C., dentist, learned about Ussing's plight. He subsequently paid her $100 a month to do research until July 1950 when she obtained a Public Health Service postdoctoral research one-year fellowship to work under the guidance of Scott. After Ussing went back to Denmark in 1951, she was married in Europe, later returned to the Institute as Marie Ussing Nylen, and distinguished herself as an electron microscopy expert and one of the few women to achieve leadership positions at the National Institutes of Health.[71]

After Ussing's experience, training became more systematic at the Institute. By the 1960s trainees with a Ph.D. or D.D.S. started research at the Institute either as associates or guest workers. Some of the guest workers arrived through arrangements with other federal dental agencies, such as the U.S. Army Dental Corps, which started sending army dentists for two-year terms in the 1960s; others came from nongovernment groups, such as the American Dental Association. Associates also received postdoctoral fellowships from the Public Health Service for work in NIDR laboratories. During the administration of President Jimmy Carter, which began in 1977, the

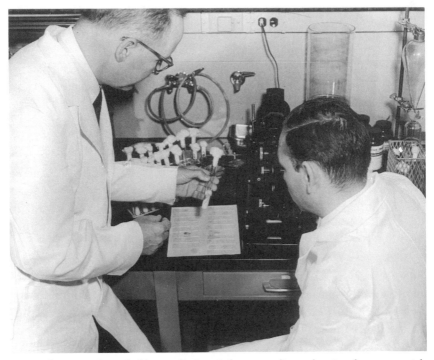

Dr. Robert Stephan (left) examining culture media and stained smears with Michael Caplow, a dental student employed in a summer training program in the mid-1950s. Courtesy of Dr. George Garrington, University of Florida College of Dentistry.

Institute greatly increased the number of trainees conducting investigations on its premises. That rise was sustained into 1985 under the presidency of Ronald Reagan. Consequently, after almost four decades of its existence, the Institute, through its own laboratories and scientists, had provided dental research training to over five hundred scientists.[72]

The first government attempts to foster careers in dental biological research outside NIH were disappointing. Such Public Health Service dental research training support started in 1946 as part of a major biomedical research fellowship program. Of 162 fellowships awarded in all fields from 1946 through 1948, only 11 went to holders of a D.D.S. in comparison to 88 with an M.D., 55 with a Ph.D., 7 with both an M.D. and Ph.D., and 1 with a D.V.M. The 11 awarded to dentists reflected the small number of applications received from dentists; yet the service had approved a higher proportion of the applications from dentists than it did from physicians. In an attempt to encourage more candidates for such fellowships, the National Institutes of Health Dental Study Section, which judged fellowship applications, urged the Kellogg Foundation to support dental graduates who wanted to conduct dental research. Also concerned about the lack of applicants, the committee on dentistry of the National Research Council attributed the indifference to the deans of the nation's dental schools. Consequently, as part of the extramural program, the Institute administrators took on the responsibility of attracting talent to the field of basic biomedical research affecting dentistry.[73]

Through a combination of circumstances the extramural training picture improved. To secure advice, Dean established a Dental Research Specialty Board on Fellowships composed of Institute scientists. The Institute started with fourteen research fellowships in July 1949 at a cost of approximately $35,000. The program made little progress through the Korean War era and the first two years of the Eisenhower administration's stringent budgets. By mid-1955, however, the Institute training budget rose to $100,000—a gain, but not enough to satisfy the dental community.

A substantial change occurred in 1956 after the National Science Foundation's Long committee, which had surveyed NIH, found the shortage of dental scientists to be a major deficiency. Following the Long committee report, Secretary of Health, Education and Welfare Folsom decided to increase funding for dental research fellowships for the 1957 fiscal year. But the nation's organized dental community lobbied for even more money for dental research fellowships. As Public Health Service Chief Dental Officer Knutson described the situation, the number of students preparing for basic dental research was "wholly inadequate." Furthermore, after Dean Roy O. Greep of the Harvard University School of Dental Medicine met with Institute Director Arnold, Fogarty's House Appropriations Committee received a proposal by Harvard that recommended establishment of training centers. The Harvard plan proved so attractive that Fogarty's committee directed that half the training appropriations go toward creating research training centers in nonprofit institutions to educate future dental school teachers and researchers. Led by Fogarty and Hill, Congress passed and Eisenhower approved a budget that gave

$500,000 for basic science research fellowships and $500,000 for training for the fiscal year beginning July 1, 1956.[74]

The additional appropriations started a trend toward greatly increased academic and institutional dental research training in the United States. The most immediate result occurred when the number of institutions participating in dental research training rose from nine in 1956 to thirty in 1957. To implement the Fogarty committee directive, the Institute and the National Advisory Dental Research Council launched "The Graduate Training Program of the National Institute of Dental Research." Between 1956 and 1958 Dr. Thomas Hill, Arnold's friend and dental school mentor, helped shape the program and select sixteen training centers in leading dental schools and hospitals throughout the country. Whereas Institute fellowships were awarded on a national competitive basis, trainees were selected locally by university training directors. The program stressed educating teachers with research abilities in clinical and basic sciences for the nation's dental schools.

Over the next decade a number of other measures also enhanced dental research training. In 1958 Institute Director Arnold assembled the largest gathering to date of dental educators to promote such training. Under the new NIH General Research Support Program, started in 1962, the Institute approved grants of over $2 million to strengthen research and research training programs in the nation's dental schools. That same year the Institute added clinical research training programs, which emphasized work with patients.[75]

In 1964 the Institute inaugurated a clinical research training grant for a six-year curriculum leading to combined doctor of dental surgery and doctor of philosophy degrees at the University of Minnesota School of Dentistry. Three sophomore dental school students entered the Minnesota program the first year.[76]

To assess the effectiveness of the various programs, the Institute conducted surveys of trainees and fellows every six years. The 1962 follow-up study showed 70 percent of the trainees in private practice. After finding that those trained in basic sciences spent three times as many hours in research as those who concentrated on clinical studies, the Institute and council staffs revised the program guidelines to favor recruiting Ph.D. candidates and to stress training in the basic sciences. By 1967 overseers assessing the programs considered the effort a failure because the application pool had declined in quantity and quality. Approximately 10 to 13 percent of the training and fellow-ship slots were then going unused because of a lack of applicants. Money was not a problem, for Congress and the Kennedy and John-son administrations provided sufficient funding, such as the $1.8 million for fellowships and $5.2 million for training available for the 1967 fiscal year.[77]

Nevertheless, by 1970 the programs had fostered an increase in dental school faculty members engaged in research. A survey found that the number of dental school professors spending 10 percent of their time in research activities grew from 400 in 1958 to over 1,100 by 1970. Yet there were 377 budgeted vacancies in the nation's dental schools and a shortage of clinical investigators.[78]

By 1972 the Institute had supported over 1,600 trainees and fel-lows since the inception of its programs. A survey in which almost 1,300 former Institute trainees or fellows responded showed that over 70 percent were teaching, 54 percent were engaged in research, and almost 51 percent conducted clinical care. In each case a higher proportion of former fellows entered research, teaching, and/or clini-cal care than trainees. A different study indicated that of all full- and part-time dental school faculty members in the United States, 7.7 percent had received some educational support from the Institute. That survey also found that former Institute trainees or fellows made up 11 percent of all scientific researchers working on the Smithsonian Institution's publicly listed dental projects in the United States, Can-ada, and Great Britain.[79]

In the early 1970s the Institute and other NIH training programs came under attack as the Nixon administration increasingly ques-tioned their necessity. Was it appropriate for the federal government to play a role in training biomedical scientists? If so, how much help should the government give? What was the proper mechanism to provide such support?[80]

By 1972 the National Advisory Dental Research Council found itself in a dilemma on the training grants situation. Where was dentistry moving? Would it retrogress to mechanical work or would it advance as a learned profession? What should be done about the polarizing effects the council perceived as a result of the congressio-nally authorized funding programs? Should support still be concen-trated in a few schools that consistently produced the best research or should the Institute finance programs that allowed more flexibility by institutions? Council members observed that other federal initiatives had increased the number of dental students but that dental schools tended to shorten the dental curriculums and de-emphasize research, contrary to the underlying purpose of the Institute's support.[81]

The council's concerns turned out to be moot because in 1973 the Nixon administration impounded Institute training funds and decided to end all future NIH research training and fellowship programs. Consequently, after January 29, 1973, the Institute discontinued awarding new training grants, and staff members asked what could be done "to resolve this incongruous situation as rationally as possible." The budget cut meant dropping a program supporting 112 Ph.D. candidates who expected to receive degrees in 1974 and 1975.[82]

Anticipating future shortages of dental researchers, the American Dental Association's Council on Dental Research complained to federal authorities and members of Congress about the prospective reduction of the Institute's research program. Even though a court decision released the impounded 1973 funds, the association's council found the prospective elimination of the program alarming.[83]

By July 1973 Dr. Robert S. Stone, director of the National Institutes of Health, compromised with Department of Health, Education and Welfare officials to propose the Weinberger Program. That plan phased out the existing training support system, including the recent NIH Research Career Development Awards, and replaced it with support for a maximum of three years for postdoctoral physician and Ph.D. research training. The Weinberger Program also required recipients to pay back the government if they did not undertake teaching or research careers after completing their training.[84]

Fearful that the United States would lose its international leadership in biomedical research, members of the 93d Congress opposed such a drastic change. Consequently, in 1974 Congress established the National Research Service Award program through Public Law 93-348 to support for a maximum of five years predoctoral and postdoctoral students training to become independent researchers. The act required that training awards favor areas where a need was demonstrated.[85]

Although funding and trainees for dental research diminished in the late 1970s, the Institute had accomplished its primary mission to increase the corps of dental science researchers. By 1975 the Institute had assisted over one thousand scientists active in research pertinent to dentistry. Support for researchers in the future would have to concentrate on maintaining the quality of the scientific manpower pool and to fill major research gaps in the 1980s and 1990s, such as those in clinical periodontal research.[86]

By 1981 each one of the Institute directors, however, had expressed concern about retaining an adequate supply of dental researchers. Dean and Arnold had courted dental school deans to encourage research. Kreshover and Scott, with considerable experience in the academic world, pressed for more research training in dental schools and had their staffs prepare studies forecasting the availability of dental researchers toward the end of the century.

In the 1980s American Dental Association and Institute appraisals showed that the Institute training and fellowship programs had contributed toward increasing the number and productivity of dental researchers in the nation. A 1982 association survey of researchers under forty years of age found that Institute-supported or -trained investigators produced more professional publications than did non-Institute trained scientists; in fact, those from twenty-six to thirty years of age published twice as much as non-Institute trained scientists. Moreover, because of Institute help the number of individuals with both a dental degree and Ph.D. had almost tripled. "A large proportion" of the Institute trainees and fellows also took jobs in university and research settings. Association evaluators concluded, "The data . . . suggest that NIDR trainees and fellows have confirmed the hopes and projections of the original planners."

The Institute study was prepared after Löe became director. Coming from a dental college to the Institute in 1983, Löe assigned a high priority to dental research training. His staff's survey determined that 31 percent of all Institute postdoctoral trainees from 1948-1982 served on the faculties of dental schools in the 1983-1984 academic year. In addition, a "significantly greater proportion" of faculty members with prior Institute support, as compared to others, devoted at least 20 percent of their time to research.[87]

But Löe was concerned about the future. Consequently, to augment the supply for the year 2000, Löe's administration initiated a new career awards program in 1984. Dentists could obtain support as individuals or through nine institutions for the Dentist Scientist Award to support five years of study to become dental clinical and basic researchers. NIDR also expanded the program to include a Physician Scientist Award for Dentists. Under the latter, dentists with advanced clinical training could develop basic science research skills during a maximum of five years.[88]

The Institute and Research Centers

Although the National Institute of Dental Research initiated extramural training centers at universities around the nation in 1956, almost a decade passed before the Institute applied the same mechanism to scientific research. During the late 1950s the Shannon administration at NIH promoted the research center concept encouraging a more comprehensive, broad approach to investigating general and categorical disease questions. Subsequently, in 1959 Congress appropriated funds for regional primate research and clinical and metabolic research centers for several NIH institutes. Dental research, however, was excluded from the initial legislation, which called for the establishment of resource centers at existing large medical research institutions throughout the nation. Through Public Law 86-158 Congress appropriated $500,000 each to several institutes to support such specific center programs as arthritis and cancer research. The legislation introduced large grant funding to the NIH extramural program, which previously consisted usually of awards to individual investigators.[89]

The dental community, from the Institute leaders to the American Dental Association, wanted dental research centers included in the new program. After studying the question, the National Advisory Dental Research Council agreed in 1960 that high priority be given to the establishment of cleft palate centers. (In cleft palate all or part of the solid surface of the roof of the mouth is missing.) Surgeon General Terry and the association joined the council in backing the cleft palate center recommendation. Thus, in 1962 the Institute started financial support of the University of Pittsburgh Cleft Palate Center. In 1964 the Institute awarded its largest clinical research grant up to that date—$428,000—to the Lancaster Cleft Palate Clinic of Lancaster, Pennsylvania.[90]

The Institute, NADRC, and American Dental Association also pressed for establishing regional interdisciplinary dental research centers similar to those of other institutes. But problems persisted with several of the other NIH center grants. Either an institute had too much or too little money to spend. Institute Director Arnold encountered the former predicament in 1963 when Congress, responding to association lobbyists, appropriated $500,000 for interdisciplinary dental research centers. Arnold found it impossible to spend the full amount, for he could not establish centers that year. Because several of the NIH center requirements proved unsuitable for dental research, Arnold and the council first had to tailor plans appropriate for dental research.[91]

For the next three years NADRC members and Institute staff planned for centers that would draw interdisciplinary research from scientists not previously associated with dental studies. Dr. Clair Gardner, the Institute's program planning officer, drew up the guidelines for the future centers. The planners expected the regional institutes to be centers of excellence with staffs of scientists of the highest order to train dental scientists, undertake frontier-type investigations, engage in interdisciplinary scientific work, collaborate on comprehensive research programs with other parts of the parent institution, and contribute to the educational programs of the parent institution. The Institute and council members hoped that the new centers would bring fresh approaches to research by combining the talents of scientific and professional personnel from dental, medical, and graduate schools as well as from other university departments. Any training under the grant would be only at the postdoctoral level comparable to that offered in Institute laboratories. To monitor the program's progress, a special centers advisory committee, aided by consultants, planned to conduct annual reviews of each center's work.[92]

Before selecting sites for the centers, the planners conferred with dental school and university deans and administrators. In 1965 a council advisory group visited prospective center locations. Planning continued as Arnold turned over the Institute directorship to Kreshover. In 1966 Director Kreshover appointed Lyman, NIDR associate director for extramural programs since 1965, as the Institute's first associate director for special programs to establish the new centers under the Dental Research Institutes and Centers (DRIC) program.[93]

Under Kreshover and Lyman the Institute awarded grants for five regional dental research centers in 1967. In February Surgeon General William H. Stewart announced the first, a three-year award to the University of Washington at Seattle for an interdisciplinary research center in oral biology to expand the University's existing investigations in genetics, immunochemistry, and mineral metabolism. The second grant went to the University of Pennsylvania for oral health research in microbiology, biochemistry, histology, embryology, and pharmacology and clinical studies, primarily in periodontal diseases. The University of North Carolina, the third selected, was chosen to investigate neural mechanisms, mineral metabolism, and hemostatic mechanisms related to oral health. The fourth center was established at the University of Alabama Institute of Dental Research to focus on the mineralization and demineralization of tooth structure and supporting tissues, the formation and metabolism of dental plaque, and the biochemistry of connective tissues. The University of Michigan, the fifth, had the mission of coordinating research in university departments of anatomy, biochemistry, genetics, pathology, and microbiology. Congress appropriated $3 million to support the first year of the centers' operations.[94]

The Institute and its consultants gave the regional centers several years to build research strengths. In 1971 reviewers recommended budget cuts for most of the centers and advised dropping some programs and investigators they found unsatisfactory. The planners had expected to open competition for nationwide bidding after completion of the program's fifth year. Budget restrictions in 1972, however, ruled out the extra expenses necessary for creating new centers. Consequently, the Institute continued grants for the existing centers instead of opening the program up for new bidders.

Institute policy on research centers shifted in the mid-1970s to an emphasis on specific purposes. The first change resulted from an evaluation of the Institute's intramural and extramural periodontal disease research initiated by Kreshover in 1974 and reported to Director Scott in 1976. The evaluation was the first done of an entire field for the Institute and one of the earliest such appraisals conducted at NIH. The panelists recommended increased support of periodontal disease investigations through "encouragement of cooperative ventures" and training programs, especially in clinical and microbiological research. In 1977 and 1978 the Institute staff responded by establishing clinically oriented periodontal research centers at the Forsyth

Dental Center in Boston, the State University of New York at Buffalo, and Virginia Commonwealth University in Richmond.[95]

A 1977 to 1978 Rand Corporation study of the entire NIH research center program also contributed to the change in Institute policy. The Rand evaluators determined that the regional dental research centers had successfully fulfilled the goal of attracting a broader segment of the research community to dental-related investigations. Whereas only 20 percent of recipients of individual investigator grants had not shown a predisposition for dental research, 55 percent of the centers' scientists had not been inclined previously toward dental research. The investigation also showed that scientists in the dental research centers published more articles in biomedical journals than in dental publications.[96]

Following the 1977 policy change on centers and the completion of the Rand Corporation study the DRIC program operated with virtually no budget increases between 1977 and 1982. As a consequence, the centers reduced research because inflation diminished the dollar value of their budgets. Institute extramural policy instead favored the traditional individual investigator grant and the addition of other kinds of centers.[97]

The change in Institute leadership from Scott to Goggins and then Löe in the 1980s led to a phasing out of the regional multidisciplinary research centers. With the help of Goggins, Löe reviewed the research center situation. Having served from 1972 to 1974 as director of the University of Michigan Dental Research Institute, Löe possessed a working familiarity with the DRIC operations.[98]

In August 1983 Löe convened an ad hoc group of consultants to evaluate the DRIC program and to advise the Institute on future policies toward these noncategorical, university-based centers.

There were four alternatives for the future program:

- to continue the existing multidisciplinary centers;

- to phase out the centers and use the funds to increase the number of regular research project grants;

- to convert the centers to core centers; or

- to phase out the centers and use the money for categorical centers.

The Institute staff favored gradually ending funding for the centers and using the appropriations for categorical centers. Because the interdisciplinary centers had met their goals but lacked a linkage between basic and clinical research, the consultants preferred diminishing support for them. The advisors differed on the most appropriate kind of replacement but agreed that competition for funds should be reopened. Needs had changed in the seventeen years since the regional centers had opened, and the panel cited the pertinence and successes of the newer periodontal centers as proof that the oral health field could use some additional categorical research institutions with clinical programs.[99]

Responding to the discussion, Löe decided to close out financing of the five DRICs and to concentrate support on the more specialized centers. In September Goggins telephoned the news to the five centers' directors. Uniting to save the funding of their institutes, deans and directors of the centers protested the action at a fall meeting with Löe in Washington. Congressional representatives and senators from the centers' states joined in opposing elimination of the centers' appropriations. Finally, all compromised by agreeing to discontinue financial support for the existing DRIC program by 1989.[100]

Meanwhile, the Institute increased the number of categorical centers. In 1984 it advertised for applications for new periodontal disease, caries, and oral health and behavioral research centers. A year later Institute-supported dental caries research centers opened at the University of Iowa, the University of Rochester, and the Forsyth Dental Center in Boston. Scientists at the new centers planned to integrate basic and clinical studies to promote preventive dental disease care.[101]

Unhappy about the fate of the multidisciplinary centers, the House Appropriations Committee in 1985 urged the Institute staff to consult the dental research community about large grant use. In addition, the committee directed the Institute to prepare plans for open competition and future use of center awards. Löe responded by establishing a twenty-member ad hoc committee to evaluate the large grant system. In 1986, after consulting with almost eight hundred individuals and organizations associated with dental research, the advisory panel recommended full but balanced support of basic, applied, and clinical research through open competition of all available NIH research grants. The consultants, however, singled out the traditional individual investigator grants as the most productive. Consequently, the

Institute gave the highest priority to individual investigator competitive grants but also decided to continue the support of multidisciplinary research centers with full and open competition.

By 1987 the Institute was supporting sixteen research centers in the United States, including the five multidisciplinary regional institutes and three caries, five periodontal, and three pain control centers. Moreover, fifteen institutions, including all of the original multidisciplinary dental research institutes, were competing to participate in the new multidisciplinary program, which was called the "Research Centers in Oral Biology."[102]

Reflections

In reviewing the activities of a scientific institute, one has a tendency to look at the accomplishments and overlook the structure that supported the science. As the evolution of the National Institute of Dental Research indicated, the expansion of the Institute's scientific effort was inevitably intertwined with the building of its bureaucratic and even concrete framework. The broadening of the Institute's research followed the expansion of the Institute's organization.

At the very base of the growth was the consistent political support of the American Dental Association and particular friends in Congress. Lobbying was necessary to obtain the essential underpinnings for the science: the building to house the intramural laboratories and additional scientists and sufficient grants to finance individual investigator research, training of researchers, and multidisciplinary centers for attracting additional scientists to dental research. The year 1956 was a turning point for the Institute in gaining substantial intramural and extramural research funding, training grants, and the long-sought intramural laboratory building.

Strong and imaginative leadership in the Institute accompanied its development. At the outset Dean set high standards, established the first three laboratories, and encouraged dental research and its training in the academic world. Arnold, Kreshover, Scott, Löe, and acting directors Gardner and Goggins built up the intramural and extramural programs. Arnold and his staff created the Laboratories of Biochemistry and Microbiology and dental research training centers, planned the multidisciplinary research centers, and helped to obtain the Institute's intramural laboratory building, which contributed significantly to the growth of the intramural program. Kreshover and his administration strengthened the links between basic and applied research, established multidisciplinary research centers, elevated clinical studies, and created the Laboratories of Oral Medicine and Developmental Biology and Anomalies. Scott bolstered the Institute's clinical department by forming two new branches, increased emphasis on periodontal disease studies, inaugurated new periodontal research centers, and strengthened NIDR's role in behavioral and social sciences. Löe oversaw the growth of additional categorical extramural research centers, started an epidemiological and preventive disease program, and instituted new dental research career programs, such as the Dentist Scientist Award.

Over four decades the Institute had grown and changed in structure to accommodate and profit from other developments in the scientific world. The results of that management could be seen by the 1980s in the increase in dental scientists and broadening of Institute-supported dental research.

CHAPTER SEVEN

Fighting Dental Decay

No amount of experimentation can ever prove
me right; a single experiment can prove me wrong.
ALBERT EINSTEIN

For most of the twentieth century, 98 percent of all Americans felt
the sudden stab of pain from a dental cavity sometime during their
lifetimes. Intermittently, the American Dental Association, European
dentists and scientists, and the National Institute of Dental Research
organized wars on the "People's Disease," the name given to dental
decay in the early part of the century. Although fluoridation started
diminishing the prevalence of that condition, dentistry still lacked
sufficient preventives to eliminate new dental caries. Consequently,
scientific work that spanned decades and continents helped to trigger
the additional anticaries effort launched in the 1960s by the dental
institute.

Dental Caries Puzzle: Locating the Pieces

Could twentieth century scientists find the clues to solve the puz-
zle of the tooth decay process? The work of van Leeuwenhoek, the
seventeenth century master microscope maker, and W. D. Miller, the
dentist-protégé of Robert Koch, provided a framework for dental
caries research. Van Leeuwenhoek and Miller implicated minute
pieces of matter, visible only through a microscope, in the tooth
decay process. Their successors faced identifying the microorganisms

in tooth decay and, if possible, explaining the roles the tiny creatures played in creating dental cavities.

Initially, most scientists in Europe and the United States investigated the nutritional and bacteriological factors suspected of causing the decay, but their results were confusing. By the 1920s a rift had developed among dental scientists on the role of bacteria in producing dental caries. Some scientists in the United States considered diet the most important factor in dental decay. A leader of the nutritional argument, Dr. Percy Howe of the Forsyth Dental Infirmary in Boston, attributed tooth decay primarily to a dietary deficiency. Howe designated bacteria as merely secondary invaders of previously damaged tissue.[1]

Although mystified by bacterial penetration of the tooth, other scientists investigating the bacterial factor disagreed with Howe. Did dental caries come from a variety of microorganisms swirling around in the mouth, as the English scientist, Sir Kenneth Goadby, suspected? Were the invaders instead localized around a vulnerable tooth? Or could only certain microorganisms contribute toward decay, as several other scientists suggested? Early in the century scientists disagreed over whether streptococcus or acid-producing bacilli were more influential in the development of dental decay. By 1922 James McIntosh, W. W. James, and P. Lazarus-Barlow of England and Capt. F. E. Rodriguez of the United States Army Medical School consistently isolated some bacillus type of bacteria, or rod-shaped microorganisms, in advanced stages of tooth decay. But was *Bacillus acidophilus*, as the British scientists classified the organism they found, also present when decay started and thus possibly responsible? Supported by the Dental Diseases Committee of the Medical Research Council, Dr. J. Kilian Clarke, another English scientist, set out in 1924 to identify microorganisms present at the beginning of tooth decay. Peering through his microscope in 1924, Clarke found strange-looking colonies of spherical-shaped microorganisms "opaque, brownish and round, with a lighter centre, a 'hairy' texture." These microorganisms had not been previously described in scientific literature. Clarke included pictures of his findings and proposed a name for them, *Streptococcus mutans*.[2]

Clarke's work did not stimulate much excitement in the 1920s. Three British scientists verified Clarke's identification of the microorganism during the remainder of that decade. I. H. McLean confirmed Clarke's observation in 1927. The following year G. F. Abercrombie, a bacteriology graduate of Cambridge University, and W. M. Scott, a medical officer with the Ministry of Health, connected *Streptococcus mutans* with fatal cases of endocarditis, an inflammation of the lining around the heart. They examined Clarke's strain of the microorganism, still available in the laboratory at St. Mary's Hospital in London, and confirmed it biochemically, serologically, and morphologically as the same bacteria found in endocarditis. After Abercrombie and Scott reported their findings, additional published information on *Streptococcus mutans* did not appear in scientific literature for at least two decades.[3]

Clarke's and McLean's individual descriptions of *Streptococcus mutans* were inadequate for biochemical confirmation, but if any American conducted such a probe, he or she did not publish the findings in any recognized scientific journal in the 1920s. To the contrary, for the next twenty years American dental scientists in universities and institutions concentrated on the relationship of *Bacillus acidophilus* to dental decay.[4]

Three schools of thought during the 1930s dominated dental caries research: the nutritional group that argued the structure or resistance of the tooth itself was of prime importance; scientists who suggested that acid-inducing organisms in the mouth mattered most; and researchers who thought the composition of the saliva was significant in the evolution of dental decay.[5]

By the early 1930s Dean found dental caries research "somewhat chaotic, the findings of certain groups being at variances with other equally known and recognized investigators." Even the nutritionists disagreed among themselves about the nutritional causes of dental caries. Lady May Mellanby of England stressed vitamin D deficiency as the overwhelming factor; Howe based his research on vitamin C; and in Baltimore Drs. Elmer V. McCollum and Henry Klein, a Public Health Service dentist, pointed to a phosphorous deficiency. Dean, however, judged as most important the work of the "Michigan group" at the University of Michigan's dental school. The Michigan team was currently examining both the nutritional and bacteriological aspects of dental caries with stress on *Bacillus acidophilus.*[6]

Who was right? In the 1930s no one knew. As Dean described the enigma, "Whether dental caries is due to a vitamin deficiency, a mineral deficiency, a change in the pH of the saliva or to an aciduric organism, we do not at present know." He predicted that the future might show a combination of contributors.[7]

Caries Research and NIH

In 1938 Dean persuaded the surgeon general of the Public Health Service to establish some organized caries research on a modest scale in the National Institute of Health to end the chaos and to find some answers on the etiology, or study of causes, of dental decay. His announcement that year of evidence on the caries preventive possibilities of fluoridated water also opened up an avenue of research on the role of fluoride in curbing dental decay.[8]

Dean's broadening of research included close collaboration with scientists at the University of Michigan's dental school, one of the few American academic groups consistently conducting oral bacteriological research. Because of the Michigan group's concentration on *Lactobacillus acidophilus*, the federal government's fluoride studies initially dealt with that bacillus organism. A proponent of the belief that the amount of *Lactobacillus acidophilus* in saliva indicated the degree of dental decay, Dr. Philip Jay of the Michigan team participated in several studies with Dean's staff on the presence of that microorganism in the saliva of children they examined.[9]

The *Lactobacillus acidophilus* studies brought the Public Health Service to the edge of the debate over the importance of lactobacilli relative to that of streptococci in promoting tooth decay. On the one hand, Drs. Basil Bibby, J. F. Volker, and M. Van Kesteren pointed to the prolific and high acid-producing streptococci as the more significant; in opposition, Dr. E. S. Hemmens gave priority to lactobacilli, which he found multiplying in early childhood tooth decay.[10]

But Dean's crew started with several different approaches to gain a better understanding of the decay process. Electron microscope studies, for instance, provided new information on the composition of tooth enamel. By the time the NIDR was founded, Scott and Wyckoff had already published results of their electron microscope work on teeth—important to understanding the decay process. As part of the Institute effort, Scott collaborated with Marie Ussing, the visiting Danish dentist, to answer a question baffling scientists for years: Did tooth enamel contain organic matter? By 1951 the two resolved that doubt by finding organic matter in the enamel through their use of the electron microscope.[11]

Both Scott and Ussing were later acclaimed for their electron microscopy work. Among the first dental scientists to use the electron microscope, Scott won the Arthur S. Flemming Award, given annually to ten of the nation's young, outstanding civil servants, and an International Association for Dental Research award in recognition of his studies of the microstructure of enamel and dentin of teeth. The International Association for Dental Research also gave its Isaac Schour Memorial Award in Anatomical Sciences to Ussing.[12]

In another area in 1951 Drs. Frank McClure and Robert Stephan, both pioneer scientists at the Institute, advanced dental caries research by providing the first rat model for studying tooth decay resembling dental decay found in humans. Prior to this development, rats were regarded as unsuitable for investigating human dental caries because the coarse diets fed rats did not produce dental decay like that contracted by humans. After trying several variations of fine particle, high-sucrose diets, McClure and Stephan published the first reports of smooth-surface caries development in the molar teeth of rats with lesions similar to those of humans.[13]

But an investigation headed by Stephan in 1952 exerted a special impact. In that effort an Institute team used a cariogenic diet to study how antibiotics affected experimental dental caries in rats. The group tested the effects of both narrow and broad spectrum antibiotics on experimental tooth decay. McClure, the Institute's fluoride expert and a member of the team, and W. L. Hewitt later found that penicillin significantly reduced dental caries in rat populations with high levels of *Lactobacillus acidophilus* in saliva. The project so intrigued another team member, Dr. Robert J. Fitzgerald, that he embarked on a hunt to identify the bacteria causing tooth decay.[14]

Fitzgerald brought to the Institute his expertise in microbiology and pharmacology. Inspired by boyhood readings of such works as *The Microbe Hunters*, Fitzgerald chose a career in scientific research. In his first assignment in 1945 for the Public Health Service, Fitzgerald studied histoplasmosis, a mimic of tuberculosis. In 1946 the G.I. Bill enabled Fitzgerald to study for his doctorate at Duke University where he later met Dr. Nicholas Leone, a physician who worked on fluoride-connected nutritional studies for Dean in the postwar period. After Fitzgerald received his doctorate in pharmacology and microbiology, Leone introduced Fitzgerald to Dean, who persuaded Fitzgerald to join his research staff in 1948. By the early 1950s the possibility of conducting research to control caries appealed to Fitzgerald, and he based his studies on the hypothesis that a bacterial agent caused caries. First he had to test for gram-positive and gram-negative bacteria, so named according to their reactions to a staining test. Using laboratory rats as models, he set out to identify the causal agent.[15]

His suspicions, encouraged by his work with the Stephan group, prompted Fitzgerald to experiment with antibiotics that interfered with the growth of gram-positive bacteria, as opposed to gram-negative bacteria. Collaborating with Dr. Harold V. Jordan and assisted by William L. Poole, Fitzgerald found the gram-positive antibiotics significantly more effective than the antibiotics that acted against gram-negative microorganisms. In the course of his observations Fitzgerald also saw some new kind of streptococci that warranted testing.[16]

Fitzgerald, however, deemed it necessary to conduct caries studies in animals infected only with specific types of microorganisms. At precisely this time new avenues opened for the kind of testing Fitzgerald required. In 1954 and 1955 experiments at the Lobund Institute for Research in the Life Sciences at the University of Notre Dame changed the course of dental caries research. The Office of Naval Research supported that research through contracts with the University of Chicago and University of Notre Dame. The Lobund Institute had developed techniques and equipment enabling scientists to experiment with germ-free animals. Using these techniques, Director Frank Orland of the Zoller Memorial Dental Clinic at the University of Chicago and his team induced dental decay in germ-free rats only after the rats were fed a cariogenic diet and inoculated with coccus-type bacteria. Bred at the Lobund Institute, the animals had remained free of dental decay prior to the Orland team's trials. Moreover, the tests showed that the germ-free animals failed to develop cavities in teeth when fed the diet provided they were not infected with the bacteria.[17] Orland's experiments verified Fitzgerald's long-held notions.

New techniques in animal research at the Institute changed substantially the dental caries research picture. The National Institutes of

Health acquired its first germ-free animals in 1955, and the National Institute of Dental Research scientists were among the first outside the Lobund group to use such animals. In addition, at the NIDR Stephan and Rachel Harris expanded on the usefulness of rats for caries observations. While working on master's and doctoral degrees in biochemistry, Harris, the first woman scientist employed by Dean, assisted Stephan in animal laboratory experiments. In 1955 Stephan and Harris disproved previous assumptions that caries lesions in rat's teeth appeared only in molar teeth. Climaxing four years of experimentation, the two discovered smooth-surface caries occurring on a variety of tooth surfaces in the Norway rat. They also improved the diets needed for caries laboratory experiments. Working with Zipkin, Stephan and Harris produced a cariogenic diet, which, under appropriate experimental conditions, could induce dental decay primarily in molar teeth.[18]

Meanwhile, yet another line of Institute research was stressed when Arnold hired Dr. Paul Keyes in 1954. With a dental degree from the University of Pennsylvania and a master of science degree in anatomy from the University of Rochester, Keyes had been receiving Institute support for several years for his development of a suitable laboratory animal at the University of Rochester and Harvard University. At Rochester Keyes had followed up on Arnold's 1942 discovery of the hamster for dental caries research. For over ten years he had bred hamsters consistently susceptible to tooth decay for use in experiments. The hamsters' mouths could be easily opened and their molar teeth examined in such detail that the scientist could follow the course of decay on a daily basis with a high degree of precision. Thus Keyes came to the Institute to study the genetics of dental caries through use of hamsters and conducted his experiments as a member of Scott's Laboratory of Histology and Pathology.[19]

In the meantime Fitzgerald, as a scientist in Scherp's Laboratory of Microbiology, traveled to Sweden in 1957 to study the lightweight germ-free apparatus developed by Dr. Bengt E. Gustafsson at the University of Lund. Fitzgerald's visit was followed by Gustafsson's appointment as visiting scientist at the Institute to advise on Fitzgerald's research.[20]

After some four years of work Fitzgerald and Keyes each announced new findings by the end of 1959. By then Fitzgerald and his team, including Jordan, Dr. Harold R. Stanley, Poole, and A. Bowler,

The Gnotobiotic Section of the Laboratory of Microbiology maintained germfree rats in steel and plastic tanks. 1964

confirmed and extended the experiments by the Orland group. Like Orland's animals, Fitzgerald's noninoculated rats did not develop tooth decay after feeding on a cariogenic diet; but when Orland and Fitzgerald experimented with gnotobiotes, the animals contracted dental caries after eating cariogenic foods. (Gnotobiotes are ordinarily germ-free animals that have been inoculated with a specific bacteria.) Unlike the Chicago team, the Fitzgerald investigators singled out a specific streptococcus group as a bacterial contributor to the initiation of decay. But Fitzgerald could not identify the microorganism, which he described as "not readily classifiable into any of the currently recognized groups of this genus." [21]

By 1959 Keyes's research showed that dental caries in laboratory animals was an infectious and transmissible disease. He traced the source in young hamsters to the alimentary tract of the mother, who passed the microorganisms on to her offspring. Antibiotic treatment, however, prevented such a transmission. He also found that animals not receiving the infection from the mother could acquire the disease by contact with caries-infected animals.[22]

Dr. Robert Fitzgerald (left) and Dr. Paul Keyes demonstrating their finding that dental caries in rats is infectious and transmissible.

But Keyes wanted other scientists to elaborate on his findings, and at an Institute meeting he issued a dramatic plea for help. Impressed by Keyes's talk, Scherp, with Institute Director Kreshover's support, persuaded Fitzgerald and Keyes to collaborate on the investigation of the dental caries process.[23]

In 1959 Fitzgerald and Keyes started working together to identify the specific bacterial agents contributing to dental caries in hamsters. They devised a model and an agent for the infectious transmission of dental caries and "tagged" different microorganisms by making them resistant to streptomycin. For the experiment Fitzgerald and Keyes selected a family of dental-caries-free albino hamsters Keyes had been breeding since 1957. Scientists had speculated that those animals lacked a cariogenic oral flora. Then Keyes and Fitzgerald injected five closely related strains of streptomycin-resistant streptococci into the mouths of hamster family members. Each ordinarily caries-free hamster subsequently developed cavities in its teeth. Conversely, after Fitzgerald and Keyes inoculated the hamsters with other bacteria, including six strains of lactobacilli from the mouths of hamsters with caries, those injections did not generate decay. Although Fitzgerald and Keyes hastened to add that these 1960 tests did not rule out the roles of other kinds of bacteria in tooth decay, their 1960 test upheld Keyes's characterization of dental caries as a transmissible disease.[24]

In their landmark work Keyes and Fitzgerald benefited from research by other NIDR scientists and by collaboration of Institute researchers with investigators in the academic world. From the Institute Dr. Anthony Rizzo had developed the mouth prop for oral examinations, and bacteriologist Dr. Morrison Rogosa and his team had isolated the lactobacilli for the study. Fitzgerald and Keyes also used a new examination technique devised at the University of Rochester by Dr. Erling Johansen, who had collaborated with Rogosa.[25]

In additional experiments Keyes and Fitzgerald established that the streptococci colonized over teeth to form plaque, a slimy extracellular material that along with sucrose enabled the microorganisms to adhere to teeth. Shielded by the plaque, the sugar fermented and formed acids inducing decay. When Fitzgerald and Keyes inoculated plaque into young animals ordinarily free of dental caries, those creatures developed decay. A control group of uninfected hamsters showed no signs of dental caries.[26]

The findings of Keyes and Fitzgerald provided a powerful basis for attacking the riddle of what caused caries in humans. In the early 1960s the scientists remained unsure as to whether results with laboratory animals also applied to humans. As Fitzgerald viewed the situation, the etiology of human dental caries still had to be clarified because of complicating circumstances:

- The disease flourished among the better nourished populations.

- Decay occurred in the most durable of the body's tissues, the enamel and dentin of the teeth.

- Not all of the teeth developed decay.

- Even different surfaces of the same tooth were unequally susceptible to caries.

- Recovery from one attack of dental caries did not immunize an individual from contracting the disease again.

- The disease operated in the part of the human body that harbored the most numerous and varied microorganisms.[27]

The Keyes-Fitzgerald streptococcus findings brought international acclaim to the two scientists. Among organizations honoring both men during the 1960s, the Fédération Dentaire Internationale awarded them the Joachim International Research Prize, awarded only once every five years for the best original scientific research in diseases, structures, and/or functions of the teeth and mouth.[28]

With a caries-inducing agent identified, Institute researchers immediately started looking for ways to apply the Fitzgerald-Keyes findings to benefit humans. The tagging of the streptococcal agents to dental decay led Institute scientists to search for inhibitors of that bacteria. In 1960 Zipkin and Dr. Rachel Harris Larson—by then married and possessing a doctorate in biochemistry—found that tetracycline appeared to act indirectly against dental caries. The antibiotic depressed the intestinal microflora implicated by Keyes as transmitting caries-inducing bacteria from parent to offspring. Jordan and Fitzgerald, along with N. D. Berger, found three different compounds—all carbonyl-binding agents—effective in reducing new dental caries in rats.[29]

Next, Fitzgerald and Keyes launched experiments to develop a vaccine that would prevent dental decay. They first inoculated hamsters with a "killed" vaccine containing a strain of one of the caries-inducing streptococci, but none of the vaccinated animals achieved immunity to dental decay. Subsequently, at an international meeting in 1962 they suggested that measures other than immunological ones might be needed to control the disease.[30]

Supplementing the search for agents to control caries-inducing bacteria, the Institute sponsored research to reduce new dental caries through diet. In the 1960s McClure investigated the use of mineral phosphates in diets to inhibit decay, and Zipkin and Larson experimented with diet as a means of controlling dental caries. Because the findings of Fitzgerald and Keyes and others suggested that tooth decay was related to the interaction of food residues, caries-inducing bacteria, and a susceptible host, or tooth, Larson and Zipkin wondered if altering any one of those factors might curtail new decay. Consequently, they found that rats fed for one-third of a day developed significantly less decay than those allowed the same amount of food over a twenty-four-hour period. The Larson-Zipkin study clearly indicated a relationship between the frequency of eating and the formation of tooth decay.[31]

By 1964 caries research took a practical turn when Fitzgerald, Keyes, and Dr. Harold R. Englander of the Institute's Epidemiology and Biometry Branch found that use of new gelatinous topical fluoride preparations as well as antibiotics controlled the development of both severe experimental caries and periodontal diseases in hamsters. As a result, the National Institute of Dental Research initiated a two-year experiment providing four hundred New York school students with flexible mouthpieces filled with a fluoride-phosphate gel for self-application. The study ended successfully with close to an 80 percent reduction in new decay.[32]

Meanwhile, inspired by the findings of Fitzgerald and Keyes, other researchers were examining similar streptococci in human dental lesions. In 1965 Dr. Doran D. Zinner and his colleagues at the University of Miami isolated microorganisms from human dental caries that corresponded with the streptococci strains Fitzgerald and Keyes had linked to caries in the hamsters and rats. Dr. J. Carlsson of the University of Umea in Sweden and Dr. Stig Edwardsson of the School of Dentistry, University of Lund in Malmö, Sweden, found that the streptococci appeared to resemble closely the *Streptococcus mutans* discussed by Clarke in 1924. In 1968 the Swedish scientists tracked down a *Streptococcus mutans* strain that Dr. W. Sims, a pathologist in the Royal Dental Hospital, had deposited in the National Collection of Type Cultures in the 1950s. The strains isolated by Carlsson and Edwardsson matched the Sims deposit in Great Britain and were closely related to the rat and hamster caries strains separated by Fitzgerald! A Swiss scientist, Dr. B. Guggenheim of the Experimental Caries Research Laboratories, Dental Institute, University of Zurich, independently arrived at the same conclusion as Carlsson and Edwardsson. Indeed, it had taken almost four decades to produce solid proof to confirm Clarke's lone research of 1924.[33]

Although many questions about the caries process remained unanswered, the significant parts of the riddle had been solved. Fitzgerald and Keyes had provided the first evidence that dental caries was an infectious, transmissible disease induced by the interaction of a cariogenic diet, *Streptococcus mutans*, and a susceptible tooth. The work was a triumph for the NIDR, for teamwork, for basic research, and for dentistry, and it opened doors to other scientific investigations.

Caries Research Task Force

While stimulating scientific research, the Fitzgerald-Keyes achievements eventually proved useful politically to the Institute leadership. The dental caries findings gained attention as hints of possible health policy changes started filtering out of the White House in the early 1960s.

Before he was assassinated in 1963, President John F. Kennedy had suggested a qualitative study of NIH. Shortly after assuming the presidency, Lyndon B. Johnson implemented Kennedy's recommendation. The new president took a special interest in national health matters because of his personal friendship with Mary Lasker, an ardent supporter of applied medical research. In calling for such an appraisal, Johnson explained, "A healthy citizenry has traditionally been one of this country's foremost goals." [34]

In 1964 Johnson requested a group of leading Americans in science, technology, and education to assess the operations of the National Institutes of Health. Led by Dr. Dean E. Wooldridge, an eminent science executive in private industry from Los Angeles, California, the committee praised the work of the National Institutes of Health but observed that the "disease category" organization confused the public because the agency actually concentrated instead on broad basic research. In its February 1965 report the committee urged that the agency's long-range planning, utilization of funds, and activities be strengthened to retain public support. Despite its criticism the Wooldridge committee strongly upheld the continuation of the NIH basic research mission. [35]

In the wake of the Wooldridge report, the Institute leadership increased organizational and public relations emphasis on both basic and applied research—steps that Kreshover, then in charge of the Institute's scientific research, considered essential to satisfy the Johnson administration. In September 1965 when NIH Director Shannon sent Johnson a report on NIH accomplishments during his presidency, for the NIDR its information officer listed first the Fitzgerald-Keyes achievements and their potential for application. [36]

Meanwhile, Mary Lasker's views differed from the Wooldridge report's recommendations, and she pressed Johnson to insist on practical results from NIH research. In response, Johnson summoned what he called his "Battle Strategy Council" to a June 27, 1966,

White House meeting to discuss National Institutes of Health operations. The "Battle Strategy Council" included John Gardner, secretary of Health, Education, and Welfare; Surgeon General Stewart; Shannon; and every institute director.

Citing the anticipated burden Medicare was expected to impose on the nation's medical community, the president was determined to insure that scientific findings from the more than $800 million annual NIH budget were being applied rapidly to cure and prevent disease and promote solutions to health problems. Johnson repeated complaints relayed to him about too little clinical testing and too much research for the sake of research. He responded that "research is good but results are better" and suggested that NIH improve its selection of priorities within the medical research programs.[37]

Several of the scientists present urged the president to protect basic research, explaining that "targeted" research was different from "organized" research and that "targeted" research posed a risk because if the researchers missed the target, virtually no payoff occurred. While Shannon and his directors agreed with Johnson that effective application of new knowledge was essential, they opposed a modification of the agency's program.[38]

Consequently, when each director described his institute's accomplishments, Kreshover told the president about the successes of fluoride administration and the potential applications of the research that had established specific bacterial causes to dental diseases in laboratory animals. Afterward the president, who asked questions of every other categorical institute director, had none for Kreshover.[39]

Following that June meeting and similar remarks by several congressmen, Shannon sensed widespread feelings of insecurity among the nation's scientists. He estimated that approximately 60 percent of the NIH research budget went toward applied research that was not well publicized. To respond to the president's concerns, Shannon asked all institute directors to contribute to an NIH report for Johnson on each institute's activities, priorities, status of directed research, future plans, and difficulties.[40]

When he replied to Shannon's call for the NIH statement to the White House, Kreshover first proposed the concept of a future Institute-targeted caries research program stemming primarily from the Keyes and Fitzgerald findings. But Kreshover's stress on applied research troubled some members of the National Advisory Dental Research Council who preferred other priorities, such as greater basic periodontal research and increased training of dental researchers. "We have to depend on basic research to provide more information" on periodontal research, Dr. Maynard K. Hine asserted. Nevertheless, Kreshover took the position that the NIDR's research accomplishments, especially the interrelated roles of streptococci, diet, and susceptible teeth, provided sufficient insight into the causes of tooth decay to guide specific research and development of preventive measures. In November 1966 Kreshover recommended to the President that "an accelerated program of research during the next decade could reasonably provide the means for the virtual eradication of dental caries."[41]

Johnson modified his stand on research, but the president's concerns nevertheless induced NIH leaders to call attention to their applied research accomplishments. On July 21, 1967, Johnson met again with NIH directors and afterward in a public appearance at the Clinical Center complimented the institute directors on the November 1966 report. "I regard these men as my Chiefs of Staff in this war on the ancient enemies—sickness and diseases," he said. While citing specific instances of applications of NIH research, Johnson also stressed the importance of the institutes' basic research.[42]

After the president's public emphasis on application of basic research, the Program Planning Committee of the National Advisory Dental Research Council recommended taking advantage of the Institute's recent scientific progress. In October 1967 Fitzgerald and Keyes described to the committee the prospects of controlling dental caries through therapy for each one of the three major contributors to tooth decay: fluoridation to increase resistance of the host teeth, regulation of carbohydrate consumption to make the diet less cariogenic, and the possible use of dextran-splitting enzymes to prevent the cariogenic streptococci from forming plaque. The two scientists thought that streptococcal dextran appeared to be the adhesive that enabled cariogenic streptococci to cling together and form caries-inducing plaque on the tooth surface. Enthusiastic about the latest proposals of Fitzgerald and Keyes, committee members urged that "the ramifications of these findings should not be overlooked, not only in terms of scientific application but also in terms of disseminating this information." [43]

The animal experiments with dextranase, as the newly discovered dextran splitting was called, gave such striking results that the scientists published their findings as early as February 1968. Working with Diane Spinell of the Institute and Dr. Thomas H. Stoudt of Merck, Sharp, and Dohme Research Laboratories, Keyes and Fitzgerald found that the dextranase reduced plaque and caries in hamsters. Although they did not know whether dextranase would curtail the disease in humans, the possibilities encouraged Institute officials to promote applications of the research.[44]

In the spring of 1968 Kreshover and the Board of Scientific Counselors created a caries task force to implement Kreshover's 1966 proposal to the president. At the same time the board expected other Institute research projects to continue on a normal basis. By this time the costs of United States involvement in the Vietnam War brought increasing pressure for budget cuts in domestic spending. A reduction in health research appropriations threatened implementation of the plan. Despite a drop of almost $500,000 in the NIDR's 1969 budget to $22.9 million, the board recommended creation of the caries task force.[45]

Kreshover's chance to act came with the celebration of the NIDR's twentieth anniversary on June 4, 1968. Stressing Fitzgerald's and Keyes's discoveries about the origins of tooth decay, Kreshover announced the formation of the Caries Task Force to lead targeted research "to give substance to our hopes that we may completely prevent caries in the United States in the next decade." In the fall he appointed Scherp, chief of the Institute's Laboratory of Microbiology since 1958, as chairman of the task force, by then composed of Institute scientists.[46]

Actually, the task force operation did not begin until 1969. Political problems made uncertain the scope of the Institute's anticaries effort because of competition between the NIDR and the Division of Dental Health over applied and epidemiological research. In addition, Institute administrators were unsure whether the new administration of President Richard M. Nixon would support the Caries Task Force concept.

In January Scherp announced proposals for the task force to deal with caries research in the intramural, collaborative, and extramural programs. Such coordination was unique for the Institute. To guide the task force, Kreshover appointed a panel of experts composed of prominent dental scientists from both within and outside the federal government.[47]

Dr. John Greene's presence on the task force panel helped to resolve the potentially troubling question of how the program would affect the spread of fluoridation in the United States. At the steering committee's first meeting in June 1969 Greene, deputy director of the Division of Dental Health, persuaded the panel to protect his division's promotion of community and school fluoridation. By supporting certain fluoridation proposals and programs of Greene's division, the advisory group made it clear that the task force's mission was to supplement, not compete with, fluoridation of public drinking water supplies.[48]

In October the task force steering committee identified possible subjects for research that included enzymes, sugar substitutes, antimicrobial agents, vaccines, sealants, and improved applications of topical fluoride. With those recommendations the group created a framework for a future caries research program.[49]

National Caries Program, 1969-1976

Even without any formal program the Fitzgerald and Keyes work had motivated researchers to investigate preventives for dental decay. By 1969 the U.S. Navy and scientists in both the United States and abroad were attempting to develop a vaccine and other methods to inhibit the growth of caries-inducing bacteria. Kreshover, however, favored a visible, structured project identified with the Institute. Consequently, the National Caries Program (NCP) emerged in the fall of 1969. When Kreshover testified before the Senate Appropriations Committee in October 1969, he announced the creation of the National Caries Program as part of the Institute's targeted approach to research. Again, he predicted, based on the findings on the causes of dental decay, a concerted effort could produce "substantial reductions of caries in the next decade."[50]

Simultaneously, the Nixon administration moved toward a sharper change in biomedical research policy and prepared to use Kreshover's proposal as part of that shift. During the fall of 1969 the office of Secretary of Health, Education and Welfare asked the Institute to provide a detailed plan for developing caries-preventive techniques. Kreshover assigned that task to Scherp. Aided by the recommendations of the Caries Task Force Steering Group, Scherp drew up a ten-year research and development program for presentation to the Nixon administration in January 1970. Besides the steering group suggestions, Scherp proposed investigating restorative materials, tooth implants, and alternate means of delivering fluoride protection. Scherp considered the latter especially important because over 40 million Americans lacked access to community water supplies.[51]

Actually, the caries proposals were in accord with the Nixon administration decision to concentrate on targeted research by declaring war against certain diseases. In January 1970 Dr. Roger O. Egeberg, assistant secretary for health in the Department of Health, Education and Welfare, announced that the president had selected the Institute's plans for a National Caries Program as a special health initiative. Subsequently, in his February 1970 budget message Nixon recommended "substantial increases in research on cancer, heart disease, serious childhood illnesses, and dental health—where current findings promise significant advances in the future." Kreshover immediately appointed Scherp as leader of the National Caries Program.[52]

After Nixon's approval of the program Scherp moved forward with the project. In March 1970 the task force sponsored the first of "state-of-the-art" conferences on dietary factors in dental caries. Scherp organized the program into branches to conduct research directly or to support it through contracts and collaboration.[53]

But a public relations problem suddenly emerged. Statements that in ten years dental caries would be preventable proved especially troubling. Tula Brocard, Institute information officer, tried to discourage such comments. "This is highly improbable. Our objective . . . is to make it more nearly preventable by developing an improved technology for prevention by the end of the decade," she remarked. Brocard attributed such publicity to press confusion and to responses to press questions by "some of our own dental scientists [who] have fallen into a semantic trap."[54]

In the meantime, Institute administrators were apprehensive about the financial effects of the program's funding on the rest of the Institute's mission. To deal with the country's troubled economy, the administration cut domestic spending. Yet while the Nixon White House was reducing other parts of the health budget, the administration increased the Institute's request for the first year of the National Caries Program from $1 million to $5 million. To the dismay of the NIDR's Board of Scientific Counselors in 1970, the level of support for the next fiscal year decreased for noncaries intramural research. Kreshover explained to the board that he foresaw difficulties in maintaining the integrity of the Institute's work in other areas such as periodontal disease, abnormalities of facial development, and soft tissue lesions. Several board members were worried about the possible infringement on the freedom of research of the intramural scientists, but Institute leaders indicated that they would try to match individual pursuits with the program's research plan.[55]

The Nixon administration's order for a reduction of federal government personnel in 1971 exacerbated the situation. The Institute had to cut its staff from 304 to 285 positions. While the greatly increased budget, if passed by Congress, contained enough money to support 304 positions, Kreshover lacked authority to hire even 5 people above the limit of 285 to build up a staff for the program. Unfortunately, at its start the NCP lacked sufficient staff members to carry out all of its first proposals.[56]

Thus the entire NCP did not commence as planned in 1970 because of funding and administrative problems. Congress failed to approve the $5 million appropriation, which appeared as a line item in the president's budget. Instead, the Institute operated with the rest of NIH on a continuing resolution. Of necessity the NCP used funds from existing grants and the intramural program, and Scherp delayed implementation of collaborative research.[57]

The issue of targeted research again arose just prior to congressional funding of the NCP. Several Board of Scientific Counselors members found the NCP as outlined in the Institute's five-year plan, *Oral Disease: Target for the 70s*, too rigid and potentially hazardous to the basic research freedom associated with the Institute. Kreshover, however, assured them that he would maintain the Institute's research flexibility. Yet the apprehensions about targeted research lingered after the NCP began. As one observer later noted, "the Board's collective feeling seemed to be a curious blend of indignance, resignation and, above all, curiosity to see how such changes in traditional NIH operations will affect them in the long run." [58]

After Congress finally approved NCP funding, the program became fully operational in March 1971. The NCP expenditures for the first year of operation amounted to slightly over $6 million, including almost $2 million in grants, $3 million in contracts, $900,000 in laboratory and clinical research, $200,000 in statistical and field studies, and $40,000 in collaborative work.[59]

In September the NCP became an official part of the Institute when the NIH deputy director for science approved an office of associate director for the National Caries Program with responsibilities for direct research, grants, and contracts. Scherp assumed the post of associate director for the National Caries Program, which, for the first time in the Institute's history, officially included intramural and extramural responsibilities within the same branch. The arrangement was unique not only for NIDR but also for NIH.

Scherp organized the research according to the concept that dental caries resulted from a combination of several factors. The NCP concentrated on four approaches:

- combating caries-inducing microorganisms;

- increasing the resistance of the teeth to decay;

- modifying caries-promoting ingredients of the diet; and

- improving delivery and public acceptance of techniques that prevented dental caries.

To prepare a base for the work, the Institute catalogued all caries projects in the United States for most of the preceding three years and held workshops and conferences on the subjects designated for study.[60]

From the outset Dr. James P. Carlos, chief of the Disease Prevention and Therapeutics Branch, and his staff were concerned principally with reducing the prevalence of dental caries in children, but they possessed no estimate of how rampant the disease was in the United States. To acquire that essential data, they conferred with the Center of Health Statistics about obtaining a survey to measure the degree of dental caries in the nation. But at the time such a survey was considered too expensive to prepare. Instead, the center conducted a limited dental caries census from 1971 to 1973.[61]

In its early years the program staff laid the foundation for other research. NIDR officials were disappointed, however, after the first clinical studies of humans with dextranase mouthrinses failed to duplicate successes inhibiting new dental caries in experimental animals. On the other hand, prospects appeared promising for the success of sealants when an Institute-sponsored two-year study proved that a sealant developed by Dr. Michael Buonocore protected tooth pits and fissures against decay. Buonocore, a pioneer in sealant research at the

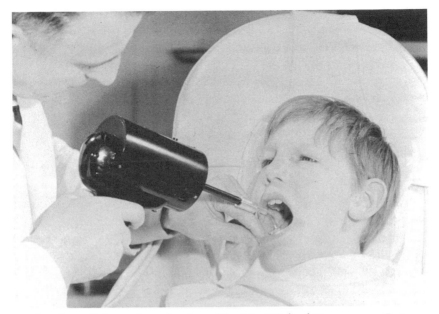

Application of the sealant developed by Dr. Michael Buonocore, Eastman Dental Dispensary, Rochester, N.Y.

Eastman Dental Dispensary in Rochester, New York, had been receiving NIDR support for his sealant investigations since 1964. Of course, the program also included the financing of studies on large-group use of alternate types of fluoride applications.

At the beginning of the NCP other potential preventive measures presented problems. There were questions about the practicability of antimicrobial agents research. Carlos was concerned about the limited interest of the pharmaceutical industry in developing such dental preventives because of Food and Drug Administration requirements for costly preclinical and clinical testing of such agents. Moreover, he doubted that antimicrobial chemotherapy would prove feasible on a mass scale. Because such preventives could help individuals, the Institute contracted with the Medical College of Georgia to screen potentially useful antimicrobial agents for pharmaceutical companies. Scherp was also pessimistic about the prospects of producing an anticaries vaccine because of the complexities of the disease. Nevertheless, he included studies in the program on the feasibility of creating a dental caries vaccine.[62]

In March 1972 Scherp retired, and Carlos, known for his epidemiological work, replaced him as head of the NCP. A dentist with a master's degree in public health from Columbia University, Carlos had analyzed data from the Newburgh-Kingston, New York, fluoridation trials. He had joined the Institute in 1967.[63]

Carlos viewed the NCP as a joint intramural and extramural operation and was determined to mount a strong intramural effort. He set out to build a highly competent staff to run the program. Already the realignment of Public Health Service dental research responsibilities had brought Dr. Herschel S. Horowitz to the NCP to organize clinical field trials of caries-preventive agents that could be used on a communitywide basis. With a D.D.S. and master's degree in public health from the University of Michigan, Horowitz previously had served as chief of the epidemiology branch of the Division of Dental Health San Francisco Dental Health Center. Carlos placed scientists from within the Institute in the program and recruited from outside the government such prominent researchers as Dr. William Bowen from the Royal College of Surgeons in London, Dr. Basil Bibby of the Eastman Dental Center, and Rudi Schamschula from the United Dental Hospital of Sydney, Australia.[64]

During the program's first four years the major problems were largely political. Departmental disarray deprived the NCP of support for additional personnel and adequate physical space. Between 1973 and 1975 the National Institutes of Health operated under three successive directors, and after Dr. Jesse Steinfeld vacated the post of surgeon general on January 20, 1973, no one replaced him during the remainder of the second Nixon administration. Even after the Watergate controversy forced Nixon to resign in August 1974, his successor, President Gerald Ford, did not appoint a new surgeon general. Moreover, for the first half of 1975 the Department of Health, Education and Welfare had no assistant secretary for health, the departmental administrator responsible for the NIH.[65]

Meanwhile, through collaboration with the private sector, the NCP staff encouraged pharmaceutical manufacturers to experiment with antimicrobial agents. Program administrators established screening services for clinical trials of antimicrobial agents at the Forsyth Dental Center in 1973 and later at the University of Pennsylvania. To foster industrial research, NCP personnel conducted a workshop in 1974 to apprise some thirty pharmaceutical firms about the screening services and later produced a manual on that assistance. Those NCP efforts led manufacturers to test close to two hundred potential preventive agents at the preclinical level and several in short-term clinical trials.[66]

On the other hand, results from a series of experiments and clinical trials sponsored by the program persuaded NCP leaders to recommend a major change in topical fluoride therapy. Research findings in Larson's intramural animal experiments indicated that regular, frequent exposures to relatively diluted fluoride solutions could provide an effective, easy way to prevent new dental decay in school-age children. Moreover, Scandinavian studies unconnected with the NCP confirmed those good effects with diluted fluoride. Carlos reacted by proposing school mouthrinsing demonstrations because they would be easy to control and an inexpensive way to provide children with caries preventives. An American Dental Association survey of the nation's dentists also had manifested support for school-based projects such as this one. Meanwhile, the Senate Appropriations Committee had been urging the Institute to provide more effective dissemination and application of research findings on dental decay. Consequently, in 1975 the NCP initiated three-year weekly mouthrinsing demonstrations of 0.2 percent solution of sodium fluoride started in seventeen communities with 75,000 students to test feasibility, cost, and public acceptance.[67]

The NCP also extended its scope to extramural training in dental caries research. Through the NIH institutional award process, the NCP staff gave the first such postdoctoral grant to the University of Minnesota School of Dentistry in 1975.[68]

During 1976 NCP-sponsored research results appeared to diminish prospects for rapid development of new methods of dental caries prevention. The requirements for antibacterial measures, for instance, seemed more complex. Dr. Ronald J. Gibbons and Dr. J. Van Houte of the Forsyth Dental Center confirmed that sucrose facilitated the colonization of *Streptococcus mutans* on smooth surfaces of teeth but pointed out that other kinds of bacterial mechanisms also might determine whether the accumulation would adhere to the teeth. In addition, more definitive evidence raised doubts about the practicability of using dextranase as a preventive; clinical trials on dextranase, the enzyme that had prevented dental plaque in laboratory animals, did little to prevent tooth decay in children. Meanwhile, a sealant

Students in Nelson County, Virginia, participating in a 1973 study to measure caries reduction in children who used fluoride tablets and fluoride rinses at school and brushed with ADA-accepted fluoride dentifrices at home.

Posters designed by the National Caries Program to emphasize the benefits of fluorides to oral health.

workshop sponsored by the NCP ended with participants recommending that dentists use sealants on patients, even though the researchers regarded sealants as in the research stage in 1976 and not yet practical for mass, or self, use. Although recent research had shown that sealants could prevent decay in tooth areas, such as occlusal surfaces where fluoride alone was ineffective, only an experienced person could apply sealant to teeth.[69]

In November 1976, the five-year point in the NCP effort, Herbert Dantzler, a supervisory auditor of the General Accounting Office (GAO), jolted Scott, Institute director for less than a year. Dantzler revealed that the GAO, the accounting arm of Congress, intended to study the entire National Caries Program. The GAO, not any member of Congress, initiated the investigation. In fact, the office's Boston branch already had planned a visit to the Forsyth Dental Center. Scott told Dantzler that "it would be nice to know what is going on, especially since we have for some time been planning an evaluation."[70]

The General Accounting Office and the National Caries Program

The GAO investigation of the program first centered on Boston but eventually affected the existing and future operations of the mouthrinse demonstration project. Unfortunately, from the outset of the study, leaders of the investigation made statements suggesting that they had already drawn conclusions about the program.

The GAO team seemed unaware that the NCP aimed at supplementing, not competing with, fluoridation. During the early days of the probe the GAO investigators contended that water fluoridation was the most inexpensive means of controlling tooth decay and asked why the mouthrinsing demonstration money was not spent instead for water fluoridation equipment. Apparently unfamiliar with almost three decades of resistance to fluoridation, especially in Boston, the investigators wanted to know why the NCP was selecting cities eligible for fluoridation for mouthrinse demonstrations.[71]

In 1977 the Boston GAO probers paid special attention to NCP participants, including the Forsyth Dental Center. The GAO chief investigator asserted the federal government had greatly deemphasized fluoridation promotion and that the NCP administrators seemed "to be backing off from that initial objective ... to eliminate dental caries as a public health problem in ten years." Director of the Forsyth Dental Center Dr. John W. Hein and his staff replied to the GAO team that fluoridation was only partially effective against dental caries and that continued research was needed for better or supplemental control of dental decay. Concerned over reports that Boston NCP administrators regarded the GAO as unreceptive to explanations on the basics of their effort, Carlos feared GAO interviews with contractors and the public might jeopardize the entire program.[72]

Ironically, while its accounting arm was investigating the mouthrinsings, Congress was pressing for dissemination of information to the public on the process. To do so, Carlos issued a film and manual promoting fluoride mouthrinsing.[73]

In July 1977 the GAO investigating team contracted with the Gallup Poll to conduct a national survey on fluoridation attitudes. The Boston branch of the office proposed expanding the probe to California and Tennessee and evaluating the antifluoridation factor through discussions with officers of the National Health Federation, a leading opponent of fluoridation.[74]

Later that year, contrary to the protests of NIH Director Donald Frederickson and Carlos, GAO investigators questioned local officials at mouthrinsing demonstration sites about fluoridation and whether the communities would adopt the mouthrinsing projects after federal funding ended. Fredrickson and Carlos worried that the GAO interrogations might distort information collected by the NCP, which wanted to identify factors influencing community decisions on implementing caries preventive programs.[75]

In 1978, anticipating GAO disapproval of the fluoride mouthrinsing school demonstrations, Carlos publicized the effectiveness and frugality of the school-based programs in preventing dental decay in nonfluoridated areas. Congressman Tim Lee Carter, a Democrat from Kentucky, also publicly praised the procedure.[76]

On April 13, 1979, the GAO released its study, *Reducing Tooth Decay—More Emphasis Needed on Fluoridation*, which criticized the federal government's negligence in doing little to promote fluoridation and recommended that Congress amend the Safe Drinking Water Act because the law's language discouraged fluoridation. In assessing the NCP, the authors declared the goal of "eliminating tooth decay by 1980" unrealistic, the fluoride gels impractical for mass use, the mouthrinsing demonstrations too costly for the government, and the school-based mouthrinsings unacceptable alternatives to community fluoridation. Although no national survey had been conducted in the late 1970s on the prevalence of dental caries, the GAO report also claimed that the research had not produced a measurable reduction of dental caries in the nation. The study further recommended that the secretary of Health, Education and Welfare require the NIH director to develop criteria for undertaking NCP demonstration projects and reassess at least annually the potential public benefits of program undertakings.[77]

While strongly endorsing the GAO call for promotion of community water fluoridation, NCP officials countered the GAO appraisal by pointing out that the program's objective was to help approximately 107 million Americans without access to fluoridated water supplies. The NCP mouthrinsing demonstrations were aimed at influencing nonfluoridated communities to adopt the process for close to 25 million children. The program's scientists also defended sealant and fluoride gels as highly effective for children and individuals at high risk to caries, such as patients who had lost salivary gland functions because of cancer therapy. The GAO charge that caries had not diminished nationally prompted Institute leaders to explain that a decrease in dental caries would depend on economic, political, and social factors beyond the control of the program operators. Adding that the GAO had neglected to recognize that the government costs of mouthrinsing demonstrations included research and data collection, Department of Health, Education and Welfare officials supported the NCP administrators.[78]

Overall, the GAO report failed to deliver a mortal blow to the NCP. Instead, the study strengthened fluoridation promotion. In 1979 Congress passed legislation providing technical and financial support to fluoridate 435 additional community water systems and 100 more school water systems. Moreover, as a consequence of the GAO examination, the Institute arranged for a nationwide survey on caries prevalence. As Scott explained to the National Dental Research Advisory Council, the Institute lacked "really good recent data on dental caries" to serve as a background for its studies.[79]

Final Years of the National Caries Program and Its Aftermath

At the same time as the NCP was the subject of investigation in 1977 and 1978, the program underwent several changes in emphasis prompted by results of research projects. Program administrators terminated some of the dietary studies because in the case of phosphate compounds clinical trials proved them ineffective. Views changed also on sugar substitutes. A cable from an English laboratory about possible side effects from high concentrations of polyol xylitol, a sugar substitute in chewing gum, prompted Carlos to fly to New York to stop a trial of xylitol-sweetened chewing gum only three days after a clinical test had commenced. But in 1978 dipeptide aspartame emerged as a promising noncariogenic sugar substitute. Meanwhile, Carlos and Scott decided to reduce industry's clinical trials of antimicrobial agents because of slow progress and the private sector's lack of enthusiasm.[80]

In November 1978 NIDR Director Scott, aided by his special assistant Dr. Lois Cohen, assembled panels of close to forty outside experts from the United States and several other countries to appraise the NCP. That evaluation was part of an effort begun in 1974 to assess all major Institute programs. A prominent dental scientist, Dr. George S. Beagrie, served as chairman of the main NCP evaluation panel. A past president of the International Association for Dental Research, Beagrie was dean of the Faculty of Dentistry at the University of British Columbia. While the GAO had examined the NCP as part of a "cost-benefit" study of several federal approaches to the dental caries problem, the NIDR advisors chose to examine the scientific strategies, organization, and management of the NCP alone.[81]

A year later, in November 1979, the consultants reported their evaluation. Using a five-point scale, the group rated the program's overall accomplishment at four, or good. They judged that the greatest strides were made in the microbiology area, which received the most emphasis and funding. Yet the evaluators found comparatively little achievement in dietary research and in improving delivery and acceptance of preventive methods. Moreover, they called attention to "a clearly identified lack of 'hard' epidemiological data" on the magnitude of dental caries in the general population and on the measure of effectiveness of preventives.[82]

In contrast to the GAO criticisms of specific NCP projects, the NIDR-sponsored examiners, who included eminent oral microbiologists, judged both weekly mouthrinsings and sealants as useful supplements in curbing new decay. Those consultants, however, recommended that the NCP promote school water fluoridation and other fluoride alternatives in communities lacking water fluoridation. To overcome the problems with sealants of application, expense, and a short retention time, the advisors suggested more research and development on sealant materials.[83]

The NCP appraisers called for a refocusing of the NCP to place greater stress on research of nutritional aspects of dental caries and on behavioral science areas affecting preventive measures. In addition, the consultants advised the Institute to create a separate epidemiology and biometry office that would develop epidemiological methods and conduct local and national surveys on dental caries. Furthermore, they suggested that the Institute establish special dental caries research centers for basic and clinical investigations at major universities.[84]

After reviewing the evaluation with his staff, Carlos implemented several of the study's recommendations. In 1980 the NCP chief restructured the effort on tooth resistance research, added an expert on nutritional research to the staff, refocused the cariology training programs, and followed some management suggestions. The course of research, personnel ceilings, and time needed to consider other options kept Carlos from making additional changes.[85]

In the meantime, NCP scientists enjoyed some encouraging research successes. Although uncertainties persisted about developing a successful caries vaccine, in 1978 NCP scientists showed that caries antibody levels increased in saliva of both humans and animals after the subjects swallowed a capsule containing killed *Streptococcus mutans* cells. Carlos called the work extremely important but warned that "we should not conclude that a vaccine against human caries is imminent" because much more basic and clinical research was necessary.[86]

Moreover, the mouthrinsing demonstrations had been completed in 1979 and had proved successful clinically and promotionally. When the demonstrations ended in 1979, the results showed that the decrease in new tooth decay ranged from 11 to 54 percent. Local officials at all the sites responded by continuing the mouthrinsing programs after federal funding ended. As the NCP finished mouthrinsing demonstrations in California, that state adopted a school-based mouthrinsing program. In 1980 over five thousand requests poured into the Institute for the mouthrinsing educational and promotional materials. Nationwide estimates showed that the number of children participating in school-based self-applied fluoride programs increased from less than 2 million in 1975, just before the program's mouthrinsings started, to over 13 million in 1981.[87]

The development by the NCP of a screening system for potentially cariogenic foods was an achievement that Carlos termed a major contribution to food-screening technology. By 1980 Bowen and his Institute NCP team had devised a highly controlled, reproducible rat-feeding technique. That method yielded data for use in assigning a "cariogenic potential index" relative to that of pure sucrose for each food tested. Subsequently, Bowen's programmed feeding model for the rat was adopted by laboratories around the world.[88]

The national caries prevalence survey, conducted in 1980, provided especially revealing findings. The surveyors found that the rate of new dental caries among schoolchildren in the United States had decreased by more than 30 percent since the last national dental survey of 1971-1973. In the 1980 survey, 36 percent of the children had no caries; in the previous count, 28 percent exhibited no decay. Nevertheless, Institute officials cautiously noted that the survey results should not be attributed to any particular factor in the NCP.[89]

Yet the 1980 survey findings suggested that the NCP had fulfilled part of Kreshover's prediction of promoting a substantial decline in new dental decay. Having passed the ten-year period originally designated by Kreshover, the program had run its course. During that decade the NCP had proved to be an important source of appropriations for dental research; from 1972 through 1978, for instance, the program had funded over 200 individual research projects, the equivalent of almost 850 project years of activity. For most of its existence the NCP had received almost 20 percent of the Institute's entire intramural and extramural program funds.[90]

But a radical change in the NCP did not take place until 1983. Scott retired in 1981, and Goggins served as acting director during 1982. In 1983, after reviewing the NCP work, Löe, the new Institute director, replaced the NCP with an expanded epidemiology and oral disease prevention program and integrated the program's intramural and extramural caries research into regular Institute programs. In reorganizing, Löe, an international authority on periodontology, wanted to extend expertise in caries prevalence to other diseases and to refocus some efforts on periodontology. From a practical standpoint, he proposed to reduce overhead and administrative costs. Löe also followed some of the suggestions in the NIDR caries evaluation by establishing three new extramural caries research centers in 1984.[91]

Löe's reorganization was greeted with mixed reactions in the dental research community. A strong advocate of extramural funding, Forsyth Dental Clinic Director Hein supported Löe's action. In Hein's view, too much money had gone into the caries intramural program at the expense of extramural projects. On the other side, Dr. Fred Emmings, chairman of the Department of Clinical Dentistry at the University of Rochester Medical Center, feared the program's abolition would indicate to the "best dental investigators in the nation" that the Institute no longer assigned a high priority to caries research. Emmings had previously served on the National Caries Program Advisory Committee and as one of the consultants evaluating the NCP for the Institute. Carlos, at the Institute, urged Löe to bolster the dejected spirits of former program personnel who had been reassigned to other parts of the Institute.[92]

Although the NCP was abolished, the Institute continued many of its projects. Additional research on food screening ended principally because the Institute had produced a usable method. But sealants, for instance, received continued backing. Since the Institute had started supporting sealant development, the nation's dentists had changed their views on using sealants. In 1974 only about 38 percent of the respondents in a survey of American dentists offered sealant treatment; by 1982 close to 58 percent administered sealant therapy to patients. At a 1983 Institute conference of the nation's sealant researchers the participants agreed that dentists, dental health agencies, and dental health educators should expand the use of sealants. The consensus was that pit and fissure sealant development had progressed to such a degree that sealants effectively prevented new decay, retention was no longer considered short term, and the cost of sealant was less than that of an amalgam restoration.[93]

Adherents to the concept of a vaccine persisted, and the Institute continued support of such research in the extramural sector. In the 1984 Kreshover lecture, an annual series sponsored by NIDR, Dr.

Roy Curtiss III of the University of Alabama predicted that a dental caries vaccine could be available in the next "3 to 10 years." [94]

Research on the relationship between diet and nutrition to prevent dental diseases, including caries, was supported by the Institute as early as 1985. Equally significant, Institute administrators were preparing another study to measure the efficacy of prenatal fluoride to prevent children's tooth decay.[95]

Meanwhile, as the NCP administrators had hoped, manufacturers of fluoride mouthrinsing supplies and school systems had assumed operation of school-based fluoride mouthrinsing. By 1985 schools in forty-four states were conducting fluoride mouthrinsing programs the Institute had promoted as part of its effort to reduce children's tooth decay.[96]

Looking Back

After almost fifty years of twentieth century research on the causes of dental caries, experiments conducted at the NIDR helped resolve many questions, contributed to a better understanding of the decay process, and opened areas of research for other scientists to explore. Several issues of the 1930s were clarified in the 1960s findings interlocking bacteria, diet, and a susceptible tooth as the keys to dental decay.

Like the successes in fluoridation research, the achievements in the dental caries studies exemplified the importance of the Institute's multidisciplinary operation and the cooperation of the dental research community outside NIH. Other Institute experimenters, for instance, developed equipment, isolated bacteria, and induced smooth-surface caries in rat teeth that helped Keyes and Fitzgerald in their investigations. Scientists not associated with the Institute initiated dental experiments with gnotobiotic animals—leading Fitzgerald to follow up on their research. Fitzgerald, who was searching for bacteria, and Keyes, who was tracing the dental caries process, worked in different laboratories; yet they combined their individual talents to produce results that excited investigators around the world.

On the other hand, the merging of research into the NCP provided a case study of both the benefits and the risks of targeted research.

One has only to recall that years before the NCP started, Keyes and Fitzgerald immediately recognized the possibilities of applying their basic results to a preventive agent. Obviously, the search for applications would have progressed with or without a targeted effort. But politics entered the picture in 1966 when President Johnson told NIH directors that "research is good but results are better," and Institute Director Kreshover realized that the Fitzgerald and Keyes work had the potential of fulfilling Johnson's belief. But Kreshover also was aware of the pitfalls pointed out to Johnson by NIH institute directors—that targeted research could end in absolute failure. Nevertheless, he seized the opportunity to give the Institute visibility. In preparation for a trend toward greater applied research at NIH, Kreshover initiated a national caries effort to expedite the work in order to produce within ten years methods that he forecast would virtually eradicate dental decay. When President Nixon's administration shifted sharply to targeted research at NIH, Kreshover's proposal was included in the administration's war on diseases.

During a period of budget reduction, the designation of the NCP brought additional funding to the Institute for studies on tooth decay. As the NCP evaluators concluded, that program achieved a moderate success. Both the basic and applied studies showed that the dental decay process was infinitely more complicated than scientists had anticipated at the inception of the NCP. While the 1980 national dental caries survey suggested that the NCP may have contributed to a significant decline in tooth decay, it was impossible to determine in any detail how the reduction occurred. Although the NCP fell somewhat short of its goal, it nevertheless succeeded in promoting topical fluoride applications through school-based mouthrinsings; it was responsible for the development of better sealants; and, of special importance, it funded research that enhanced the understanding of the dental caries mechanism.

Ultimately, the basic research that flourished under the NCP might lead to techniques that could eliminate dental caries disease. As the NCP demonstrated, politics could only furnish encouragement and financial support to research, but results depended on human progress in understanding and harnessing nature.

CHAPTER EIGHT

Sleuths of Science: Basic Research at NIDR

Science moves, but slowly slowly, creeping on from point to point.

ALFRED LORD TENNYSON

"We're devoting entirely too much attention to patching up people after they get sick, and nowhere near enough attention to the job of finding out what causes the sickness in the first place," Dean told a national radio audience in 1950. Dean's personal experience with the first NIH dental research project convinced him that the answer lay in fundamental research into the causes of dental diseases. Dean recalled that a dental epidemiologist, a water chemist, and a biochemist cooperated in the landmark work that led to fluoridation. By 1950 half of the NIDR investigators were Public Health Service dental officers, most with graduate school training, and the rest were scientists with Ph.D.s in the basic sciences.[1]

But Dean would not deny that dental research had "a long way to go, after a late start." He pointed out that more information was needed on the evolution of dental caries but that "we know even less about periodontal disease." While in 1950 most of the Institute's research concerned dental caries and fluoride, its scientists had already published significant basic science contributions. Through electron microscopy they had disproved a theory that decay originated in extremely fine cracks in the tooth, and they had developed techniques for preserving oral microorganisms in a dried and frozen state that would be helpful to bacteriologists. Dean wisely predicted that

216

major strides in controlling dental disease would eventually arise through interdisciplinary collaboration with scientists around the world.[2]

The family of periodontal diseases presented a particularly difficult problem. The dental science community used the words "periodontal disease" as a general term for an inflammatory process affecting the gums that could proceed to destruction of the soft tissue and bone supporting the teeth. Scientists did not understand what triggered this kind of disease or how the condition developed.

Starting usually with gingivitis, a mild inflammation of the gums, the pathological process can advance until the gums separate from the teeth and form "periodontal" pockets. Debris fills the pockets and exacerbates the damage to the surrounding tissues until the teeth become loose. Worldwide, virtually everyone eventually contracts some form of periodontal disease.

Unlike dental decay, that was curtailed by fluoridation, periodontal diseases had no miracle deterrent in 1950. As Dean suggested to his radio listeners, basic research seemed to be the most appropriate means of attacking the periodontal disease problem.[3]

The rewards of basic research were impossible to predict, however. Years might pass before scientists could determine if their findings were significant. Yet fundamental inquiries into the causes of dental problems could prove instrumental in explaining the processes of dental as well as other diseases because, as Dean explained, "We can't divorce the mouth from the rest of the body." Studies of gum tissue and bone, for instance, could apply to connective tissue and bone elsewhere in the body and, consequently, to such conditions as rheumatoid arthritis and skeletal disorders.[4]

Dean and Arnold, his scientific director, set the precedent at NIDR for fostering basic and other kinds of research. They and their successors operated the intramural program as both a broad-based research center and a postdoctoral training ground. Although each director and intramural chief exercised personal judgment in building the intramural program, each was limited by general NIH policies, politics, and budget considerations. In addition, Congress and the presidents influenced the amount of emphasis on basic research. From the late 1960s on, Congress clamored for more visible results from research, particularly after Hill retired from the Senate. Johnson and Nixon favored targeted studies that took the form of wars on diseases, which were easier for the public to understand. The administrations of Presidents Jimmy Carter and Ronald Reagan stressed basic research.[5]

From 1948 through 1987 intramural research received an average of 18.8 percent of the total Institute appropriations, ranging from a low of 11.7 percent in 1949 to a high of 36.1 percent in 1956. Congress increased intramural research appropriations every year except for slight reductions in 1962 and 1978. (See charts and tables in appendices.) Further, Institute administrators apportioned these funds to change research priorities. For instance, in 1973 the Institute leadership allocated 30 percent of the intramural research budget to caries, 27 percent to periodontal disease, and 17 percent to soft tissues; the remainder covered a variety of topics. In 1979 for the first time the largest share of intramural research funding went to periodontal diseases. By 1983 periodontal research absorbed 31.4 percent of the intramural research expenses; caries, 25.2 percent; and soft tissues, 26.6 percent.[6]

A different set of circumstances governed extramural activities. Covering a broader range of disciplines than the intramural effort supported, the extramural program depended on several factors beyond the control of Institute administrators, including the nature and scientific promise of both the research grant applications and the candidates for research training. From 1948 to 1987 extramural research grants received an average of 42.8 percent of the Institute appropriations, ranging from a low of 8.8 percent in 1949 to a high of 64.4 percent in 1986 and 1987. During the Vietnam War, Congress cut extramural research grant appropriations almost 3 percent in 1965, 5 percent in 1970, and 12 percent in 1974. Yet the extramural research emphasis, according to data for the period from 1973 to 1983, generally matched the proportions for the intramural research expenditures.

The overall trend in Institute obligations for intramural, extramural, and contract research reflected a shift from 1973 to 1983 to more emphasis on soft tissue research and somewhat less support to work on periodontal diseases and caries. The shares were:

	1973	*1983*
caries	32 percent	24.0 percent
periodontal	29 percent	27.9 percent
soft tissue	9 percent	18.4 percent[7]

Basic studies could affect any of these areas and nondental conditions as well. Initially, the Institute's intramural fundamental research focused on the causes of major dental problems and, as Dean observed, had evolved from modest beginnings. Over the Institute's four decades the basic research of its intramural laboratories and extramural program grew and diversified to become part of mainstream biomedical basic research.

Mineralized Tissue and Bone

Studies of bone and mineralized tissue, ultrastructure of teeth, and enamel surface structure were among the oldest basic dental research fields at NIH. In 1945, prior to the establishment of NIDR, dental researchers examining bones and mineralized tissues concentrated first on the reaction of fluoride and the dental decay process. McClure also conducted some of the initial biochemical studies of the effects of fluoride on bone.

Electron microscopy of mineralized tissue actually started after Dean introduced Scott to Dr. Ralph W. G. Wyckoff, a prominent crystallographer, who joined NIH in 1945. Wyckoff had come to NIH to establish a program to study the fine structure of tissues with new instruments, such as the electron microscope. Dean encouraged Wyckoff and Scott to collaborate; his strategy was successful. Wyckoff became Scott's mentor and by 1949 the two had published numerous papers on tooth structure, including results showing changes with age, the fibrous components of dentin, and optical and electron microscopy of tooth surface structure.[8]

While Wyckoff's laboratory was eventually housed in the National Institute of Arthritis and Metabolic Diseases, Dean placed Scott's laboratory in the Pathology and Histology Section of NIDR. Within a year of the Institute's founding, Scott's laboratory began a tradition of serving as a training and research center for scientists from around the world. Dr. Poul O. Pedersen of Denmark, the Institute's first foreign visiting scientist, came to the laboratory in 1949. Others who followed included Drs. S. Takuma from Japan, G. Helmcke from the Federal Republic of Germany, Knut A. Selvig from Norway, and J. Theilade from Denmark.[9]

As in other fields of science, the mineralized tissue work at the Institute benefited from the mentor system. After his fruitful relationship with Wyckoff, Scott in turn served as a mentor to Marie Ussing, a graduate of the Royal Dental College of the University of Copenhagen. She started working in the laboratory in 1949.[10]

Scott achieved international recognition for his development of new methods for applying the electron microscope to the study of enamel and dentin and for his use of other physical methods, including X ray and electron-diffusion contact radiography. He also devised a new technique for studying tooth structure. By 1954 Institute Director Arnold had elevated Scott's section to a laboratory and designated him as its chief. Then specializing in mineral-related tissue ultrastructure and chemical microscopy, the laboratory focused on biology.[11]

Meanwhile, Marie Ussing had left the Institute and had married Aage Nylen. By 1955 she had returned to the Institute to resume research with Scott on the structure and integrity of dental enamel.

In the late 1950s another fruitful period of research was initiated. Using the electron microscope to full advantage, Nylen, Scott, and Takuma at NIDR and scientists elsewhere in the United States and England for the first time traced the development of enamel from embryonic to mature stages. During this same period the Institute researchers devised techniques for obtaining previously unavailable electron micrographs of the stages of crystallization. Their signal studies disclosed crystals forming at the first stage of enamelization and growing out to the edge of the teeth. The electron microscope revealed tooth crystals arrayed in a prism with all crystals oriented the same way within each prism; yet the structure differed for each kind of animal. The scientists found that adult tooth enamel actually was a fossil of the mouth because all living cells and almost all of the enamel's proteins were removed prior to eruption. Because of their achievements in analyzing tooth structure, Scott and Nylen attained such renown as forensic dentists that the Federal Bureau of Investigation sought their aid in criminal investigations.[12]

The laboratory's mineralized tissue program expanded in 1962 with the establishment of a crystal chemistry section under the supervision of Dr. Aaron Posner, who had established a crystallography laboratory for NIDR. Posner's research team used X ray diffraction and infrared spectroscopy techniques to study various stages of development of tooth enamel and dentin.[13]

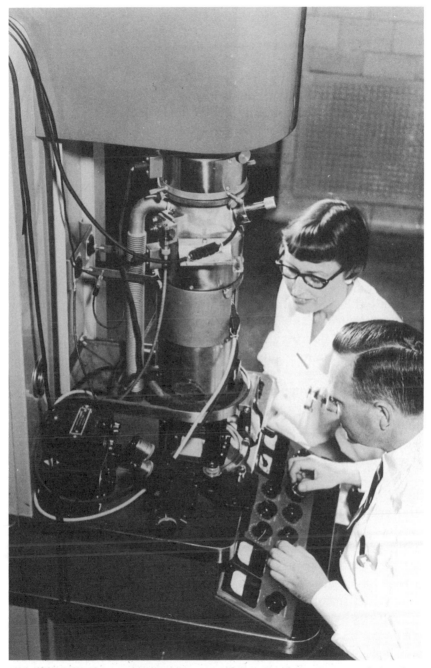

Drs. Marie Nylen and David Scott studying tooth structure and development with the aid of an electron microscope in 1958.

In a striking advance in 1963 Nylen, Dr. Edward D. Eanes, and Dr. Karl-Ake Omnell employed electron micrographs to show precise changes in crystals during enamel mineralization of rat teeth. Included in scholarly journals and an oral biology textbook, the work of the Nylen group encouraged other scientists to concentrate on molecular biology investigations of tooth enamel.[14]

In the 1960s and 1970s the laboratory's scientists were instrumental in confirming the relationship between tetracycline therapy and tooth discoloration. The staining detracted from the individual's appearance and resembled that seen in the severe forms of fluorosis. Tetracycline was developed after World War II and administered to children for a variety of ailments, from sore throats to cystic fibrosis. In the late 1950s signs of underdevelopment and brown and yellow streaks started to appear in the tooth enamel of children who had been treated with tetracycline. Almost immediately dentists suspected the antibiotic. In 1962 Drs. Carl Witkop, Jr., and Robert O. Wolf of the Institute's Human Genetics Branch initiated clinical investigations into the problem that they presumed was caused by tetracycline administration in the period of tooth formation during pregnancy and early childhood. As a result of their study, they advised judicious use of the antibiotic in children because it could damage baby and permanent teeth.

Subsequently, Nylen, who became the laboratory chief in 1966, conducted a series of experiments with Drs. Omnell and Claes-Goran Lofgren from Sweden and Dr. J. Westergaard from Denmark to trace the effects of tetracycline on calcifying tissue. Initially the team employed microradiography and optical microscopy to examine the teeth of rats given tetracycline. Later they depicted the effects with the electron microscope and established the relationship between tetracycline and tooth discoloration. In response to these findings, the Institute prepared statements for publication in the *Journal of the American Medical Association* that warned against administration of tetracycline to pregnant women and children under eight years of age because of the risk of staining youngsters' teeth. Because intensive tetracycline treatment was necessary for certain illnesses, such as cystic fibrosis, dental scientists continued to seek methods to counter or conceal the discoloration.[15]

When Civil Service Commission Vice-Chairman Jayne B. Spain awarded Nylen the Federal Woman's Award in 1975, she singled out

Nylen's work on tetracycline's side effects on dental enamel and the research's influence that led to restrictions on the use of the antibiotic. Nylen was one of only six women in the United States that year to receive the award, established to honor women for their outstanding contributions to the career government service. The commission recognized Nylen for her achievements as a leading expert on the morphology of tooth enamel and the use of the electron microscope in dental research as well as for her administrative capabilities as chief of the laboratory.[16]

Meanwhile, the laboratory branched out into other areas of research. In a reorganization at the end of the 1960s the pathology section was separated from the laboratory, and Nylen's group became known as the Laboratory of Biological Structure. Researchers interested in saliva and molecular biochemistry joined the unit.

Stimulated by the 1963 Nylen team reports illustrating crystal changes during rat tooth enamel mineralization, the laboratory moved further into molecular biochemistry as a new generation of scientists joined its staff. The work of the newcomers in basic research exemplified how very fundamental, seemingly esoteric probes could eventually produce applications beneficial to humans.

One such case started with a mineralization investigation. In 1970, through Eanes, Nylen met and recruited Dr. John Termine, a biochemist, to join Eanes's laboratory as a special research fellow. In the 1960s Posner and Eanes had left the Institute to work in a laboratory at the Hospital for Special Surgery in New York City where they collaborated with Termine. In his doctoral and postdoctoral studies Termine had examined the nature of bone mineral and the interactions between the mineral and organic phases of bone by using such techniques as electron spin resonance spectroscopy, X ray diffraction, and vibrational spectroscopy. In New York, Termine, Eanes, and Posner concluded that the mineral portion of bone and dentin was more complex than previously believed. Supported by the Institute's extramural research grant program, the investigators described the complicated intermediate phases involved in the deposition of bone mineral.[17]

Their investigation, which concerned how calcium phosphate formation took place, continued as an intramural project at NIDR after Eanes returned to Nylen's laboratory as a section chief with Termine on his team. Termine was among the first scientists to describe the

physical chemistry of the calcium phosphates, the inorganic components of bone mineral, as formed under physiological conditions.
Essential to this work was extracellular matrix, which was produced
and secreted by cells to form the major structural elements in most of
the body's tissues. Theorizing that the mineralization pattern in bone
and tooth was controlled by their extracellular matrix, Termine
worked for about a year with Drs. Karl Piez and Edward Miller,
Institute collagen experts in the Laboratory of Biochemistry, to establish expertise in protein chemistry. Collaborating with Eanes and
Nylen, Termine found that synthetic calcium phosphate formation
under alkaline or high-temperature conditions was physiochemically
similar with some modifications, primarily kinetic in nature, to the
processes of calcium phosphate formation in tissues. But the biological picture changed drastically under physiological conditions. The
researchers observed that the matrix proteins had a profound effect
not only on the kinetics but also on the three-dimensional pattern of
mineralization. Consequently, they determined that the way the matrix proteins were elaborated in tissues (by the bone and tooth cells)
directly controlled the mineralization process.

Eanes subsequently pursued basic research in the chemistry of cal-
cium phosphate compounds and later received the International
Association for Dental Research Biological Mineralization Research
Award for his work. Meanwhile, the calcium phosphate study led
Termine into molecular biological investigations. Termine received
the same award later in his career.[18]

As a consequence of the calcium phosphate work, the laboratory
supported an international effort to characterize biochemically the
proteins in tooth enamel. Because the Institute had the best techniques for such research, experts from three nations joined Termine
to unravel this problem in the late 1970s and early 1980s. Dr. Alan
Fincham, a major force in English research on the subject; Dr. Alain
Belcourt, a French expert on adult teeth; and Dr. Hitoyata Shimokawa, a Japanese scientist studying the biosynthesis of enamel protein, spent the better part of six years working with Termine. By
1981 they had identified two classes of proteins in enamel: enamelins,
attached to growing tooth crystals on the surface of the tooth, and
amelogenins, providing the bulk of the growing embryonic tooth.
Their studies showed that tooth enamel resulted partially from a
blend of the amelogenins and the enamelins, each produced by its

own gene. The team eventually confirmed the theory that bone and tooth matrix proteins regulated the crystallization process.[19]

With the tooth enamel proteins biologically characterized, the race ensued to clone the genes for tooth enamel. While intramural researchers pursued their objective of isolating a bovine gene, the Institute supported outside efforts with extramural funding to separate and copy a mouse gene. The leader of the latter search was Dr. Harold Slavkin, professor of biochemistry at the University of Southern California School of Dentistry Laboratory for Developmental Biology and one of the nation's leading dental molecular biologists. In 1983 Slavkin, a long-time Institute grantee, and his team isolated and cloned the cDNA encoding mouse amelogenin, one of the two major classes of tooth enamel proteins. Using recombinant DNA technology, Slavkin and his colleagues in California and researchers at Baylor Medical College in Texas decoded the genetic instructions for mouse amelogenin. At the Institute a group led by Termine and Shimokawa, the visiting scientist from Japan, cloned the bovine amelogenin gene in 1986. Subsequently, the NIDR laboratory started a three-year project with the University of Pennsylvania School of Dentistry to characterize and sequence the entire amelogenin gene.

Potentially, such research could lead to the creation of synthetic tooth enamel indistinguishable from the natural product. But, as Institute science writer Patricia Sheridan has pointed out, considerable research would be necessary before the realization of such a development. For instance, the NIDR scientists would have to determine if the human and animal proteins were alike and would have to isolate and clone the other three proteins. Nevertheless, the Slavkin and Termine results could furnish important clues to determining the role of amelogenin in forming the primary mineral component of teeth and could help scientists understand more about how the gene regulation process dictates the development of all normal and defective tissues in animals and humans.[20]

While the work leading to isolation of enamel genes was under way, the laboratory's scientists also made significant progress in bone research. The laboratory chief of the Proteoglycans Chemistry Section, Dr. Vincent C. Hascall, led a group that achieved international recognition for its studies of proteoglycans, the ground substance portion of cartilage and other connective tissues. That research began as Hascall's doctoral dissertation at the Rockefeller University in the

1960s and was continued when he joined the Institute. During the 1980s the Hascall team shed light on the structure and biosynthesis of proteoglycan molecules, which determined the compressive-cushioning properties of all cartilage in the body and which were integral components of much of the body's cell surfaces and connective tissues. The work contributed toward understanding degenerative diseases of the connective tissues, especially osteoarthritis, and suggested that proteoglycan metabolism could be useful in studying degenerative changes in periodontal diseases.[21]

Elsewhere in the same NIDR laboratory, Dr. Dennis Torchia, a nuclear physicist who had switched to biophysical research, directed nuclear magnetic resonance (NMR) spectroscopy studies of proteins and intact tissues. From 1980 to 1985 Torchia and his group showed how various components of the tissues interacted with each other and how the components were altered by "mechanical loading," such as walking or exercise on cartilaginous tissues and on bone development. The Torchia team used recombinant DNA procedures to construct and modify proteins to determine their molecular structure as they existed in body tissues. Those studies added to the knowledge about the structural dynamics of the protein constituents of bone, cartilage, and ligaments.[22]

During the 1980s Termine also supervised a team that focused on the molecular structure and cell and molecular biology of bone. That group subsequently discovered most of the major noncollagenous proteins of bone, such as osteonectin, and cloned many of their genes in order to learn more about the regulation of bone development. The researchers found that specific noncollagenous proteins were modified in genetic diseases of bone, such as osteogenesis imperfecta, a brittle bone disease found in children. This finding added to dental knowledge because most osteogenesis victims also suffered from dentinogenesis imperfecta, a condition in which imperfectly formed teeth tended to fracture easily.[23]

In addition, in the early 1980s Dr. Pamela Gehron Robey and Termine developed procedures to isolate and study in culture human osteoblasts—bone-forming cells. These techniques were adopted by investigators around the world, including researchers at the Mayo Clinic in Rochester, Minnesota. The Gehron Robey methods led the Mayo Clinic team to show that human bone cells had estrogen receptors—an advance that opened up the possibility of making further studies to clarify the development of osteoporosis, a degenerative bone disease especially affecting postmenopausal women.[24]

In the meantime Dr. A. Hari Reddi of NIDR was engaged in a long-time basic research project on the induction of bone formation. That investigation originated with Reddi's research at the University of Chicago. With an interdisciplinary background in cell biology and endocrinology, Reddi was introduced to bone research by his post-doctoral mentor, Dr. Charles Huggins of the University of Chicago's Medical School. In the 1930s Huggins had found that teeth implanted in subcutaneous spaces induced bone formation. Huggins then had turned to prostate cancer research, which won him the Nobel prize in 1966. But his interest in bone induction research was revived during Reddi's fellowship. Both Huggins and Reddi were stimulated by the 1965 discovery of Dr. Marshall Urist, an Institute grantee and orthopedic surgeon at the University of California at Los Angeles Medical School. Urist had successfully induced new bone growth by intramuscular implantation of demineralized segments of bone in rabbits. Reddi and Huggins had studied the sequential cascade of bone formation processes in rats at Chicago.[25]

Appointed by the University of Chicago in 1972 as an assistant professor, Reddi set out to identify the agents in the demineralized bone matrix that promoted bone repair. To enhance his research, he came to the Institute on sabbatical leave in 1975 to learn collagen chemistry from Piez, a leading scientist in that field. Instead of going back to Chicago when his sabbatical ended, as he had originally planned, Reddi was hired by Nylen and stayed with the Institute.[26]

Thus, Reddi became the first intramural scientist to investigate bone induction. Like the enamel work, the NIDR bone inquiry grew into an international effort engaging visiting scientists from several nations, including India, Israel, Poland, and the People's Republic of China. In 1981 Reddi's team devised a quantitative technique for the bioassay of soluble proteins by reconstitution with insoluble collagenous matrix. The method was adopted universally by those in the field. By then Reddi had systematically studied the cellular and biochemical changes occurring during bone induction.[27]

In 1983 Urist's team, supported through extramural funding, isolated "bone morphogenic protein," an agent that induced new bone formation in the laboratory. But the basic biology of the bone induction process and the properties of that protein continued to remain under investigation.[28]

Meanwhile, Reddi and his group pursued their bone growth work. In 1987 they isolated "osteogenins," bone inductive proteins named after a 1945 published prediction by Lacroix, a Belgian scientist. Urist and Reddi, however, were uncertain about whether their protein factors were identical because their methods of isolation differed. The continuing work on the chemistry of bone morphogenic protein and osteogenin was expected to resolve this issue and to lead to the isolation and cloning of the genes for osteogenin by recombinant DNA methods.

Knowledge of the growth potential in bone matrix agents led surgeons at Children's Hospital in Boston to investigate bone induction in patients with craniofacial defects and trauma. In these cases, the surgeons stimulated bone growth by implanting bone matrix at the replacement site.[29]

In the meantime, the broadening bone and tissue research prompted administrative changes. In 1980 Director Scott and Intramural Research Director Nylen, instrumental in bringing early international recognition to the Institute's bone and tissue work, established the Skeletal Matrix Biochemistry Section under Termine. Nylen and Löe, the newly installed Institute director, created the Bone Research Branch in 1983. The following year Löe appointed Termine as head of the branch, which included investigators and sections from both the hard tissue and biochemistry laboratories of the Institute.[30]

Saliva and Dental Diseases

The major fluid in the mouth, saliva plays a key role in protecting and maintaining the oral tissues and serves as an important washing and transporting solution for the human body. Basic research on saliva has led to significant discoveries about saliva components that help control dental and other diseases. In addition, fundamental studies of the function of salivary gland cells have enhanced the understanding of the secretory process and the nature of secretory immunity.

In 1939, early in his career, Dr. Joseph Volker, who became one of the nation's leading dental scientists, produced a landmark finding on

Saliva collection.

saliva. While conducting research at the University of Rochester, Volker showed that saliva expedited blood coagulation, a primary factor in healing. Despite Volker's work, little subsequent investigation of saliva took place until the 1950s.[31]

The 1950s research proved especially important because the laboratory studies demonstrated that normal saliva provided humans with an impressive defense system. Studies at the Institute initially took place in McClure's laboratory. There, in 1954 NIDR scientists reported that children free of dental caries had a more alkaline saliva that also was richer in dehydrogenase-type enzymes than youngsters with tooth decay had. In 1956 Institute research findings confirmed that a decrease in saliva was associated with an increase in dental caries.[32]

In a 1967 report to President Johnson, Institute scientists identified the antibacterial action of saliva as crucial to dental health. The researchers based their conclusion on tests in which rats experienced almost a tenfold increase in tooth decay, a rise in oral bacteria, and severe gum recession after their salivary glands were removed. The laboratory results resembled those of patients with malfunctioning salivary glands.[33]

Basic research conducted under NIDR's intramural and extramural programs brought additional information on saliva mechanisms in the late 1960s and early 1970s. Clinical investigations also expanded during the same period, particularly in extramural areas.

In 1968 new investigations on saliva began in the Laboratory of Histology and Pathology following the arrival of Dr. Arthur Hand, who had just graduated from dental school. Hand was attracted to research by his summer work in the University of California at Los Angeles anatomy department and was recruited by Dr. Richard Greulich, his former anatomy professor who had become NIDR's intramural director. Hand had intended to stay only for the two years of his Public Health Service term; but after starting his first research project on von Ebner's gland, he decided to make a career of dental research. Hand was the only saliva researcher in that laboratory until 1974 when Dr. Constance Oliver arrived to collaborate with him.[34]

Von Ebner's gland is one of the minor salivary glands, with ducts opening on the surface of the tongue. Its function has been described as one of helping the mouth to wash out taste substances and prepare for new ones.

Hand's work on von Ebner's gland—initiated to clarify the role of saliva in dental conditions—fostered understanding of nondental disorders, including cystic fibrosis. His 1970 publication on von Ebner's gland was the first to describe the gland's structure in rats at the electron microscope level. Hand later collaborated with Dr. Margit Hamosh, a biochemist with the National Institute of Arthritis, Metabolism, and Digestive Diseases. Hamosh had discovered earlier that von Ebner's was the only salivary gland producing lingual lipase, an enzyme that broke down dietary fats and initiated the digestion of dietary fats. In 1977 Hamosh and Hand traced the development of lingual lipase in the rat from the prenatal to adult stages. They suggested that the enzyme might be instrumental in aiding in the dietary fat digestion of infants when their levels of pancreatic lipase were low. The International Association for Dental Research honored Hand with its 1978 "Basic Research in Oral Science Award" for that work.[35]

Meanwhile, Institute extramural scientists also produced useful information on saliva. In the late 1960s, through their development of collecting devices and application of new techniques, grantees contributed to the discovery that salivary secretions were highly complex. Further, Drs. Edward A. Azen of the University of Wisconsin at Madison and Frank G. Oppenheim of Boston University—both NIDR research grantees—identified four new proteins in human saliva by 1973. Their studies suggested a hereditary link in the composition of the saliva between parents and offspring.[36]

By the 1970s Dr. Irwin Mandel, professor of dentistry at Columbia University and an Institute grantee of long standing, began investigating the role of saliva in caries resistance. Mandel, a saliva expert, was attracted to saliva research through studies of caries-resistant persons who were found in approximately 1 out of 750 adults. Such individuals, who had not been exposed to fluorides during their tooth development years, did not develop dental cavities even after ingesting caries-inducing diets. In Institute-sponsored studies in the 1970s Mandel and A. N. Zengo confirmed that caries-resistant subjects showed much lower levels of demineralizing plaque acids but a higher rate of acetic acids than normal individuals who were not resistant to caries. The acetic acids, as a later computer simulation confirmed, could act as a buffer to prevent the demineralizing acids from eroding tooth enamel.[37]

Saliva researchers in the late 1970s and 1980s cast additional light on secretory processes as the Institute team grew with additions of new investigators and visiting scientists from Israel, Canada, and Guatemala. Much of the research focused on the rat parotid gland, the best biochemically characterized of the major salivary glands in the rat and thus an important experimental model for scientists investigating secretions. In 1984 Oliver and Hand described the secretory role of a membrane system near the Golgi apparatus of salivary gland cells. Hand also furnished a detailed description of the Golgi apparatus, a cellular component instrumental in modifying, transporting, and packaging proteins secreted by salivary cells. In 1986 and 1987 Hand and several visiting scientists studied the ability of rat parotid gland cells to take up or remove abnormal proteins prior to the secretion of saliva into the oral cavity.[38]

The basic saliva research that helped expose the secretory process was especially relevant to both intramural and extramural clinical studies of individuals with xerostomia, or "dry mouth." Although not a disease in itself, xerostomia was found to be a common side effect of more than two hundred medications and some medical treatments, especially chemotherapy and radiation treatment to the head and neck. Xerostomia also was recognized as a symptom of certain diseases, including Sjogren's syndrome, an immunological disorder. Patients with "dry mouth" were especially susceptible to tooth decay and difficulties in speech and swallowing. They complained of dry, rough, sticky mouth and throat, hoarseness, sore mouth, difficulties in eating, and loss of teeth and fillings. Mandel, the Columbia University saliva expert, noted that by the 1980s xerostomia had become a significant clinical problem.

To enhance such clinical research Institute administrators hired Dr. Bruce Baum in 1982 to head the Institute Clinical Investigations and Patient Care Branch. A dentist with a Ph.D. in biochemistry from Boston University, he had previously worked for the National Institute on Aging (NIA), the National Heart, Lung, and Blood Institute, and the Dental Sciences Department of the National Naval Medical Center. Baum was especially interested in salivary gland function and age-related changes in the mouth.

After Baum's arrival the direction of Institute saliva research shifted. Baum described the action involved in the neurotransmitter control of secretion, one of the major interests in the field since the late 1970s. In the extramural sector, Dr. James Putney of Virginia Commonwealth University in Richmond produced significant findings on the regulation of salivary secretions. In addition, extramural research by Dr. Michael Levine of the State University of New York at Buffalo contributed to knowledge on salivary mucins, the chief constituents of mucus. Donald Hay, a grantee at the Forsyth Dental Center, added information on a variety of salivary proteins.[39]

Under Baum's leadership the Institute established the NIDR Dry Mouth Clinic at the NIH Clinical Center in 1983 with Baum and Dr. Philip Fox as the principal investigators. Initially, they screened patients with complaints of xerostomia to ascertain the status of the salivary gland function and the origin of the discomfort. Their observations led to experimental use of a nineteenth century saliva stimulant, pilocarpine.

Pilocarpine had been discovered in the 1800s by missionaries in South America. They had reported their observations of natives chewing the leaves of the pilocarpus shrub to increase saliva production while they worked in the heat. Acting on that information, scientists had extracted the alkaloid, pilocarpine, from that shrub in the 1880s and had confirmed that pilocarpine stimulated salivary and sweat glands. When scientists had tested pilocarpine in the 1960s, they had discovered that the substance also increased heart rate and blood pressure—grounds for rejecting it.

In the 1980s, tests by Baum and Fox showed that a single, very small 5 milligram dose of pilocarpine, a drug used in prescription eyedrops, could stimulate saliva production without affecting heart rate or blood pressure. The pilocarpine was effective, however, only if some functional salivary gland tissue remained in the subject. In 1986 the two investigators began to conduct long-term trials with both time-release and altered-dose regimens of pilocarpine to provide longer-term relief.[40]

The Institute-supported saliva research results brought national awards for the scientists in the 1980s, including the ADA's first Gold Medal Award for Excellence in Dental Research to Mandel and the Association of Military Surgeons of the United States Carl A. Schlack Award to Baum. In 1986 the Institute paid special homage to the importance of saliva research and the outstanding work of Mandel by selecting him as the fourth Seymour J. Kreshover lecturer.[41]

Collagen Investigations, Developmental Biology, and Anomalies

Circumstance and Dean's philosophy led the Institute into studies of collagen, one of the major components of teeth, bones, and their supporting structures.

Without collagen all forms of animal life, including human, would find chewing, lifting, and moving virtually impossible. As a principal body protein, collagen endows the body's connective tissues with the strength and form to resist breakdown under mechanical, chemical, and enzymatic stresses. Dental scientists study collagen because it is part of the bones, teeth, and periodontium, or the connective tissues surrounding the teeth, as well as the major protein of dentin. Inflammation of the periodontium in the course of periodontal disease can lead to a breakdown of collagen and eventual loss of teeth.

The role of collagen in dental diseases seemed to be an appropriate choice for investigation in 1952 when Dean was seeking to expand Institute research beyond fluoridation studies. Determining the makeup of collagen could facilitate greater understanding of dental structures and tissues and their diseases. The collagen molecule, however, presented a formidable challenge to the scientist seeking to expose its secrets. Before 1950 Dr. Frank Schmitt and his colleagues at the Massachusetts Institute of Technology had characterized the protein by electron microscopy. In the early 1950s Drs. Alexander Rich and Francis Crick in England and G. N. Ramachandran in India had examined collagen structure by using X ray diffraction.[42]

In the 1950s Piez, a protein chemist, set out to examine collagen at the molecular level. After working as a technician at the Institute from 1948 to 1949, Piez had entered graduate school at Northwestern University in Evanston, Illinois. There he had concentrated his doctoral studies on protein chemistry, particularly in the investigation of the complex amino acid structures of proteins. For his dissertation Piez had analyzed amino acids by ion exchange chromatography, at that time a new technique. In 1951 when Piez, with a new Ph.D., wanted to return to the Institute as a research scientist, Dean placed him in the biochemistry laboratory headed by McClure. There he continued his investigations of amino acids under Dean's sensible policy of giving scientists the freedom to choose research areas relevant to dental science and thus to prove their worth as researchers.[43]

When Piez started his Institute research, biochemists considered the determination of the amino acid composition of a protein a tour de force. In McClure's laboratory the young scientist focused on several rare amino acids, including hydroxylysine, that were unique to collagen. Piez separated isomers of hydroxylysine and hydroxyproline by ion exchange chromatography, the chemical technique he had used for his doctoral dissertation, and reported his findings in the March 1954 issue of the *Journal of Biological Chemistry*.[44]

When Piez embarked on collagen research in the 1950s, chemists knew little about the three-dimensional structure of collagen and its chemistry. Scientists used X ray diffraction and electron microscopy as their major tools for analyzing the collagen molecule. Thus, Piez's application of chromatographic procedures represented a major methodological advance in collagen research and formed the basis of the chemical characterization of collagen.

One of the Institute's earliest collagen publications was produced when Piez collaborated with Dr. Robert L. Likins, a pioneer member of the Institute, to explain some of the chemistry of collagen. Piez and Likins applied a modified ion exchange chromatography procedure to the collagen in mineralized tissue in a study of the biosynthesis of hydroxylysine and published their work in 1957 in the *Journal of Biological Chemistry.* Piez later used the modified technique to separate hydroxyproline, another amino acid found in collagen.[45]

One of the first protein chemists to enter collagen research, Piez collaborated with scientists from other institutes and the academic world. Because collagen affected the research of virtually every institute on the Bethesda campus, the protein was a natural subject for collaborative studies. An early collaborator, Dr. Bernhard Witkop, an organic chemist with the National Institute of Arthritis and Metabolic Diseases, worked in the laboratory next door to Piez in the 1950s. Through Witkop Piez met another colleague, Dr. Jerome Gross, a medical biologist and subsequently a professor at Harvard Medical School. During their early collaboration Gross encouraged Piez to specialize in the collagen field. In 1958 Gross and Piez announced the results of their examination of the amino acid composition and structure of some invertebrate and vertebrate collagens. Their findings showed the persistence of the proteins throughout a very long period of evolution.[46] That work marked the beginning of a long, fruitful collaboration.

Dr. George Martin joined Piez's group in 1959. Martin held a doctorate in pharmacology from the University of Rochester and had come to the National Heart Institute as a postdoctoral fellow. He moved to NIDR as an American Dental Association research associate in 1959 and by 1961, with Piez and others, published additional reports explaining collagen chemistry.[47]

Having discovered some of the chemical properties of collagen, Piez, Martin, and their colleagues set out to elucidate its molecular structure. Their quest was aided by the development of cellulose ion exchangers in the late 1950s by two National Cancer Institute biochemists, Drs. Herbert Sober and Elbert Peterson. Using the Sober-Peterson procedure, Piez, Marc S. Lewis, Martin, and Gross separated the polypeptide chains of collagen. They found that skin and tendon collagen contained two distinct chains, which existed alone and in dimeric and trimeric compounds created by the cross-linking of the two chains. The discovery of the cross-links, or chemical bonds between the chains, was especially important because such cross-links were unusual and undetected before this work was done. The collagen work was so important that by 1961 McClure, the laboratory chief, and Arnold, Institute director, established a protein chemistry section with Piez as its chief.[48]

Using the Piez methods and findings, researchers produced further information about the structure and properties of collagens. In collaboration with Gross at Harvard, Martin, Piez, and Lewis found that lathyrism, a form of poisoning caused by ingesting certain sweet pea legumes, prevented the formation of collagen's intramolecular cross-links. Lathyrism was characterized by a great loss of tensile strength, and its victims experienced a general weakening of tendons and ligaments or spastic paraplegia. Sheldon, Pinnell, and Martin discovered the cross-linking enzyme, lysyl oxidase, and showed that it was inactivated by the factors causing lathyrism. The team demonstrated the importance of cross-links in the development of collagenous tissue and suggested that cross-link destruction or interference with cross-link formation could be factors in connective tissue disorders such as periodontal diseases. In 1964 Dr. Paul Bornstein, a research associate formerly with the Pasteur Institute, Martin, and Piez showed that each collagen molecule contained three helical chains with short nonhelical ends where cross-links originated.[49]

Through the 1960s the number of collagen researchers grew, and collaborative efforts expanded. In 1966 Piez became chief of the Institute's Laboratory of Biochemistry, and close to a dozen biochemists from the United States and abroad joined in Institute collagen investigations.[50]

Martin and Dr. Edward J. Miller, an American Dental Association research associate, succeeded in extracting bone collagen in 1966 and found that, contrary to other evidence, bone collagen resembled other types of collagen. Their analyses indicated that bone collagen's structure was more highly cross-linked than that of other types of collagens. The higher cross-linking thus accounted for the insolubility of bone collagen.[51]

A series of experiments conducted from 1969 to 1971 by Miller, Piez, and Dr. Victor Matukas in collaboration with Dr. Ervin Epstein of the University of California Medical School revealed collagens as a family of different gene products rather than as a single protein. Miller and Matukas had opened that new branch of inquiry with their 1969 paper on the discovery of a new type of collagen chain appearing as the major collagen in cartilage. The group's studies identified

Dr. Karl Piez (left) and Dr. George Martin (right) examining a model of collagen fibrils.

three types of collagen: type I, the only one previously described; type II, unique to cartilage; and type III, a constituent of skin and certain other tissues. After this initial breakthrough scientists elsewhere later identified additional types of collagen.[52]

In 1971 two teams of researchers independently discovered procollagen, the soluble biosynthetic (synthetic production by a living organism) precursor of collagen: the Institute group of Dr. Don Layman, E. B. McGoodwin, and Martin; and the University of Washington investigators, Dr. Garland Bellamy and Bornstein, formerly of the Institute. They found that collagen was synthesized as a larger molecule, procollagen, which then was converted to collagen outside the cell. The existence of a soluble precursor, procollagen, could explain how collagen, an insoluble protein, was transported to the site of fiber formation.

The procollagen papers opened another line of research at the Institute and elsewhere, including the University of Liege, Belgium, and the Max Planck Institutes in Germany. The Belgian group related an accumulation of procollagen to a genetic disease of cattle.

Thus, by the 1970s the Institute was an acknowledged world leader in collagen research. An analysis of collagen research by the Institute for Scientific Information showed that from 1970 to 1972 the National Institute of Dental Research dominated the field in publications on collagen structure most frequently cited by researchers, a measure used by scientists to determine the impact of particular scientific publications.[53]

Moreover, international recognition had been growing for the Institute's collagen researchers. The International Association for Dental Research had honored Martin in 1965 for his basic research on bone metabolism; the Helen Hay Whitney Foundation had named Piez a recipient of the T. Duckett Jones Memorial Award in 1970; and Miller had received the 1971 International Association for Dental Research Award for Basic Research in Oral Science.[54]

Following these successes the Institute collagen research program branched out, with Piez taking one direction and Martin another. In the early 1970s Piez changed the focus of his research from biochemical to structural investigations of collagen. Still searching for more clues on the relationship of collagen with disease and disorders, Piez and a British scientist, Andrew Miller of Oxford University, investigated the process of collagen fiber assembly. In the mid-1970s the two scientists found that the fibers coiled like rope but, unlike rope, were composed of a single molecular species packed together "in a highly ordered way." Those fibers imparted strength, toughness, flexibility, adherence, endurance, and resilience to the final products, such as bone, skin, and teeth. While scientists knew that hereditary defects could alter the cross-links holding the ropelike chains together, investigators still needed to determine how such processes as inflammation and aging affected collagen. Piez continued this line of investigation until he retired from the Institute in 1982 to lead research directed to applied ends in private industry.[55]

For his part, Martin initiated studies in the early 1970s on the developmental aspect of collagen studies. His research had progressed so impressively that in 1974 Kreshover established the Laboratory of Developmental Biology and Anomalies with Martin in charge. By 1975 Martin's work showed that properly assembled collagen cross-links were essential for normal health. He collaborated with scientists at The Johns Hopkins University on studies of several connective tissue disorders, including the Ehlers-Danlos syndrome, a genetic disorder discovered at the National Institutes of Health. Occurring in at least thirteen variations, Ehlers-Danlos IV syndrome affected the stretching properties of the skin and probably was the physical condition underlying the India rubber men appearing in carnival sideshows. Investigators observed that Ehlers-Danlos IV syndrome patients lacked a certain type of collagen that appeared in healthy persons.[56]

Additional studies revealed some of the contributions of collagen to life processes. Scientists at various university laboratories previously had clarified collagen's organizational role in embryonic life. In 1975 two investigators in Martin's laboratory, Dr. Malcolm C. Johnston, a visiting scientist, and Dr. Robert M. Pratt, showed how collagen contributed toward the formation of part of the jaw and beak of laboratory animals.[57]

Procollagen research flourished as well in Martin's newly established laboratory. Dr. Robert J. Klebe of the University of Texas at Galveston demonstrated that there were specific proteins, known as fibronectins, that bound to collagen. His research led to the Institute's entry into the study of cell attachment proteins in 1975. While conducting research at the Salk Institute the previous year, Klebe had observed fibronectins. Scientists at the University of Oregon, the Massachusetts Institute of Technology, and the National Cancer Institute made similar finds. Newly arrived at the Institute's Laboratory of Developmental Biology and Anomalies in 1975, Dr. Hynda Kleinman, a nutritional biochemist who specialized in glycoprotein biochemistry, started research on the interaction of collagen with fibronectin. She initially described the interaction of collagen with fibronectin, a glycoprotein, and located the site on the collagen molecule to which fibronectin bound. With Dr. A. Tyl Hewitt, a postdoctoral fellow at the NIDR, Kleinman identified and named chondronectin, a cell attachment protein associated with cartilage.[58]

At this point, in 1976, the Institute's collagen research might have been abolished had Institute administrators followed the advice of an evaluating panel. Despite the acclaim for the Institute's connective tissue work, not everyone approved of the amount of Institute support for the basic collagen studies. A group of outside periodontal disease experts evaluating the Institute's periodontal disease research program criticized the Institute for spending nearly 50 percent of the periodontal research funds on the structure and metabolism of connective tissue and bone. While admitting that such work was significant and of high quality, the consultants suggested that those investigations be performed by other NIH institutes and divisions interested in connective tissue and bone diseases. Questioning the propriety of that portion of the evaluation, members of the National Advisory Dental Research Council took exception to that recommendation. Subsequently, connective tissue and bone studies remained within the Institute, yielding interesting developments.[59]

In 1979 Pamela Gehron Robey, a young graduate student working in the Laboratory of Developmental Biology and Anomalies, triggered a series of exciting events when she discovered laminin, a basement membrane glycoprotein. These circumstances resulted from investigations involving basement membranes, the thin barriers of collagenous and noncollagenous extracellular material lying under the skin and surrounding blood vessels, muscles, and nerves—important to dental research because of their role in tooth development and in oral cancer. Gehron Robey, who later worked in the Institute's Mineralized Tissue Research Branch, identified and helped describe the laminin, a large protein with several useful properties found only in basement membranes.[60]

Other laboratory scientists subsequently investigated laminin. In 1980 Drs. Victor Terranova, David Rohrbach, and Martin were the first to describe a principal function of laminin—promotion of cell adhesion. Kleinman joined the effort in 1982 when she collaborated with scientists from the National Institute of Neurological and Communicative Disorders and Stroke to show that laminin also promoted nerve growth. Scientists in the private sector subsequently used the Institute information to develop laminin commercially as a nerve growth stimulant and as an additive to promote the growth of cells in culture in laboratories.[61]

In 1984 Drs. Makoto Sasaki and Yoshihiko Yamada of the Institute took on the challenge of isolating and characterizing the genes for the chains of laminin. Especially difficult because of the molecule's size and complexity, this work took three years to finish. Utilizing the latest recombinant DNA technology, the NIDR team cloned the genes that encoded laminin and from their sequences deduced the order of amino acids in the molecule. With 6,555 amino acids arranged on three chains, laminin was the largest protein ever to have been sequenced by 1987. With this information as a basis, the two scientists, Dr. Jeanette Graf, and others attempted to identify biologically active domains in the protein by synthesizing short peptides that corresponded to sequences found along the length of one of the laminin chains. These studies led to the demonstration that a peptide of five amino acids, abbreviated YIGSR, represented a major site on laminin for cell binding.[62]

Laminin research also contributed to the NIH war on cancer. Laminin study was relevant to cancer research because tumor cells had to break through basement membranes in order to invade other tissues of the body. From 1982 through 1987 Martin, Kleinman, Terranova, and several other Institute and visiting scientists studied the relationship of laminin to tumors. In 1984 the researchers discovered that tumor cells treated with laminin mestastasized more frequently than untreated cells and could adhere to laminin more easily than benign cells could. The investigators found that mestastasis, the complex process of invasion of healthy tissues by cancer cells, occurred when the malignant cells migrated to basement membrane, attached to laminin, and generated enzymes that destroyed the membrane. The tumor cells then crossed through the broken membrane to enter the blood stream and other tissues.

After other research identified the sequence of the cell binding site on laminin—the YIGSR peptide, a group led by Dr. Yukihide Iwamoto investigated the use of this peptide to block tumor cell attachment to basement membrane. Results of their experiments showed that YIGSR peptide stopped the spread of lung cancer cells beyond the basement membrane by blocking the binding of cancerous cells to laminin. Moreover, *in vitro* studies of the YIGSR peptide demonstrated that the peptide stopped the spread of a variety of other malignant tumors and also prevented growth of blood vessels formed to nourish growing tumors. The latter reaction suggested that the peptide also might help treat certain diseases related to blood vessel accumulation at the skin surface, such as the AIDS-associated Kaposi sarcoma.[63]

The assay developed in the YIGSR peptide research brought acclaim to the Institute team for its advancement of cancer research and reduction of animal use in experiments. In 1987 the Doerenkamp-Zbinden Foundation of Switzerland awarded $26,000 to Drs.

Adriana Albini, Iwamoto, Kleinman, and Martin for "an outstanding contribution that will reduce the dependence on animals for drug development." The technique furnished a rapid test for invasiveness of tumor cells, and its utilization of laboratory equipment allowed researchers to use one mouse instead of two hundred mice for such studies.[64]

As a result of the basic research, Institute scientists, including Martin and Kleinman and Drs. Yamada and Sasaki, applied for patents for products they subsequently developed, including a reconstituted form of basement membrane and the synthetic peptides from the laminin studies. Private industry started extensive laboratory use of the reconstituted form of basement membrane as an aide in analyzing the culture and growth of cells for such studies as those of nerve regeneration and wound healing. Peptide-11, the nine-amino acid peptide containing the smaller YIGSR peptide, showed biological activity, including antitumor action, that also attracted commercial users.[65]

These applications were among several outstanding Institute connective tissue research contributions. Moreover, the Institute had encouraged collagen studies elsewhere and had helped to create and stimulate a corps of experts in that area by providing a research and training center for over one hundred investigators, including post-doctoral fellows, guest workers, and visiting foreign scientists.[66]

Enzymes

Enzyme specialization was another basic research field that emerged from the Dean administration and engaged the interest and talents of Institute biochemists and histochemists.

An enzyme is an organic substance produced in cells that effects change in other substances without undergoing change itself. Dental scientists study enzymes to determine their origins and roles in altering the structures and processes affecting teeth.

With intramural fluoride research diminishing in the early 1950s McClure wanted to develop a strong basic research program in the biochemistry laboratory. Consequently, when Dr. John Folk, who had just received a doctorate in biochemistry from Georgetown University, arrived as an American Dental Association research associate in 1952, McClure assigned him the task of discovering what caused a diet of heated milk powder to induce tooth decay in rats. While searching for a link between the onset of tooth decay and nutrition, Folk investigated proteolysis, the breakdown of protein during normal digestive processes. Intrigued by that research, he took a special interest in proteolytic enzymology, the study of enzymes involved in the digesting or dissolving of proteins, and decided to specialize in pancreatic proteolytic enzymes.[67]

The study of proteolytic enzymes was especially significant for understanding dental and other degenerative and organic diseases because of the involvement of enzymes in the breakdown of collagen and other proteins essential to teeth, bones, and periodontal tissues. Folk's task involved investigating how specific enzymes contributed to the biological activities of organs and tissues affected by degenerative and organic diseases, whether they played a role in periodontal diseases, and how these agents operated.

When he started, Folk was one of the few scientists specializing in enzymes at the Institute. His early work included collaboration with Dr. Marvin S. Burstone, a histochemist in the Laboratory of Histology and Pathology. Folk isolated and studied the enzymes' mechanisms, and Burstone located the enzymatic processes in the tissues. In the mid-1950s they devised some of the early techniques for locating enzymes in tissues, including an enzymatic hydrolysis method.[68]

Through independent research in 1956 Folk described an enzyme, which he called basic carboxypeptidase (BCP). Folk's observation showed that BCP was responsible for the rapid availability of lysine and arginine, two amino acids essential to life. That work led to Folk's collaboration with Drs. Jules Gladner and Koloman Laki of the National Institute of Arthritis and Metabolic Diseases (NIAMD) on BCP structure and function. Renaming BCP "carboxypeptidase B" in 1957, Folk and Gladner produced studies promoting investigations of other proteolytic enzymes. Subsequently, Folk alone and in collaboration with several other investigators found and described additional enzymes, including aminopeptidase A in 1962, three forms of carboxypeptidase A in 1963, and chymotrypsin C in 1965. These studies showed aminopeptidase A and the other enzymes examined as vital to the mammalian digestive processes because of their roles in the breakdown of proteins in the digestive systems of all animals. Their findings engendered protein structure studies in laboratories elsewhere.[69]

In the mid-1960s Folk, by then chief of an enzyme chemistry section in the biochemistry laboratory, switched to studying transglutaminase enzymes, which were involved in binding protein molecules together. When Folk began those investigations, transglutaminase enzymes were a curiosity in the scientific world, and their biological functions were obscure. During almost twenty years of research Folk and Drs. S. I. Chung and Michael Gross, a postdoctoral fellow, described the metabolism of the enzymes and helped to clarify their role, distribution, and formation. The investigations added new information on the function of transglutaminase enzymes in wound healing and blood clotting and in the formation of hair and the outer layer of skin.[70]

Meanwhile, other Institute scientists also conducted enzyme research. From 1966 to 1976 Dr. Harold Fullmer, a histochemist, and his co-workers made important observations on collagenase, an enzyme first described by Dr. Jerome Gross at Harvard Medical School. In 1966 Fullmer and Dr. William Gibson suggested that an enzyme might be involved in tissue destruction in periodontal diseases after both had observed collagen destruction in over one hundred cultured specimens of gum tissue removed from patients undergoing periodontal disease treatment. The enzyme proved to be collagenase. Subsequently, Fullmer and his colleagues were the first to find collagenase in bone and cartilage tissue and in excessive amounts in the cutaneous tissues of two-thirds of a group of individuals with amyotrophic lateral sclerosis, also known as Lou Gehrig's disease. In 1968 a team that included Fullmer, scientists from the NIAMD, and Walter Reed and George Washington Hospital demonstrated the relationship of collagenase activity to the severity of rheumatoid arthritis. From 1974 to 1976 Fullmer, by then conducting research at the University of Alabama's Institute of Dental Research, was the first to show the source of collagenase in human periodontal tissues, the activation of latent collagenase by microbial plaque, and the production and stimulation of collagenase by macrophages, a type of white blood cell.[71]

By the 1980s enzyme investigations were spread among several Institute laboratories, and Folk's Enzyme Chemistry Section, a center for visiting foreign enzyme researchers, was focusing on the molecular and physiological structures of enzymes.[72]

Microbiology and Immunology

Microbiological research at the Institute started with a single individual. Hampp, the first American Dental Association research associate at NIH, had begun his work before the Institute's creation. Within the first year of its establishment the Institute gained recognition for a noteworthy scientific achievement by Hampp. In 1949, with the aid of the electron microscope, Hampp isolated an organism he named *Borelia vincentii*, a spirochete he associated with trench mouth. The Washington Academy of Science awarded Hampp its 1949 award in biological sciences for his discovery. Hampp became the first dental scientist and third scientist from the National Institutes of Health to receive such an honor in the academy's history. Following Hampp's achievement the Institute concentrated on other kinds of periodontal disease organisms.[73]

Meanwhile, Dean hired additional bacteriologists, including Fitzgerald and Morrison Rogosa, but the Institute's major increase in basic research in microbiology and later in immunology occurred during Arnold's administration. Arnold and Kreshover established a separate microbiology laboratory in 1958 after recruiting a prominent scientist, Dr. Henry Scherp, to serve as its chief. The need to probe the origins of caries and periodontal diseases lay behind the expansion. Subsequently, Fitzgerald, Jordan, and Keyes made their spectacular observations on the role of *Streptococcus mutans* in triggering dental caries, but they also were concerned with the etiology of the periodontal diseases.

The most common form of periodontal disease was chronic destructive periodontitis (CDP). Much of the knowledge gained by researchers on the immunopathology of CDP was applicable to the mechanism of tissue destruction in other chronic inflammatory diseases, such as rheumatoid arthritis. Consequently, a considerable amount of the basic research undertaken by the Institute in microbiology and immunology directly bore on such nondental chronic degenerative illnesses as rheumatoid arthritis.[74]

In the 1950s experiments by scientists in Europe and the United States revealed the infectious nature of periodontal diseases. That breakthrough opened the path for Institute research. Scientists knew little then about the origins of periodontal disease, but most, including Fitzgerald, suspected a bacterial role.[75]

Dr. Edward Hampp (right), the first ADA research associate at NIDR, whose career focused on bacteriological research on spirochetes, shown here in 1957 with Dr. H. Trendley Dean, then secretary, Council on Dental Research, ADA.

While experiments of all kinds—laboratory, epidemiological, and clinical—upheld the labeling of periodontal diseases as infectious, the advances of research kept changing scientists' concepts of how such infections started and progressed. At the beginning of the 1950s scientists thought mechanical irritants such as hard deposits of dead bacteria on teeth (calculus) caused tissue destruction. But further research in the 1950s demonstrated that calculus played a minor role. The findings of the University of Oslo's Dr. Jens Waerhaug brought revolutionary change to periodontal research. Waerhaug reported that periodontal lesions were derived from bacteria that colonized on the gingiva and subgingival areas. Waerhaug influenced Löe, the Norwegian periodontal expert who later became Institute director, to conduct periodontal research that focused on gram-negative bacteria. Those observations stimulated investigations at NIDR that demonstrated the importance and function of bacteria in fostering periodontal disease.[76]

Institute basic microbiological research increased after Scherp took charge and built up the new laboratory. Scherp was joined by a young scientist with a doctorate in bacteriology from the University of Rochester, Dr. Stephan E. Mergenhagen, who started his Institute career in 1958 by examining the breakdown of gum tissues after exposure to bacteria. He and Scherp observed that a mixture of oral microorganisms brought about the degeneration of collagen fibers associated with periodontitis. Later Mergenhagen and Dr. Anthony Rizzo, a dental scientist who also came to the Institute in 1958, found that gingival tissues in rabbits were susceptible to toxins associated with certain oral bacteria.[77]

Understanding the nature of bacteria normally present in the mouth (the oral flora) was fundamental to clarifying dental disease processes. Consequently, in the early 1960s Drs. Arden Howell, Jordan, and Stephan of the Institute studied bacteria found in various places in the mouth and in saliva. Howell, a microbial taxonomist, studied the oral flora and classified the actinomyces family of bacteria, a group highly prevalent in the mouth. A combination of work by Howell and others at the Institute along with Dr. Basil Bibby at the University of Rochester straightened out the actinomyces taxonomy.

Howell's familiarity with the actinomyces family led to a productive collaboration with Jordan, who had played a significant role in the *Streptococcus mutans* research with Fitzgerald. Because of his animal studies with Fitzgerald, Jordan introduced the use of hamsters to Howell. In 1963 Jordan, also a microbiologist, and Howell learned that by implanting bacteria into hamsters, they could induce a periodontal disease-associated plaque. In an experiment that helped confirm a bacterial role in periodontal disease, they isolated a filamentous microorganism that appeared in that plaque.[78]

That work prompted Jordan's further collaboration with Keyes, also noted for his research with Fitzgerald on the caries process. Consequently, in 1964 Jordan, recognized for his designs of experiments, and Keyes, with the reputation of proposing "terrific ideas," linked a periodontal disorder in hamsters with the filamentous organism Howell and Jordan had previously isolated. By 1965 Howell and Jordan identified *Odontomyces viscous*, a filamentous microorganism, in periodontal plaque of hamsters, and Jordan, Fitzgerald, and Stanley showed the production of periodontal disease in germ-free rats by injection of an oral actinomycete. Those experiments furnished the first demonstration of a causal linkage between a single specific organism and a periodontal-like infection that was transmissible in animal models. Later investigations located both the bacteria and the disease in humans.[79]

Shortly after the Jordan and Keyes report several observations of human periodontal disease puzzled scientists. For instance, a classic study by Löe, then a professor at the Royal Dental College in Denmark, showed that gingivitis, an early stage of periodontal disease, could be induced as well as reversed in healthy young adults if they suspended regular oral hygiene for several weeks and then returned to daily oral cleaning. Löe's experiment demonstrated that plaque accumulation preceded and triggered gingivitis but that oral hygiene procedures leading to the removal of plaque resolved the inflammation problem. On the other hand, clinicians saw some cases in which individuals exhibited little plaque and inflammation but lost much of the periodontium; other persons suffered from severe gingivitis but displayed no damage to supporting structures of teeth.[80]

Following the various clinical studies and the Jordan-Keyes report, scientists increased emphasis on investigating the immune response evoked by actinomyces. In a logical expansion of his work, Mergenhagen turned to immunological research on host-parasite interactions, especially on bacterial toxins, in oral infections. In response to his work, the Institute created a new section on immunology headed by Mergenhagen within the microbiology laboratory. In 1966 the International Association for Dental Research recognized the significance of his host-parasite work by presenting Mergenhagen with its award for basic research in oral science.[81]

In his immunological investigations Mergenhagen found an unsuspected individuality in the production of antibodies to oral bacteria. By 1968 results in experiments caused Mergenhagen, along with Rizzo and Dr. S. E. Berglund of the Institute, to suspect that immunological reactions to bacteria in diseased gum tissues played an important role in periodontal disease.[82]

By 1970 the immunological detective work yielded more evidence. At the Institute Dr. T. R. Tempel, a guest worker from the U.S. Army, Mergenhagen—by then chief of the laboratory, Dr. Henry Gewurz, and Dr. Ralph Snyderman, a research associate, investigated the effects of the encounter of antibodies with oral bacterial products. The team concluded that with constant exposure to such bacteria some of the normal body defenses, such as complement,

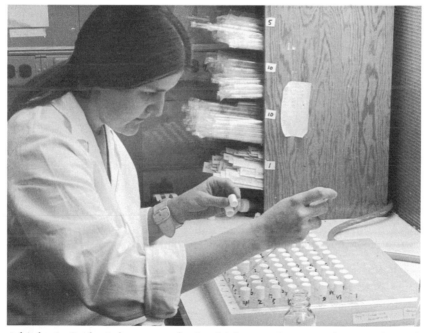

A biologist in the Laboratory of Microbiology and Immunology works with tissue cultures in studying the contribution of allergic reactions to caries and periodontal disease in 1973.

could contribute toward the inflammation associated with periodontal disease. They found that an endotoxin, a major component of certain bacterial cell walls, activated the complement system, a series of serum proteins acting in sequence that could induce a wide variety of inflammatory reactions. The investigators identified one of the products generated during the complement activation as a potentially important stimulant for migration of white blood cells toward the site of infection. Such a reaction could provoke swelling, redness, and permeability of gum tissues. Their finding helped explain a second pathway of complement activation and its role in human disease. The report presenting their findings became one of the ten most cited research articles on periodontology between 1960 and 1976.[83]

Later information on endotoxins was put to practical use. In an extramural project during 1975, investigators at Temple University found in a tissue culture system that without special measures to remove endotoxins involved in periodontal disease, gum tissues did not grow back over the root surfaces of extracted teeth. In laboratory experiments the researchers observed that repair did not occur because fibroblasts, collagen-producing cells, did not, in culture, adhere in the presence of endotoxins. If the experimenters scaled away the endotoxins and other bacterial contents in plaque accumulated after removal of a tooth, then the fibroblasts attached to remaining tooth root surfaces and produced collagen for new tissue.[84]

In 1976 Institute and other investigators produced additional evidence on the process of bone destruction in periodontal disease and rheumatoid arthritis. The collaborators included Dr. Ann L. Sandberg and Mergenhagen of the Institute, Dr. Lawrence G. Raisz of the University of Connecticut, Farmington, and Dr. Jo Max Goodson of the University of California, San Francisco. The team demonstrated a new function of the complement system. They found that interaction of antibodies with bone-cell surface antigens activated the complement system which then stimulated production of prostaglandins, substances detected in high concentrations in inflamed joint and periodontal tissues. In turn, the prostaglandins destroyed adjacent bone.[85]

In another collaborative effort, Mergenhagen and his fellow scientists learned that two types of white blood cells, lymphocytes and macrophages, also influenced bone destruction. The team included Mergenhagen, Dr. Sharon M. Wahl, Dr. Larry M. Wahl, and Dr.

Joost Oppenheim—all of the Institute, Raisz, and Dr. John E. Horton of the United States Army Institute of Dental Research. They learned that chronic stimulation of immune reactions led to the accumulation of lymphocytes and macrophages in inflamed tissue. When combined with stimulated lymphocytes, the macrophages secreted collagenase, an enzyme known for its destruction of collagen. During the same study the Mergenhagen group discovered a bone-destroying substance produced by the combination of stimulated lymphocytes and macrophages. The new substance, named "osteoclast activating factor" (OAF), did not appear unless the two cells made direct contact with each other. The results of this work suggested involvement of immunological factors in bone loss in periodontal disease and in damage to joint tissues in rheumatoid arthritis.[86]

Through work in cellular immunology in the 1970s and 1980s other Institute investigators brought new insights into the nature of inflammatory processes. Oppenheim, a pioneer in cellular immunology, defined hormonelike factors, or cytokines, that are secreted by lymphocytes and monocytes and participate in the body's inflammatory and immune responses. Adding to the discovery of what came to be known as the Interleukin-2 molecule by Dr. Robert C. Gallo of the National Cancer Institute, the Institute's Dr. John Farrar purified and defined the characteristics and functions of Interleukin-2, including its role in inflammation. Meanwhile, Dr. Steve Mizel described the workings of Interleukin-1, produced by macrophages and also involved in fever and inflammation. Those fundamental expositions stimulated other investigations within the Institute and elsewhere and proved useful to understanding periodontal disease, cancer research, and, later, AIDS.[87]

While Mergenhagen's group was penetrating some of the immunological aspects of chronic inflammatory diseases, researchers funded by the extramural program were exploring the bacteriological role. At the Forsyth Dental Center, for example, scientists obtained samples from human volunteers in order to identify bacteria contributing toward gum tissue destruction. Research conducted primarily by Dr. Sigmund Socransky, a leading dental microbiologist, and his Forsyth team in the late 1970s showed a difference in the kind and number of bacteria between healthy and diseased mouths. The microorganisms appeared in different arrangements in various stages of periodontal destruction. In some periodontal diseases, such as local-

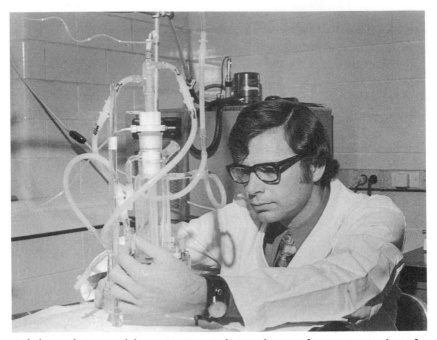

While studying oral bacteria, Dr. Jack London performs a procedure for separating proteins in 1973.

ized juvenile periodontitis that affected young people, the scientists found strong evidence to implicate certain species; in other cases, they saw no clear patterns. Dr. Ronald Gibbons, associate director at the Forsyth Dental Center and professor at the Harvard School of Dental Medicine, also produced landmark findings on the specificities of attachment of different oral bacteria to the tooth surface. Gibbons observed also that specific proteins found in human saliva that exhibited a high affinity for tooth surfaces could serve as sites of attachment for certain oral bacteria.[88]

In bacteriological work at the Institute Drs. Charles Wittenberger, Jack London, and John Thompson explained how bacteria metabolized dietary sugars. In the 1970s and 1980s the three researchers identified enzymes essential to the process by which sugars were converted to acids involved in tooth decay.[89]

In a major piece of basic research in the 1970s, Dr. Elliott Schiffmann, a biochemist, and his team cast additional light on the immune system mechanisms. The Schiffmann group detected and clarified the process by which a chemical signal alerted the body's white blood cells following the intrusion of a bacterial infectious agent. In response to that warning, the body's immune system mobilized by sending cells to the site to eliminate the invading bacteria. These descriptions added to the understanding of human tissue repair, disease development, and human growth and encouraged work leading to cell motility studies. As Dr. Julius Axelrod, 1970 Nobel Prize winner for his research on nerve transmission, appraised Schiffman's findings, "He has done fundamental work on how certain white cells, the neutrophils, are turned on, and these observations had important implications on immunological research."[90]

Scientists in the 1970s and 1980s turned their attention to questions about bacterial adhesion to teeth and to other bacteria. Previously, researchers had examined such matters when studying plaque and its relation to dental caries and periodontal diseases. At the Institute Drs. John Cisar and Sandberg depicted complicated processes contributing to periodontal disease. Cisar and Sandberg described how long fibrillar structures on the surface of certain bacteria could adhere to different tooth surfaces or to other bacteria and to mammalian cells that could ultimately destroy the bacteria. During the process, leukocytes eventually released agents harmful to the tissues surrounding the teeth. Subsequently, Drs. Paul Kolenbrander and London of the Institute described various bacterial attachment processes. In connection with that work, investigators at the University of Florida led by Dr. William Clark, an extramural grantee, initiated studies into the possibility that vaccines might be developed to prevent the fibrillar structures from initiating the bacterial attachment.[91]

Although originally undertaken because of its relevance to periodontal diseases, the immune system research also disclosed new information on the course of arthritic diseases. In the early 1980s the Wahls turned their attention to the pathology of arthritis. In a collaborative study of rheumatoid arthritis patients, they observed that by manipulating the body's immune system and the number of certain white blood cells (lymphocytes), they could alter the course of the disease. Later the effectiveness of a fungal-derived drug, Cyclosporin A, as an immunosuppressive agent confirmed the importance of the white blood cells in the disease process. Cyclosporin A specifically limited proliferation of helper lymphocytes and lymphokine production and controlled arthritis during clinical testing.[92]

The accumulation of significant contributions to basic micro-biological and immunological research brought acclaim from outside experts. In a 1981 evaluation of the laboratory, the Institute's Board of Scientific Counselors and five ad hoc experts praised the work of the scientists as outstanding, highly regarded in the international community of immunology, and "a credit to the Institution."[93]

Furthermore, outside groups recognized Mergenhagen, the labora-tory's chief, for his role. In 1981 the Alexander von Humboldt Foundation of West Germany granted him the United States Senior Scientist Award, and in 1982 he received his second International Association for Dental Research award, this time for his major con-tributions to the understanding of the pathogenesis of periodontal diseases.[94]

Virology

Under Arnold's directorship basic research expanded with the ad-dition of viral studies to the Laboratory of Microbiology in 1956. Prior to that year scientists had lacked adequate techniques to conduct such work. The change resulted from advances in poliomyelitis re-search that allowed the Institute to initiate investigations into latent viral infections. In such cases the infection appeared sporadically, but the virus remained in tissues regardless of whether the infection was active or latent. The cold sore or fever blister of the lip and mouth represented the most common manifestation of a suspected latent virus, namely herpes simplex, that was estimated to affect up to one-third of the population in the United States. For Institute scientists the course of such a probe was unpredictable. As the 1956 annual Institute report stated, "Where such investigations may lead is not known at the present time." The first official chief of the Laboratory of Microbiology, Scherp endorsed that philosophy. He wanted to build a strong base of research and thus encouraged scientists to choose their own fields and problems relevant to oral diseases.[95]

Consequently, Drs. Irwin I. Ship and Harold R. Stanley, Jr., were among the earliest at NIDR to investigate what appeared to be an oral viral disease. Instead, in their 1959 collaboration with scientists from other institutes, Ship and Stanley found that another condition, known commonly as canker sores and called aphthous stomatitis, produced symptoms similar to those of herpes viral infections but did not appear to be of a viral origin. Subsequently, other scientists at the Institute, including Dr. E. A. Graykowski, attempted to clarify the issue, but their results, too, were inconclusive.[96]

Scherp also conducted viral research. By 1965 he and Drs. Berge Hampar and Warren K. Ashe found that virus strains from recurring fever blisters in the same individual showed distinct characteristics. Their research indicated that such strains were partially resistant to the person's body defense against herpes.[97]

Meanwhile, sensing a future in viral studies, Scherp sought a virologist, especially for herpes research. Consequently, he approached Dr. Abner Notkins, who had joined the National Cancer Institute in 1960. Inclined toward tackling the unknown, Notkins had earned his medical degree from New York University with the intention of entering research. After years of observing his father's medical practice, Notkins had decided to help the sick through research into the development of disease. In 1961 Scherp offered Notkins an Institute position along with the opportunity to establish his own laboratory in the new dental research building, a technician, and the freedom to select his own oral disease investigations. Already immersed in virus-connected work, Notkins accepted the job and proceeded to teach himself virology.[98]

During his first few years at the Institute Notkins collaborated with other NIH scientists in probing an obscure transmissible agent associated with tumors in mice. To obtain the kind of information for the research, Notkins found he needed to specialize in combining methods of virology, immunology, and experimental pathology. The investigations concluded that the tumors concealed a virus. Study of that virus provided a new understanding of the mechanization by which antibodies inactivated viruses. Because of that work Notkins was the first to show that a virus could persist in the bloodstream for life in the presence of an antibody and that the virus could affect the functional capacity of the immune system. Notkins later applied what he had learned from the mouse virus to the herpes simplex virus.[99]

In the late 1960s Notkins led a team studying in depth the immune response to herpes simplex virus. The group's findings described the way that antibodies adhered to and made the virus powerless. Those results suggested that the viruses eventually might be controlled if scientists could learn more about the deficiencies in the defenses that allowed the viruses to persist.[100]

A new kind of laboratory established in 1973 enabled Notkins to conduct the research that would advance the studies of herpes and other oral ailments, including certain glandular diseases. With Notkins as chief, the Laboratory of Oral Medicine was unique in the Institute because it combined clinical medicine and dentistry with virology, pathology, electron microscopy, and cell biology. As constituted, Notkins' laboratory could serve as a bridge between basic and applied sciences.[101]

In the case of the herpes simplex virus just such a link materialized. In the spring of 1985 Notkins and Dr. Bernard Moss of the National Institute of Allergy and Infectious Diseases (NIAID) reported successful vaccination in laboratory animals against herpes simplex virus type 1, the virus strain associated with cold sores. A year later Notkins and Moss found that the vaccine still protected the test animals from a latent, recurrent infection and, moreover, appeared to safeguard its subjects against herpes simplex type 2, associated with genital herpes. The scientific team, however, concluded that they needed to continue more animal testing for greater safety and effectiveness and explained that extensive trials were necessary before considering application to humans.[102]

A congressional mandate also plunged the Laboratory of Oral Medicine into diabetes research during the time that its scientists had been investigating herpes. In 1974 Congress charged the Institute and six other institutes at NIH with the responsibility of coordinating research on diabetes. That directive led Notkins' team into research that shed light on juvenile diabetes, a devastating disease that usually left its victims totally dependent on insulin, reduced their life span by as much as 50 percent, and subjected them to the risks of blindness, limb amputations, kidney failure, and stroke. Since the beginning of the twentieth century physicians had theorized that a virus might induce juvenile diabetes, a different disease from the diabetes that started in adulthood.

By 1976, while studying diseases of the salivary gland and pancreas, scientists in Notkins' laboratory found a genetic factor in the development of virus-induced diabetes in mice. That work set Notkins and his colleagues on a trail to determine whether a virus

A researcher in the Laboratory of Oral Medicine works on developing a vaccine against herpes simplex virus.

caused human diabetes and whether that disease was hereditary. In 1979 Institute scientists, including Drs. Takashi Onodera, A. Bennett Jenson, Ji-Won Yoon, and Notkins, found several viruses common in human infections that caused a diabeteslike condition in certain strains of mice; other strains did not contract the disease after exposure to the virus. Shortly after they completed that animal experimentation, the Institute scientists in collaboration with Dr. Marshall Austin of the National Naval Medical Center in Bethesda recovered one of those viruses, Coxsackievirus, from the pancreas of a child who had just died from acute-onset diabetes. They injected mice with the virus obtained from the child and witnessed the onset of diabetes in the strains of mice previously shown as susceptible to a diabeteslike condition. That 1979 report was the first documentation of a recovery of a Coxsackievirus from the pancreas of a person with juvenile diabetes.[103]

But Institute investigators warned that it was premature to assume from the one case that the viruses alone triggered diabetes in susceptible individuals. Then Dr. Takashi Onodera, a visiting scientist, and others in the Laboratory of Oral Medicine observed in 1980 that, along with other influences such as genetic background, certain viruses could help trigger the disease. The Onodera team and other scientists began to suspect that juvenile diabetes might have an autoimmune component; in such circumstances the body's defense system went askew and attacked the tissues it normally defended. Subsequently, in collaboration with Dr. Fredda Ginsberg-Fellner at Mount Sinai School of Medicine in New York City, Notkins and others described a triad of markers for identifying individuals at high risk of coming down with diabetes long before clinical symptoms developed. As Notkins noted in 1987, a number of complex factors could induce that disorder, "but at least now, there are some very promising leads and some new tools and approaches that should help us study not only diabetes, but other autoimmune disorders."[104]

Both governments and organizations in the United States and abroad acknowledged Notkins' accomplishments in research in viral immunology, immunopathology, and virus-induced diabetes. In appreciation of the diabetes research, American agencies awarded him the Department of Health and Human Services Meritorious and Distinguished Service Medals, the Paul E. Lacy Research Award of the National Diabetes Research Exchange, and the David Rumbaugh Scientific Award of the Juvenile Diabetes Foundation. In Europe Notkins was honored for his work on viral immunology and diabetes by receiving the 1986 Paul Ehrlich and Ludwig Darmstaedter Prize.[105]

Commentary

By 1988 Institute support of basic research had demonstrated how the federal government's involvement in science could ultimately benefit humanity. Both the intramural and extramural investigations had broadened the base of health science knowledge through productive work, training, and international collaboration.

Significant progress in dental research had occurred since 1950 when Dean had observed that scientists needed more information on the evolution of dental caries and knew "even less" about periodontal diseases. By the 1980s when Löe, a periodontal disease expert, took over the directorship, Institute-sponsored basic research had contributed information on bacteria, infection, and immune responses associated with the periodontal diseases. Others had clarified the development of connective tissue, affected in periodontal diseases. Virological research had explained the process of such soft tissue problems as herpes simplex and had led to the development of an experimental vaccine. By conducting investigations relating to dental problems, scientists had advanced understanding of such fundamental biomedical subjects as the role of connective tissue in human systemic disorders, the operation of the body's immune system, and the actions of viruses within the body.

Furthermore, the NIDR researchers had identified genes and gene products essential to enamel and bone development. Already these studies had prompted experiments on preventives and therapies. Institute findings, too, had added to knowledge about such nondental conditions as rheumatoid arthritis, juvenile diabetes, and genetic disorders.

Through its support of investigations into green fields, the Institute also functioned as a scientific mission by stimulating dental research on an international scale. The evolution of particular lines of study originated with the hiring of scientists for specific purposes, such as virological investigations, and from the Institute policy started by Dean of giving scientists freedom to select their research preferences. The success of the Institute effort opened up new research directions for other institutions and investigators, brought postdoctoral fellows as well as seasoned scientists to the Institute, established the Institute as a training ground, and made NIDR an international center for a number of areas, most notably collagen studies.

Further, with Institute support both intramural and extramural scientists kept pace with the latest biomedical research developments—applying as well as creating new techniques. Scott, for instance, demonstrated to dental scientists the significance of such sophisticated methods as electron microscopy, and Piez introduced a major advance when he used chromatographic procedures to investigate collagen. Other researchers at the Institute, such as those in bone, enzyme, collagen, and viral studies, and grantees, such as Slavkin at UCLA, moved into the growing field of molecular biology and proved its value to dental science.

As indicated by the distribution of Institute funds, periodontal diseases, caries, and soft tissue received over 70 percent of Institute research financing. For most of the Institute's four decades, responsibility for the majority of that research lay with the extramural sector; by 1985 almost two-thirds of the Institute research budget went to the extramural area. The proportions of the budget for the periodontal, caries, and soft tissue disease programs were similar for both intramural and extramural work. The most important change was the increase of support for soft tissue studies from 1973 to 1983—a rise in funding that coincided with the Institute's striking achievements in viral research on herpes simplex.

In the long run, the Institute financial support paid dividends for the biomedical community. During forty years of operation, scientists in Institute programs delivered results that advanced the understanding of dental conditions and other health problems—achievements acknowledged by national and international groups through awards to the Institute's scientists. Consequently, Institute basic research proved faithful to the expectations envisioned by the framers of the original National Institute of Health and the National Institute of Dental Research.

CHAPTER NINE

Diseases, Disorders, and Therapy

So many worlds, so much to do.
ALFRED LORD TENNYSON

In a contemplative piece on the significance of dental research, the editor of *Dental Survey*, Dr. Hamilton Robinson, compared the basic researcher to the ore prospector, the "next level of biomedical researcher" to the miner, and the clinical investigator to the refiner. Next, he categorized the research and development scientists and industry as preparators of practical applications and the dentist as the user for disease prevention or therapy. Over its forty years of operation the Institute engaged in virtually all stages cited in this analogy. Indeed, this perceptive editor attributed the tremendous growth in dental research in the twentieth century to both federal grants and the operations of the National Institute of Dental Research.[1]

Various factors determined the course of Institute projects. As Dr. Anthony Rizzo, familiar with both intramural and extramural periodontal activities, viewed part of the picture, the pattern changed from individual to team investigations as research progressed. Training and availability of appropriate researchers and sufficient financial support for both intramural and extramural activities were vital.

During its four decades, Institute research appropriations increased from $217,000 in 1948 to almost $130 million in 1988. Beginning with 1973, when the Institute first reported financial obligations by research topic, over half of the Institute research budget went toward basic, clinical, epidemiological, and research and development studies on caries and periodontal diseases, with 21 percent, the largest share of funding, going to the latter by the 1980s. That trend generally continued to 1987—the latest year reported. Modifications in emphasis began in 1976 when caries and periodontal disease investigations obligations dropped and all other areas received substantial increases for that year alone. A rising trend started that year for pain and soft tissue research expenditures, but support for craniofacial anomalies studies declined in 1982 and 1983. The distribution of research obligations in percentages by category for the base and years of sharp change was as follows:

	Pain	Restorative Materials	Soft Tissues	Craniofacial Anomalies	Periodontal Disease	Caries
	(%)	(%)	(%)	(%)	(%)	(%)
1973	3.0	8.0	9.0	19.0	29.0	32.0
1976	5.0	11.0	11.0	30.0	20.0	22.0
1977	6.0	6.0	13.0	18.0	28.0	29.0
1982	8.0	8.0	16.0	16.0	29.0	23.0
1983	8.4	8.0	18.4	13.3	27.9	24.0

Changes in pain expenditures, for example, reflected increased efforts in that area, especially at the intramural level, and the decline in craniofacial anomalies support coincided with reduced expenditures in the intramural work. Although figures were unavailable on the amounts devoted to basic research, the titles of publications of the intramural staff suggested that, on the average, more than 50 percent of the intramural annual research budget went to fundamental studies.[2]

While basic research absorbed much of the Institute's funding, other kinds of significant investigations—including epidemiological, clinical, and applied work—received substantial Institute support. Consequently, over the course of forty years the Institute actively promoted the advancement of knowledge in the areas of epidemiological and clinical periodontal studies, dental genetics, facial abnormalities, restorative materials, pain research, and, most recently, the behavioral and social science programs.

Periodontal Diseases: Epidemiological and Clinical Research

The loss of teeth is a disturbing experience. Leaders in the dental community recognize that fluoridation can save children's teeth from decay but that teeth can be lost later because of periodontal disease.

When the Institute formally began operation in 1948, little research was under way on periodontal diseases. The Public Health Service supported periodontal disease research performed by grantees, but except for the work on trench mouth, no other intramural periodontal research was being conducted.[3]

In assessing the state of periodontal disease research in 1953, Dr. George C. Paffenbarger, Capt. J. A. English, and Dr. Edward Hampp warned that "only a small proportion of dental research concerns itself with periodontal disturbances." All were in positions that allowed them to make such a judgment. Paffenbarger served as the American Dental Association senior research associate at the National Bureau of Standards; English headed the Dental Division, Naval Medical Research Institute, and Hampp worked as the American Dental Association senior research associate at the National Institute of Dental Research. The three dental scientists attributed that paucity to the difficulty of reproducing periodontal diseases in laboratory animals and the scant knowledge about the development and prevention of periodontal disorders. They concluded that basic research offered the best approach for penetrating "this complex and devastating dental problem."[4]

Early in the 1950s Institute administrators met the challenge of probing periodontal diseases by expanding the coverage of basic research as well as epidemiology. Dr. Albert L. Russell, an epidemiologist and chief of the NIDR Epidemiology and Biometry Branch, produced some of the Institute's earliest studies on the severity and prevalence of periodontal diseases. In 1956 he completed a periodontal disease index that established numerical scores to measure the severity of periodontal disease. That classification system provided epidemiologists with a tool to gauge the prevalence and degree of periodontal disease among various population and age groups.[5]

Epidemiological studies conducted by Russell helped determine the extent of periodontal disease in the United States and other countries. Based on his United States surveys in the 1950s, Russell estimated that 75 percent of all adults over sixty years old suffered from periodontal diseases. Even more important, he identified periodontal disease among teenagers—a finding that encouraged clinical investigations of that illness. In his 1958 surveys in Alaska, Russell observed that some seven hundred men he examined showed virtually no dental caries or periodontal diseases if they lived in primitive villages. Yet his findings showed that Eskimo males living in civilized conditions had about the same prevalence of oral diseases as the average male in the United States. The Institute supported dental and nutrition surveys in other parts of the world in cooperation with the World Health Organization to compare this periodontal disease problem in different population groups. An accumulation of surveys revealed that race and nutritional deficiencies had little bearing on the magnitude or severity of periodontal disease. A correlation, however, appeared between the "societal status" and the severity of the condition. As Russell later noted, "we find more severe periodontal disease in the residential area that has the highest case rate of juvenile delinquency, or the highest case rate of people on welfare."[6]

In 1958 an Institute-sponsored committee called for improvement in the management and extent of periodontal disease research. The committee recommended fuller cooperation between basic science investigators and clinicians, training of researchers in periodontology through graduate training centers, a published compilation of literature on periodontal disease, and priority for basic scientific research pertinent to periodontal disease.[7]

Subsequently, in 1959 Surgeon General Leroy E. Burney supported increased funding for periodontal disease research. Of almost $1 million spent nationally for periodontal disease research, almost 80 percent came from Public Health Service funding, according to a study by the Research Committee of the American Academy of Periodontology. Of this amount, the Institute awarded grants of close to $700,000 to multidisciplinary periodontal disease research in academic institutions.[8]

Institute experts by 1963 estimated that over 50 percent of Americans over forty years of age had lost one or more teeth because of periodontal disease at a cost of more than $1 billion a year to the nation. Russell's surveys indicated that periodontal disease was the major adult dental illness. Clinical management of the condition was costly and time consuming, and therapy produced mixed results.[9]

Research on humans posed special problems involving ethical considerations over allowing the disease to go untreated as well as the length of time necessary to follow through on chronic gingivitis. To solve that dilemma, researchers used animals whose gingivitis resembled that of humans.[10]

In November 1963, addressing the need for more investigation, the NADRC recommended strengthening periodontal disease research. In response Arnold and Kreshover organized categorical programs that included periodontal disease in the extramural sector. And fortunately, the Johnson and Nixon administrations and Congress increased pressure to conduct targeted and applied research on such illnesses as periodontal disease.[11]

LOCALIZED JUVENILE PERIODONTITIS RESEARCH

Clinical research in both the extramural and intramural areas produced breakthroughs on localized juvenile periodontitis (LJP) and furnished an example of how the NIH system functioned. That illness struck teenagers, who suffered a bone loss in front of their first molars and in their upper front teeth.

Scientists in the 1920s had regarded that condition as a chronic, degenerative, noninflammatory disease of periodontal tissues. In his 1950s epidemiological studies in six states, Russell had called attention to advanced destructive periodontal disease in teenagers and had noticed that it tended "to be somewhat more severe in young girls than in young boys." Later studies had estimated that the disease affected between 0.1 and 2.3 percent of children between ten and nineteen years of age in the United States. Until 1970 scientists had classified the affliction as a syndrome.[12]

Dr. Paul Baer, an Institute clinical researcher, in 1971 published the first data tracing the development of localized juvenile periodontitis, as the condition was later called. Baer found that in the first twenty years of life the bone loss occurred so rapidly that the youth usually lost the incisor and first molar teeth before reaching the age of thirty. The model established by Baer and others suggested that the condition tended to affect members of the same family. Their findings encouraged investigations in other institutions.[13]

Since the 1950s an eminent scientist and grantee at the Forsyth Dental Center in Boston, Dr. Sigmund Socransky, had suspected that specific bacterial species contributed to onset of the disease. Following the suggestion of a young female assistant that he study the worst cases, Socransky and his researcher isolated a microorganism that they associated with the disease. By the mid-1970s Michael Newman, a graduate student with a training grant from NIDR, compiled and published Socransky's findings. In 1976 Dr. Max Listgarten of the University of Pennsylvania, another long-time Institute grantee, strengthened Socransky's findings when he observed with the electron microscope that the pattern of the bacterial colonization in juvenile periodontitis differed from that seen in adult periodontal disease.[14]

Some grantees investigated the hereditary factor. Using the method and basic immunological information developed by the Institute's microbiology laboratory, Dr. L. J. Cianciola, for example, led a team in an experiment in 1977 at the State University of New York at Buffalo that concluded certain family members might be more susceptible to the illness because of an inheritable defect in their immune systems.[15]

In 1979 and 1980 scientists at both the Forsyth Dental Center and the State University of New York at Buffalo isolated and named microorganisms associated with the disease. Dr. Robert Genco and his group at the State University of New York at Buffalo further implicated the specific bacteria by demonstrating that victims of the disease developed high levels of antibodies against it. The following year Genco, who had been a grantee of NIDR since the late 1960s, established that tetracycline treatment benefited patients with the condition.[16]

Successive experiments revealed increasingly explicit information about how youngsters acquired the disease. In 1982 Dr. Richard R. Ranney, a grantee at Virginia Commonwealth University in Richmond, discovered a link between severe forms of juvenile periodontitis and defects in a key defensive cell that normally protected the body against periodontal disease. The next year Dr. Joseph Zambon and his Buffalo, New York, team implicated certain bacteria that were transferred among family members.[17]

By 1985 the Institute-supported research had reached the stage where the scientists could advise the nation's dentists on successful treatment of the disease. Dr. Lars Christersson and his Buffalo colleagues showed how a combination of mechanical removal of the organisms inside the affected tissues and systematic treatment with antibiotics could alleviate the disease.[18]

MANAGING PERIODONTAL RESEARCH AFTER 1970

Because of the Nixon administration's targeted biomedical research policy, in 1972 the Institute benefited through increased funding of $1.3 million for periodontal disease research. To obtain advice on strengthening the program with the added funds, NIDR Director Kreshover convened the first of several committees of leaders in the field. The committee recommended the following:

- studies to prevent dental plaque by chemical and mechanical means;

- coordinated clinical and laboratory studies to understand the biology of plaque;

- studies of the severity of periodontal diseases in patients with connective tissue disorders and immune deficiencies;

- studies of the natural history of periodontal diseases, beginning with the eruption of permanent teeth;

- study of the effects of periodontal disease on general health; and

- development of experimental models and methods to measure periodontal diseases.

NIDR administrators implemented some of those suggestions when they expanded clinical research collaboration with Institute laboratories and with other institutes at NIH.[19]

In 1974, after the Department of Health, Education and Welfare and the Office of Management and Budget placed greater emphasis on program evaluations to justify budget requests, Director Kreshover initiated a scientific evaluation of the Institute's periodontal research program by an ad hoc panel of distinguished periodontological researchers. Dr. William D. McHugh, director of the Eastman Dental Center in Rochester, New York, led the project.

The group included Löe, then dean of the School of Dental Medicine of the University of Connecticut Health Center at Farmington.[20]

The panel gave the Institute a mixed review. Evaluators urged that the Institute's objectives aim at eliminating periodontal diseases through developing a better understanding of the condition, preventive techniques, and improved treatment. Using that framework, the panel concluded that the Institute had made "immense contributions . . . to the knowledge of connective tissues and to the understanding of immune responses." Nevertheless, the evaluators found major weaknesses: insufficient clinical research, inadequate support for periodontal microbiology investigations, and uneven scientific quality in research projects. The group especially wanted more done to bridge the gap between basic and applied research, particularly for use in prevention and diagnosis.[21]

Evaluators suggested that NIDR use its funds differently. Because almost 50 percent of periodontal research money went to tissue structure and metabolism, panel members thought that other NIH components with relevant interests should give more support to connective tissue and bone work. Only 20 percent of the NIDR's 1976 budget went to periodontal research, a decrease from earlier years that evaluators regarded as "quite dramatic if account is taken of the effects of inflation." While rejecting the concept of a national targeted program like the National Caries Program, the panel encouraged the creation of cooperative projects with other institutions and special training programs for periodontal biomedical research.[22]

In 1975 and 1976, during the periodontal program evaluation, several changes occurred that eventually affected the course of such research. First, Kreshover reorganized the Institute's clinical research program to concentrate more fully on diagnostic research. Gardner, who became acting director after Kreshover retired in 1975, continued strengthening the relationship between clinical and basic research units. When the panel finished its study in 1976, Scott, the new director, and the National Advisory Dental Research Council agreed with the report's contention that clinical research deserved greater attention. In 1977 and 1978 the Institute established periodontal disease research centers at the Forsyth Dental Center in Boston, the State University of New York at Buffalo, and Virginia Commonwealth University in Richmond to advance knowledge for prevention, diagnosis, and treatment.[23]

The Institute had met many of the recommendations proposed by the ad hoc panel by 1979. In order to increase the intramural effort on periodontal microbiology studies, the Institute almost doubled its 1975 research staff of twenty-three to a 1979 complement of forty-three by adding visiting scientists and guest workers to its laboratory of microbiology and immunology. Of the Institute's seventy individual periodontal research grants or projects, twenty-three went toward defining host mechanisms, twenty-two for investigating periodontal microbiology, eighteen for studying connective tissues, and eight for conducting clinical investigations. Periodontal microbiology took up almost one-third of the total extramural program in 1979, the direction sought by the 1976 panel.[24]

Controversy erupted in 1979 after a journalist took part in a periodontal clinical research project directed by Dr. Paul Keyes published an account of her experience in the *Washington Post.* The article appeared before the test had ended and prior to any published reports by the investigators. The writer credited the therapy with saving her gums and teeth and preventing expensive surgery. Other newspapers repeated the story, and by April 30 close to five hundred readers across the country had asked the NIDR for information about the treatment. But organized periodontists, dentists specializing in treating periodontal diseases, called for an investigation.[25]

Although press reports brought periodontal disease to the public's attention, the publicity also misrepresented the project. Originally Keyes, famous in the dental research community for his previous caries and periodontal microbiological discoveries, had launched the study to learn more about the relationships between bacteria and the stages of periodontal disease. He also wanted to test the efficacy of a different kind of microscope in diagnosing the disease. Therapy was not the main purpose of the project. Keyes's team treated diseased subjects by removing bacterial deposits from necks and roots of teeth, training the patients in complicated home care methods, monitoring with microscopic bacterial examinations, and administering antibiotics whenever the condition did not respond to the other procedures. The investigators also directed participants to use an old-fashioned remedy, a mixture of baking soda and hydrogen peroxide smeared over gums and teeth. Keyes called the treatment "monitored and modulated therapy" (MMT).[26]

Periodontists complained to their congressmen that the claims were misleading and could be harmful, especially for people needing surgery. Scott and NIH Director Donald S. Fredrickson explained the purpose of the work to inquiring members of Congress, and Scott held a workshop, "Surgical Therapy for Periodontitis," in May 1981. The workshop panel supported subgingival scaling and root planing as fundamental procedures in treating periodontitis but also recommended that dental schools expand their curricula to improve the skills of dental students in methods to prevent periodontal diseases. Fredrickson pressed for publication of Keyes's results, but Keyes retired in August 1981. Two years later Keyes and Dr. Thomas E. Rams, a former Institute fellow, published their findings. They concluded that phase-contrast microscopy, instead of light microscopy, demonstrated potential for improving diagnoses of stages in mild periodontal disease. Keyes and Rams also reported that the administration of tetracycline reduced bacteria when other procedures failed.[27]

Meanwhile, after a special committee of the American Academy of Periodontology examined the project's data, the periodontologists declared that Keyes had not proved his case and that the work had lacked controls and objective criteria. The academy committee subsequently disseminated to the public flyers explaining their disagreement with Keyes's project.[28] Nevertheless, the controversy continued, with opposition among periodontists but some support from other dentists and the press for Keyes's MMT.

The Keyes episode had attained unsolicited notoriety, but it was an extremely small part of the Institute periodontal disease effort, which, in the intramural sector, was principally basic research. The controversy occurred just when Institute scientists had received awards and praise from international organizations, including the International Association for Dental Research, for outstanding basic research on periodontology.[29]

Of equal significance, the Institute supported strong intramural and extramural periodontal programs to improve diagnosis of periodontal disease. By 1983 scientists in the NIDR Diagnostic Systems Branch had collaborated with researchers at the State University of New York at Buffalo to use fixed geometry techniques and a computer to obtain precise measurements of bone changes—some so small that they were not visible to the naked eye with traditional dental X rays. The following year Dr. Ira Lamster, a grantee, and his group at the Fairleigh Dickinson College of Dental Medicine described a biochemical profile of gingival crevicular fluid that was potentially promising as a diagnostic test for periodontal disease.[30]

Special periodontal research centers also played a prominent part in clarifying the periodontal diseases—contributing substantially to the understanding of localized juvenile periodontitis. In the 1980s scientists in the center at the State University of New York at Buffalo focused their research on the relationship between diabetes and periodontal diseases. Previous investigations had indicated a link, particularly between juvenile-onset diabetes and periodontitis. In a study of over four hundred youngsters under ten years of age, half of whom had insulin-dependent diabetes, the Buffalo scientists identified periodontitis with bone damage as appearing in 10 percent of the thirteen- to eighteen-year-old diabetics with only three cases appearing in the control group of nondiabetics. Genco, the center director, reported that the gum disease developed sharply with the onset of puberty.

In another study center investigators found Type II adult-onset diabetes in 40 percent of the Pima Indian adults examined—the highest rate in the world. In comparison, 5 percent of the general population suffered from adult-onset diabetes. By 1985 the Pima Indian study of over two thousand people showed that severe periodontal disease was a common complication of adult-onset diabetes. One-third of the diabetic Pima Indians had lost all their teeth, but less than 2 percent of the nondiabetic Pimas had exhibited such a tooth loss. In addition, researcher Dr. Marc Shlossman also detected a microorganism suspected of causing the gum disease.[31]

Meanwhile, the Institute's status in periodontal disease research rose further in 1983 when Löe became director. One of the world's leading experts on periodontal diseases, Löe brought his expertise in research, his stature in the international dental research community, and experience in administration to the Institute. His clinical gingivitis studies had influenced the course of National Institute of Dental Research microbiological and periodontal disease investigations after 1965. Of all authors publishing between 1960 and 1974 in the *Journal of Periodontology* and between 1966 and 1974 in the *Journal of Periodontal Research*, Löe was the most frequently cited, with 584 papers referring to his gingivitis work.[32]

Under Löe the Institute increased its funding of periodontal disease research. After his first year as director, NIDR extramural spending on periodontal disease research rose from $12.9 million to $15.9 million, a greater increase than in any other extramural category. The enhanced program funded biochemical and biotechnical research and development of techniques for future diagnosis and treatment of periodontal diseases.

This rise in NIDR periodontal disease research funding coincided with another significant development in that field—the commercial introduction and availability by prescription in the United States of chlorhexidine, an antimicrobial mouthrinse developed in Europe after World War II. During the 1970s Löe and his colleagues had conducted extensive clinical trials in Europe on the safety and effectiveness of chlorhexidine, a plaque-inhibiting substance that helped prevent caries and reduced periodontal inflammation. In the late 1980s the NIDR extramural program supported a clinical trial of the effectiveness of work-site applications of chlorhexidine to prevent periodontal disease in adults.[33]

Also, concerned about the status of dental health, Institute officials initiated collection in 1985 of specific data on periodontal lesions as part of the National Survey of Adult Dental Health. The results released in 1987 showed that 43 percent of working adults and 47 percent of senior citizens experienced gingival bleeding. Tartar deposits were on the teeth of 84 percent of employed adults and 89 percent of seniors. At least one site of periodontal attachment loss appeared in 77 percent of the working adults and 95 percent of the older group.

While the survey revealed that periodontal diseases continued to be prevalent in the nation, the study also disclosed a significant drop in toothlessness observed in the previous two decades. In comparing the results to surveys conducted in the two previous decades, Löe remarked that oral health had improved significantly. Although no one factor could explain the improvement in Americans' dental health, the change had come with increased understanding of the periodontal diseases and as a result of caries prevention efforts fostered over the years by the Institute. "It's clear," he said, "that people are keeping their teeth longer today."[34]

Dental Genetics: the Epidemiological Aspects

While the periodontal diseases constituted a major subject of investigation, the Institute promoted several unique projects. One such effort, human genetic investigations, resulted from the policy of allowing scientists freedom of opportunity to select research areas.

In 1950 Dean had hired Dr. Carl Witkop and had sent him back to the University of Michigan, where he had earned his dental degree, to obtain a master's degree in oral pathology. After his return to the Institute, Witkop had worked with Russell in his epidemiological studies across the country. During one of those surveys he had encountered Dr. Joseph Henry, a dentist with Howard University in Washington, D.C. Intrigued by Henry's references to an unusual family in southern Maryland and its members' susceptibility to defective enamel and dentin, Witkop initiated the NIH Genetic Field Study, more popularly known as the "Brandywine Study."[35]

The Brandywine, Maryland, jail served as Witkop's first dental examining site in 1955. From there Witkop took his study of some five thousand residents to tobacco sheds and houses in the isolated southern Maryland community. Of triracial origins of American Indian, white, and black, the inhabitants were all interrelated and descended from seven families who had intermarried since 1750. Such a group provided a rare opportunity for scientists to study the effects of heredity. Within a year the scope of the investigation had expanded with the addition of six other NIH institutes and local Washington, D.C., institutions, including Howard and Catholic universities. Witkop's team subsequently included Public Health Service physicians, dentists, nurses, a geneticist, a sociologist, and a statistician. Under his direction, they conducted medical, dental, ophthalmological, and neurological examinations and sifted through local church, hospital, and medical records to obtain family inheritance patterns.[36]

The Brandywine Study, too, provided a wealth of fascinating information to health professionals. Using a control group of 63,000 Michigan schoolchildren, Witkop found *dentinogenesis imperfecta* "almost 20,000 times higher than normal" in the Brandywine subjects. In *dentinogenesis imperfecta* the teeth were as fragile as porcelain and by the late teens or early twenties worn down to the gumline. The Witkop team also identified albinism, glaucoma, ankyloglossia (tongue-tiedness), and the highest percentage of sickle cell anemia of any group studied in the United States up to that time.

Out of the Brandywine project came a procedure that helped prevent blindness. One of the nurses, Mrs. Hazel R. Dyson, developed a method for prediction and early detection of glaucoma through a study of inheritance patterns. Because treatment of early stages of glaucoma contributed toward thwarting blindness, the Prevention of Blindness Society adopted the Dyson test.[37]

Witkop's successful Brandywine study prompted the creation of the Human Genetics Section in the Institute's Clinical Investigations Branch and more varied genetic research. In 1958 Institute geneticists initiated studies of chromosomal anomalies in human cells and were able to identify twelve discrete chromosomal abnormalities associated with oral lesions, some of which were connected with such growth defects as cleft palate.[38]

Scientists from the Human Genetics Section expanded their surveys within and outside the United States. In 1960 in Halifax County, North Carolina, Witkop and his fellow investigators found intermarried Haliwa Indian families with a high incidence of cleft palate and hereditary intraepithelial dyskeratosis, a disease first identified by the Witkop team. Symptoms of hereditary intraepithelial dyskeratosis included lesions on the mouth, tongue, and lining of the eye. Witkop next examined Chilean populations that showed a markedly lower incidence of two oral congenital anomalies frequently detected in groups in the United States. For example, out of nineteen hundred Chilean dental examinations he observed only one case of *torus mandibularus*, a bony outgrowth on the inside of the jaw that affected about 15 percent of the United States population.[39]

As early as 1961 when only three dental schools in the United States offered courses in genetics, the Institute led in promoting research in dental genetics in the nation. That year the Institute and the Council on Dental Research of the American Dental Association cosponsored the first international scientific symposium on genetics and dental health. Twenty-seven investigators reported on various aspects of dental genetics. Over one hundred geneticists and dentists from the United States, Canada, Denmark, and Sweden at the meeting approved a resolution urging dental schools to include genetics in course work and to use genetic information in clinical and research judgments. Extramural training and research grants further encouraged outside research on dental genetics, a field with a shortage of investigators in the early 1960s. By 1962 the Institute had awarded seventeen grants amounting to more than $300,000 for specific genetic projects.[40]

Genetics research continued to rise in importance in the dental research institute in the 1960s. The Human Genetics Section was elevated to a branch in 1963; the Cellular Biology and Cytogenetics Section was added to the Human Genetics Branch during the following year.[41]

The scope of the Human Genetics Branch began a downward turn following major personnel losses in the late 1960s. The program suffered after Witkop departed in 1966 to take a professorship in human genetics at the University of Minnesota. In 1967 the Human Genetics Branch's Cellular Biology and Cytogenetics Section headed by Dr. Herbert L. Cooper, a physician and geneticist, was transferred to the Laboratory of Biochemistry. Greulich, the Institute's intramural director, justified the move on the grounds that Cooper's research had changed from a focus on hereditary to a concentration on biochemical factors involved in genetics—obviously a reflection of the impact of the advances in molecular biology.[42]

Dr. Jerry Niswander, who succeeded Witkop as head of the genetics branch, struggled to retain the genetics branch programs. Niswander had participated in several genetic surveys, including one in Japan and another in the Brazilian jungle, and considered the epidemiological work of signal importance. Faced in 1969 with a reorganization attempt, Niswander's branch was threatened with abolition. "I believe it would be a mistake to entirely disband the Human Genetics Branch at this time," Niswander advised Greulich. Niswander expected the Institute to become increasingly concerned with the problems of normal and abnormal growth and development that his branch was studying.[43]

Niswander got a reprieve, but only for a few years. In preparing a 1974 intramural reorganization, Greulich recommended elimination of the Human Genetics Branch and transfer of Institute support in dental genetics and abnormalities to extramural activities. Nevertheless, the intramural chief admitted that to "move the NIDR out of a position of balanced intramural and extramural capacities in developmental biology is manifestly tragic."[44]

Responding to several investigators' appeals to Director Kreshover, himself a strong advocate of basic research, the Institute director retained and continued the basic research in the new Laboratory of

Developmental Biology and Craniofacial Anomalies but abolished the Human Genetics Branch. Niswander took the position of chief of an epidemiology and genetics section in the new laboratory, and most of the former branch's thirty-two staff members turned to work on craniofacial anomalies.[45]

Although in 1974 the intramural epidemiological dental genetic activities diminished considerably, overall NIDR had stimulated research and education in dental genetics. A review of the *Index to Dental Literature* provided an example of the Institute's impact on the growth of interest in dental genetics. In 1955 the *Index* contained no category for "genes" or "genetics" and listed only five articles under "heredity." After the Institute and American Dental Association held the 1961 dental genetics symposium, dental genetics research grew appreciably. In 1965 the *Index* added a "genetics" category, and by 1986 the *Index* cited forty-three articles under "genetic" categories. Furthermore, by 1985 fourteen United States dental schools offered courses in genetics as compared to three in 1961.[46]

Craniofacial Anomalies

Related to the genetics studies, the field of dentofacial defects commanded considerable attention in the United States. Undoubtedly, the appearance of children with such severe abnormalities touched the compassionate side of some professionals who dedicated their careers to alleviating those disabilities. To help such cases, dentists set up clinics years before the Institute was founded. Consequently, NIDR support of research in abnormal facial defects started as an extramural program in 1949. Health scientists regarded craniofacial malformations as a major public health problem because significant congenital abnormalities accompanied close to 7 percent of all live births in the United States. Of eleven major craniofacial deformities, cleft lip and palate drew the earliest attention because they constituted the most common and noticeable facial birth defects and the third most prevalent birth defect after heart malformations and clubfoot.[47]

In 1949 health specialists estimated that one of every seven hundred American babies started life with cleft lip or palate. In cleft lip the defect consisted of a split in the upper lip; in cleft palate there was a break in the roof of the mouth. Cleft palate deprived the child of a solid surface between the tongue and nasal passages and interfered with chewing, drinking, swallowing, speaking, and hearing. The cleft palate condition made the bearer susceptible to ear, nose, and throat diseases and increased the need for dental treatment. Such abnormalities caused emotional and financial difficulties for children and their parents.

Obviously, for humane reasons, at the outset of the extramural program, research in such abnormalities ranked in priority above more common anomalies, such as malocclusion (imperfect bite). In 1949 scientists believed that genetic and/or environmental factors contributed to cleft lip and palate but knew little else about the causes of such deformities.

Starting in 1949, the Institute supported a longitudinal growth study that followed for many years the same subjects born with cleft lips and palates. Dr. Samuel Pruzansky initiated the study at the Cleft Palate Center of the Chicago Professional Colleges of the University of Illinois and in 1954 continued it at the Institute, which processed the data collected by the Cleft Palate Center. As of 1955, the Cleft Palate Center had collected data on more than five hundred children. Pruzansky and other investigators at the Illinois center and at the Institute learned that adequate surgery could repair cleft lip but not all clefts of the palate. Essential aid to persons with inoperable cleft palates was provided when the Pruzansky group collaborated with Dr. Ralph S. Lloyd, chief of the Clinical Center Dental Department, to design speech appliances.[48]

Scientists concerned about craniofacial anomalies banded together at an international symposium sponsored by the Institute in Gatlinburg, Tennessee, in 1959 to form a framework for handling craniofacial genetics and developmental biology. Volker, then dean of the University of Alabama School of Dentistry, told the 125 researchers at the meeting that the time had come for dental faculties to incorporate the findings of numerous scientific disciplines in dealing with the skull's congenital abnormalities.[49]

Several months later members of the National Advisory Dental Research Council expressed similar concerns when the council's planning committee looked into the question of cleft lip and cleft palate research. After a council subcommittee suggested establishment of a multidisciplinary facility to cope with such anomalies, the council favored establishment of cleft palate research centers. Kreshover, then Institute scientific director, took a special interest in expanding support of craniofacial anomaly research. Thereafter, in 1961 the Institute awarded the first program-project grant for such a center to New York University. The following year the University of Pittsburgh, which organized a cleft palate team in 1950, received extramural support to establish a cleft palate research center.[50]

By 1961 Institute intramural scientists had turned to the laboratory to learn about the onset of such abnormalities as cleft lip and palate. They established that the fetuses of oxygen-deficient pregnant rats showed a high incidence of cleft palates and other birth defects.[51]

Through intramural research and extramural grants and training programs the Institute reinforced research on cleft palate, spending close to $2.5 million on cleft palate research in 1963. By 1964 the Institute was supporting cleft palate studies with the newly formed National Institute of Child Health and Human Development and the National Institute of Neurological Diseases and Blindness. The emphasis changed from concentration on surgery to broader research to determine causes, prevention, and growth to maintain the effectiveness of treatment. Once the domain of the surgeon, cleft palate research by the 1960s drew in the talents of pharmacologists, physicians, dentists, physiologists, embryologists, pathologists, psychologists, social workers, geneticists, biochemists, and speech therapists. Moreover, six Institute-funded multidisciplinary cleft palate centers conducted research ranging from causes to treatment. In the 1960s Institute grants also supported training programs to develop specialists for treatment and research.[52]

In 1964 the extramural program provided funding for the largest clinical research center in the nation for the study of cleft lip and palate at the Lancaster, Pennsylvania, Cleft Palate Clinic. Institute Director Arnold credited the project's director, Dr. Herbert K. Cooper, as one who "has dedicated his life to treating the orally handicapped, and to training medical, dental, and educational specialists who share the responsibility of treating these children." A pioneer in rehabilitation of cleft palate patients, Cooper had founded the facility in 1938. His center received a grant of more than $428,000 to begin a seven-year study of cleft palate and cleft lip from their origins to treatment of patients and their families.[53]

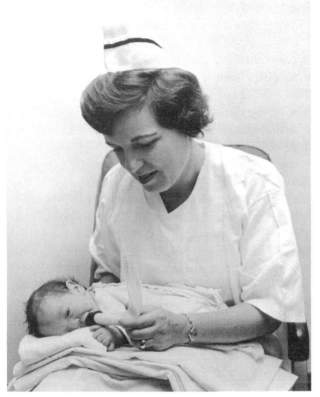

Feeding a cleft palate baby.

Scientists in 1964 suspected that complicated circumstances during fetal growth influenced the deformity, including factors such as genetic, mechanical, chemical, nutritional, infectious, and metabolic. Some studies already showed that a chromosomal anomaly, with three extra female chromosomes in a male child, accompanied the condition. Meanwhile, laboratory research showed that excessive cortisone given to pregnant mice or folic acid deficiency during pregnancy produced offspring with cleft palate.[54]

In the Institute's clinical section Dr. Yasau Takagi, a visiting physician, developed a new technique to facilitate feeding of infants with Robin's Syndrome, a combination of birth defects that included cleft palate. In addition, the Institute collaborated with the Lancaster Cleft Palate Clinic and the Halifax County, North Carolina, Health Department to study facial malformation. The Halifax study, run by

Witkop's team, found cleft palate five times more prevalent than normal in the highly interrelated Haliwa Indians.[55]

Laboratory research both outside and within the Institute showed by 1964 that certain substances in pregnant laboratory animals induced cleft palate in their offspring. A team headed by Dr. Theodore H. Ingalls at the Henry Phipps Institute observed chromosomal changes accompanying cleft palate in mice embryos of mothers with 6 aminonicotinic acid in their systems. Dr. C. G. T. King of the Institute's biochemistry laboratory reported cleft palate and other malformations in offspring carried by rats given meclizine hydrochloride, an antihistamine commonly used for motion sickness. His work in facial abnormalities advanced to the point that McClure, his laboratory chief, established a pharmacology section in 1965 with King as its chief.[56]

An American Dental Association research fellow, Dr. Anthony Steffek, collaborated with King to develop an animal model system for experimental production of cleft palate. Dr. Andrew G. Hendrickx, an embryologist who produced the first known case of cleft palate in a nonhuman primate, lent the Institute his baboons for these experiments. Scientists eventually abandoned the use of nonhuman primates as cleft models because they were less genetically specific than the mouse or rat. Steffek and King then borrowed ferrets for research from Dr. John Sever of the National Institute of Neurological and Communicative Disorders and Stroke. Subsequently, the ferret became the animal of choice for studying cleft palate.[57]

During this period the preponderance of extramural funding for cleft palate continued to support research concerned with treatment. From 1957 through 1966 the Institute awarded $8 million for sixty-eight extramural research projects in cleft palate and cleft lip. Of those projects, 33 percent included speech studies. Of the $1.6 million granted in 1966, for instance, only a little more than $200,000 supported individual research projects. From 1959 through 1966 the Institute provided most of the funding in the United States for cleft palate and cleft lip projects; the rest of the federal government, including other institutes and nongovernment institutions, contributed $3.5 million.[58]

As part of the NIH shift toward a more targeted research policy, the Institute leadership launched the Oral-Facial Growth and Development Program in 1966. The program underwent several name and administrative changes in later years but essentially covered extramural studies of skull abnormalities, including investigations at the Institute-supported regional multidisciplinary research centers.[59]

Nevertheless, both research and funding were sparse for other areas affecting craniofacial problems. For instance, Dr. K. Kenneth Hisaoka, extramural administrator of the orofacial growth and development program, estimated that malocclusion and orthodontic treatment affected from one-fifth to one-half of the school-age population in the United States in 1966. The Institute spent only 10 percent of its orofacial extramural budget, or $304,000, on malocclusal studies that year.[60]

Expansion of the scope of extramural support for cleft palate did finally occur. By 1969 the Institute funded five general areas of investigation: surgical improvement, speech capacity, psychological management, genetic causes, and environmental origins. Yet the Institute still provided almost all of the funding in the United States for research into the causes of the deformity, including both epidemiological and laboratory studies.[61]

An understanding of skull abnormalities was enhanced through the intramural program's continuation of epidemiological studies. Niswander and the genetics group recorded family histories of persons with cleft palates and cleft lips. Their analyses indicated that isolated cleft palate was a different condition from cleft lip, with or without cleft palate. By 1969 the evidence suggested that 25 percent of all clefts were associated with some hereditary influences; the remaining cases appeared to stem from environmental or unknown causes. Even those cases connected with genetic origins seemed to vary; isolated cleft palate appeared linked to dominant genes and cleft lip to recessive genes.[62]

A 1972 review sponsored by the extramural program highlighted additional milestones in the field. According to the reviewers, population studies had produced no evidence that major environmental factors influenced the frequency of cleft lip and cleft palate, either isolated or combined. That finding weakened the hypothesis implicating the environment as a contributor toward cleft lip and cleft palate. The statement stressed as well the beginnings of the application of molecular biology to mammalian teratology, the study of abnormal development and congenital deformities in mammals.[63]

Institute studies in 1973 provided data on the economic impact of skull abnormalities in the United States. The nation's physicians annually delivered from six thousand to seven thousand babies with cleft palate. Rehabilitation for a cleft patient through age eighteen cost an estimated $14,000, which totalled $100 million yearly. NIDR officials reckoned that approximately 14 million American school-children needed orthodontic treatment for malocclusion but that the majority did not receive such help. They estimated that Americans spent annually $500 million for orthodontic treatment.

Significant animal research on cleft palate by 1973 had identified a wide variety of chemical agents as causes when applied at critical times during fetal development such as the time of palatal closure. Because of the difficulty of studying comparable human growth, the origins of cleft palate in humans remained uncertain. Epidemiological studies, however, suggested that one of twenty children born to mothers who already had delivered a child with cleft palate also would have cleft palate. Utilizing this finding, the Institute planned to monitor susceptible pregnant mothers and their environments, particularly at the stage of palatal closure in the fetus.[64]

Fortunately, applied investigations brought significant gains in surgical techniques. By 1973 surgery had been developed that meant "those afflicted with deformities of the face and head need no longer suffer the social stigma of grotesque deformities in isolation." A three-day workshop sponsored by the Institute brought experts together to exchange information on these new developments.[65]

Family emotional problems caused by such abnormalities became an area of Institute research in the 1970s. To determine the effects of cleft defects on parents and associates of patients, the Institute initiated a different kind of research. Five of the cleft palate centers supported by the Institute held group therapy sessions for mothers of cleft palate children and later trained mothers as paraprofessional group therapy leaders. Researchers followed this up with a workshop in 1974 that brought together behavioral and biomedical scientists to discuss the psychosocial aspects of craniofacial malformation. Dental and behavioral scientific collaboration grew out of this workshop, and the Fédération Dentaire Internationale and the American Psychological Association planned subsequent meetings to deal with the subject.[66]

In 1974 extramural funds helped to establish the New York University Center for Craniofacial Anomalies, a program of intensified research. The university's medical school already was known internationally for its surgical reconstructive work in craniofacial cases and had included a pilot surgical-dental therapeutic team in its operations since 1970. Institute Director Kreshover, an alumnus of the medical school, encouraged the medical school, which was handling an increasing number of patients with facial deformities, to form the research center.[67]

As the subject of skull deformities attracted greater national attention, the Institute program expanded further. To coordinate research, specialists conducted almost twenty workshops from 1967 to 1974 on the state of the science. Based on discussions in later conferences, Kreshover advocated expanding the Institute program in craniofacial anomalies. He proposed to the Secretary of Health, Education and Welfare that craniofacial anomalies be included in the special research initiative of the Department's Forward Plan for Health for the 1976-1980 period. Next, the Institute submitted craniofacial anomalies funding requests as part of the NIH Forward Plan. In 1974 the Senate Appropriations Subcommittee voted to increase funding for such research, a sign to Kreshover that Congress, too, wanted more done in that field. Institute responsibilities broadened in 1979 with the addition of acquired dentofacial defects, which included deformities resulting from automobile accidents and other mishaps.[68]

As part of the Institute's program evaluations, twenty distinguished scientists from the United States, Canada, and Europe reviewed the craniofacial anomalies research activities for the 1974 to 1980 period. Dr. James W. Bawden of the University of North Carolina, Chapel Hill, served as chairman of the effort. The study panels concluded that the basic science portion of the research was the most productive and had provided new information on basic normal developmental processes. The evaluators praised discoveries in thirteen areas, including investigations that helped researchers understand better the mechanisms of congenital malformations, the formation of the palate, development of the head and neck, and both solitary and multiple defects associated with the head and neck. The evaluation concluded that in the realm of applied science progress might not have been possible without Institute funding. In listing achievements involving application, the evaluating panel first cited new orthodontic and orthopedic procedures devised as a result of studies of the relationships between natural and therapeutic stresses on facial bones.[69]

The assessors recommended more support for epidemiology and prevention. They saw a need for further genetic studies of craniofacial anomalies at the molecular and human levels. Reporting to the National Advisory Dental Research Council on the evaluation, Chairman Bawden advised, however, "if you want more research done in this area, you've got to spend more money. . . . There isn't any other alternative that occurred to us, in spite of these recommendations."[70]

By 1985 most of the extramural research in craniofacial malformations concentrated on basic developmental biology and origins of congenital defects. Four percent of grant funding went to acquired defects, a major area that one evaluator, Dr. Harold Slavkin, had found difficult to assess because information was so scattered. Prevention and epidemiology, however, received no extramural funding.[71]

As the Institute approached its fortieth year, the intramural sector's involvement in craniofacial problems was largely in basic research while extramural support included both applied and basic research. During the 1980s five research centers participated in the extramural program: the University of Pittsburgh Cleft Palate Center, the University of Iowa Cleft Palate Center, the Center for Craniofacial Anomalies, University of Illinois at Chicago, the Center for Craniofacial Anomalies within the New York University Institute of Reconstructive Plastic Surgery, and the University of Michigan Center for Human Growth and Development.[72]

With considerable justification extramural funds increasingly supported basic research in molecular genetics and molecular biology in the 1980s. Grantees in that area had produced significant findings. Slavkin, for instance, had been instrumental in the first successful isolation of a gene involved in the formation of tooth enamel. Dr. Marshall Urist, a grantee since the early 1960s at the University of California at Los Angeles, had been the first to isolate a protein from demineralized bone that, when implanted, induced new bone growth to repair some fractures. By 1987 plans were under way to support new craniofacial anomalies research centers that would emphasize the newer techniques and information on molecular biology and genetics.[73]

Other clinically important information emerged from extramural work during the 1980s as well. For instance, studies showed that use during pregnancy of sodium valproate, an anticonvulsant to control epilepsy, could disrupt fetal tissue growth and could leave portions of the spinal cord or brain exposed at birth. A 1985 report from the University of Pittsburgh Cleft Palate Center indicated that corrective surgery for one-year-old children appeared safe and did not undermine normal facial growth. In 1986 the Pittsburgh researchers found that surgery at three months of age could prevent hearing loss induced by middle ear disease, common in cleft palate victims. Other grantees produced a new restorative material, chlorinated polyethylene, for artificial replacement of portions of the face and jaw. For 1987, NIDR extramural program administrators planned a series of clinical evaluations of commonly used clinical strategies for treating orthodontic problems in children and adults. When completed, these evaluations would be the first trials to differentiate between alternative approaches with respect to their efficacy.[74]

Dental Restoration

For centuries restoration has been important for anyone who has ever had a cavity, lost a tooth, or coped with a dental defect or injury. Revolutionary technological advances in the post-World War II period have made restorations easier for dentist and patient. The Institute's part in this area has been unusual because it has involved a special relationship with the National Bureau of Standards (NBS), which has conducted research on and tested dental materials.

After the NIH established a grants award division in 1946, that division, advised by a dental study committee, awarded grants for investigations on restorative materials at Indiana University and Tufts College. With the Institute's creation in 1948 its administrators retained materials research as an extramural program and later established the NIDR Committee on Adhesive Restorative Materials. Institute scientists subsequently studied the biological effects of newly developed materials and dental techniques.[75]

Precedence had much to do with leaving direct restorative materials research out of the early intramural program because since 1919 NBS had operated a dental materials research program. Combined with support from the American Dental Association (ADA) since 1928, the bureau's staff had achieved international respect for out-

standing work in setting standards and developing materials and
equipment useful for world dentistry. Under the leadership of Dr.
George Paffenbarger, the ADA unit at the bureau had developed the
base for specifications and certification programs for dental materials
used around the world.[76]

As the NIDR Committee on Adhesive Restorative Materials later
stressed, development of satisfactory restorative dental materials depended on the basic structural and chemical properties of the affected
biological area and special characteristics of instrumentally prepared
tooth surfaces. Consequently, the earliest NIH work affecting restorative dental materials involved structural studies of tooth surfaces.
Progress in technology contributed to such investigations through
the introduction of tungsten carbide burs and diamond stones in the
1940s, providing improved tooth cutting tools. Using the electron
microscope in 1945, Wyckoff and Scott examined details of tooth
surfaces cut with the new rotary instruments. Because of the interest
in dental caries and fluoridation, research in the structure and properties of the hard dental tissues constituted a significant part of NIH
dental research.[77]

A few years later a major bureau technological contribution to
dentistry encouraged Institute scientists to undertake a new line of
research. In 1953 Dr. Robert Nelsen of the ADA group and John
Kumpula of the bureau revolutionized dental practice by succeeding
with basic research that culminated in the high-speed dental drill.
After the Nelsen work made possible the production of the first
commercial high-speed hand pieces in 1957, an American Dental
Trade Association survey reported that over 94 percent of practicing
dentists in the nation switched to its use within a few years.[78]

In 1957 Institute clinicians and pathologists started testing the
biological responses of dental tissues to treatment with the air turbine
high-speed drill. Dr. Harold Stanley of the NIDR staff recalled that
he had been reluctant to take on the study of human pulpal response
to the high-speed drill even though Dr. Herbert Swerdlow, his research partner, had predicted that the work would take only two
months. Instead, the research stretched out into years, and Stanley
made pulp studies his specialty. The studies by Swerdlow and Stanley
recorded the reactions of human dental pulp to the various drill
speeds with and without coolants and air-water sprays and to various
kinds of restorative materials. Because of the tests by Swerdlow and

Stanley, the ADA and the Food and Drug Administration consulted Institute scientists on the efficacy and safety of restorative techniques and materials.[79] What had started as a modest support of a bureau invention had evolved into a significant contribution to dental practice and by 1964 had made the Institute a world leader in dental pulp research.

In the meantime, the experiments on tooth surface bonding by Dr. Michael Buonocore and his team at the Eastman Dental Center in Rochester, New York, advanced both dental materials research and restorative dentistry. In the 1950s Buonocore proved that phosphoric acid coated on tooth enamel gave the tooth surface a better retention capability for acrylic restorative materials. His subsequent acid-etch technique, developed with extramural funding, sealed the tooth structure from leakage from the oral cavity and enabled composite materials to adhere more successfully when a tooth was filled. Buonocore's method proved useful for sealing pits and fissures in children's teeth to prevent new cavities, to affix plastic materials to restore fractured teeth, and to bond orthodontic plastic brackets to teeth.[80]

Along with the Buonocore results, the work of Dr. Rafael L. Bowen in the bureau ADA unit added another milestone to restorative dentistry with his synthesis of BIS-GMA, a substance constituting part of most dental composites today. Bowen, who published some of his findings in the early 1960s, benefited from Institute extramural support that started in the ADA unit in 1958 with Paffenbarger's leadership. He synthesized the addition reaction product of a combination of epoxy and acrylic resins. Thus, he invented a resin composite that when compared to traditional fillings improved the physical appearances of filled front teeth because the composites could be made to match tooth color.[81]

Again ADA researchers at the bureau produced another significant achievement funded by the extramural program. In 1962 Drs. N. C. Demaree and Duane Taylor, son of the first ADA research associate at the bureau, developed the spherical alloy amalgam that needed less mercury. Taylor's amalgam ultimately received international acceptance, particularly in Japan.[82]

About the time of Taylor's and Bowen's accomplishments a political controversy, the "AD-XZ Battery Dispute," almost ended dental materials research at the bureau. The disagreement involved the propriety of the bureau's publicly announced assessment of a commercial product. The problem originated in 1959 after Pioneers Incorporated sued the federal government because bureau scientists had declared the company's AD-XZ battery worthless after testing it. Although the court had dismissed the case, political pressures had forced the firing of Dr. Allen Astin, bureau director. An outcry from the scientific community led to Astin's reinstatement. In reaction to this turmoil, Astin discontinued the bureau's trade product testing, which included dental materials. Further, he wanted to stop all dental materials research at the bureau and shift that responsibility to NIDR.[83]

Paffenbarger and ADA Washington, D.C., representatives encountered a bureaucratic snarl when they tried to arrange for continuation of the bureau dental materials program. Neither Astin nor NIH Director Shannon wanted the responsibility. Shannon opposed any NIH connection with setting standards or certifying materials, tasks he regarded as beyond his agency's domain. Institute Director Arnold was interested initially only in new materials research and was concerned about protecting the Institute's extramural commitments in restorative materials projects. After pleading their case up through the bureaucracy to the Public Health Service surgeon general, ADA officers engaged Dr. Jesse Beanes, chairman of the physics department of the University of Virginia, to study the issue and recommend solutions. After reviewing the question, Beanes suggested retention of the government dental materials research at the bureau with financial support from the Institute.[84]

The combination of the jurisdictional dispute and major research developments created an odd situation for dental materials research. The National Advisory Dental Research Council became so concerned about the status of dental materials research that in 1960 and 1961 the members formed committees to advise Arnold on the subject. The groups provided suggestions on the research priority for bonding restorative materials to tooth structure and on the Institute's expansion of intramural and extramural research in dental materials and related fields. Consequently, before the disagreement was settled, the financial and working relationships improved. In 1963 the Institute's extramural support for dental materials quadrupled over that of the previous year; two bureau scientists worked temporarily in Institute laboratories, and Dr. Walter E. Brown of the bureau and Dr. David Eanes of the Institute joined to teach a course on crystallography and X ray diffraction to bureau and Institute staff members.[85]

After numerous conferences the dental restorative materials research bureaucratic impasse finally ended in 1964. On August 28 Arnold signed the first cooperative research agreement between the Institute and the NBS. The accord took effect October 1, 1964. In the new arrangement the bureau supplied the physical facilities and personnel for continuing dental materials research and the Institute paid for additional staffing at the bureau for research of special interest to the Institute, such as physical characterization of restorative dental materials. Arnold committed the Institute to supplying from $75,000 to $100,000 for the projects for Fiscal Year 1965.[86] That agreement marked the beginning of a long-term growing relationship between the NBS and the Institute.

In 1965 Dr. John Stanford, assistant director of the ADA unit at the bureau, took the NBS program of standards development and materials evaluation to the ADA Chicago headquarters to form the base of what later became the Council on Dental Materials, Instruments, and Equipment, which he headed. Beginning in 1965, the Institute provided extramural support of $200,000 annually to the ADA toward developing and evaluating methods and instrumentation used for setting specifications and standards for dental materials, instruments, and equipment.[87]

In the 1960s dental restorative materials research started to grow in popularity, with the help of increased Institute support through workshops, grants, and a closer working relationship between the bureau and the ADA. Stanford recalled meeting less than three dozen dental materials researchers at 1950s meetings of the International Association for Dental Research. Further, when he started the dental materials project at ADA headquarters in 1965, the staff consisted of only two scientists.[88]

The broadening of Institute extramural support extended in the mid-1960s to studies of the barnacle and other forms of marine life for clues on developing a permanent bond for teeth fillings. Researchers selected the barnacle because it could attach to surfaces under water with its shell adhering long after the animal died. In one of the investigations conducted by the Battelle Laboratories of Columbus, Ohio, scientists found the adhesive of another species, the sea mussel, composed of a protein of low molecular weight. The Ohio group identified dityrosine as possibly controlling the mussel's adhe-

sive qualities but also determined that the resulting cement was unsuitable because of its dark brown color.[89]

Support also continued for more conventional areas, such as basic
research on amalgam. From the 1960s to the 1980s extramural grantees reached important conclusions that contributed toward understanding amalgam failures. From the late 1960s to 1976 Dr. Evan H.
Greener, professor and chairman of the biological materials department of the Northwestern University Dental School, directed extensive investigations of the electrochemical corrosion and microstructure of amalgams. Ultimately, his team demonstrated that corrosion
of a certain interconnected phase reduced amalgam's tensile strength
by at least 25 percent. In 1980 Greener's group described the behavior
of amalgam's "creep," the time-dependent deformation accompanying the application of stress to a material and a factor conducive to a
filling's failure.[90]

Such projects as research and development of better dental prosthetics also were funded by the Institute. Extramural grantees worked
to improve dental prosthetics in the 1970s. Dr. Kamal Asgar, an
expert in metallurgy with the School of Dentistry at the University
of Michigan, developed a new "super alloy" system capable of improving base metal alloys used for removable partial dentures. In
addition, the ADA group at the bureau, including Paffenbarger and
Bowen, designed a technique that strengthened the bond between
synthetic teeth and the denture base.[91]

Although the Institute did not take a position on various procedures to aid individuals who had lost teeth, it did finance studies of
other methods to solve these problems. During the twentieth century
dentists used implants, transplants, and replants of teeth.

Implants are artificial teeth permanently placed in the jaw. A replant is an extracted or avulsed tooth placed back in its own socket,
and a transplant is a tooth transferred from one part of the mouth to
the other.

Of those replacement types, the implant was the most controversial, even though the technique had been used for centuries. Extramural grants in the 1970s provided for investigations to find appropriate
test animals and materials for implant tests, techniques to prolong the
functioning of a transplanted tooth, and the best means to achieve
success in replanting a tooth. Experiments supported by the Institute
indicated soaking a tooth in a fluoride solution might extend the use

of a transplanted tooth and that the highest degree of success in replanting teeth occurred in young persons when the replant had been out less than thirty minutes.[92]

Problems in cavity-filling materials remained a concern followed in both the extramural and intramural programs. In the 1970s and 1980s scientists progressed in dealing with water-leakage problems in fillings, including the composite resins. With extramural support, Bowen and his colleagues confronted the problems of water sorption with the resins. In 1982 his team developed a strong adhesive bonding of a conventional composite product that adhered to dentin. Later, Dr. Michael W. Roberts, chief of the Institute's patient care section, found leakage problems with long-term usage of the composite resins, but his clinical tests showed that they could be used successfully to restore children's primary molars if the dentist followed meticulous procedures.[93]

In the 1980s the Institute had to cope with a situation reminiscent of the Amalgam War days of the nineteenth century. The twentieth century episode started when the Institute and the ADA received inquiries from dentists and patients about the safety of mercury in amalgam fillings, a question that had split the dental community in the preceding century. One person claimed that he had contracted multiple sclerosis from the mercury in the fillings; others reported stories of miraculous recoveries from mysterious illnesses after removal of all amalgam fillings. Available scientific evidence from several sources, including the ADA, indicated that no health hazard resulted from amalgam except for a small segment with hypersensitivity to mercury. Such individuals, stated NIDR Director Löe, should be protected from exposure to amalgam. Because of the outcry Drs. Joyce Reese, health science administrator at the Institute, and John Stanford of the ADA organized a joint workshop in 1984 that issued a statement on the state of the science and recommended areas of additional research. In 1985 the Institute convened a meeting with representatives of other federal agencies to develop additional ideas on research.

Some stories in the newspapers and on television programs heightened public anxiety. Dr. Preston Littleton, then assistant director for program operations at the Institute, noted a growing concern in the dental community that extended to recommendations by some dentists that their patients have all amalgam restorations removed and replaced with precious metal or composite restorative materials. In 1985 Nylen, by then associate director for extramural programs, agreed to increase Institute efforts to encourage research in amalgam safety.[94]

Meanwhile, the increased numbers of dental materials researchers by the 1980s represented tremendous growth of interest in the field. John Stanford's ADA standards group, which started with two scientists in 1965, contained twenty researchers by the mid-1980s. The number of dental materials investigators he met at IADR meetings rose from about thirty in the 1950s to more than eight hundred in the 1980s.[95]

Advances in biotechnology changed the dental materials research picture by the 1980s as well, especially for Dr. J. Herbert Waite, a grantee at the University of Connecticut. Waite acquired more than three thousand mussels for his project. After experimenting by painstakingly collecting minute amounts of adhesive from each of the mussels, he used molecular biology to isolate an adhesive protein from mussels that created the properties of a "superglue." The glue set in a wet or dry environment and had potential for numerous dental and medical uses. In 1986 the University of Connecticut received a patent for the process and prepared to produce it commercially through a biotechnology firm with the use of synthetic, recombinant DNA methods.[96]

Ultimately, after several years of negotiation by Nylen as intramural director, the Institute expanded its relationship with the bureau's dental materials research laboratory in the 1980s. With the support of Nylen and Löe, the two agencies created a new cooperative program that combined the biological research of the Institute with the physical measurements work of the bureau to run from 1984 to 1993. This new project did not disrupt the other extramural projects at the bureau but linked the calcium phosphate research of Dr. Edward D. Eanes with the bureau effort. Eanes, who had achieved distinction with his mineralized tissue research, became the first NIDR scientist to set up an intramural research section at the bureau. As part of the agreement, Eanes headed the Institute's skeletal biophysics section of the mineralized tissue research branch located physically at the bureau. Under the arrangement, the Institute and the bureau operated jointly in the study of the chemistry of calcium compounds and how they related to living systems.[97]

Pain Research

For centuries pain has been one of dentistry's most incessant problems. Approximately 25 percent of all chronic pain occurs in the face and mouth.[98] Basically two kinds of dental and/or facial pain exist: acute and chronic. The oral-facial pain troubling individuals ranges from the common toothache to a postoperative complication known as "dry socket" and chronic conditions such as facial neuralgia.

After he joined NIDR in 1954, Dr. Edward Driscoll initiated and championed Institute research on anesthesia in dentistry. Driscoll had worked for the Public Health Service since his graduation from Loyola University's dental school in New Orleans in 1936. Under Driscoll, Institute collaboration on anesthesia started in 1958 with the Anesthesiology Department of the NIH Clinical Center. The Driscoll group measured important physiological responses, such as blood pressure, brain activity, and heartbeat, to administration of general anesthesia to healthy individuals for dental treatments. In 1959 his team published the first of a series of physiological studies on general anesthesia for ambulatory dental patients. Using extraction of wisdom teeth to obtain information, Driscoll developed a clinical model for acute suffering that applied to the sharp pain resulting from surgery in other parts of the body. In 1967 Driscoll received the Horace Wells Club Award for his group's anesthesiology studies, which by then included data on over twelve hundred operations.[99]

Despite Driscoll's work and the importance to dental practice of curbing suffering, most American dental institutions neglected education and research on pain. Actually, pain research in the United States in the 1960s was extremely limited but had dedicated advocates, especially Dr. John Bonica. The founder of pain research in the United States, Bonica established the first pain clinic in the world at the University of Washington at Seattle. Only the Institute, the University of Washington pain clinic, and the pain control center at Harvard University Medical School conducted such studies then. In the extramural program in the 1960s the Institute awarded only one grant each in local and general anesthesia—a total of $40,000 out of annual budgets for training and research of almost $20 million. Driscoll attributed such a void to a lack of interested researchers. Bonica suggested that the "staggering difficulties" of pain research and control discouraged scientists from such investigations.[100]

Nevertheless, English and Canadian scientists stirred scientific interest in such studies when they produced the Gate Control Theory of Pain. In the 1960s they hypothesized that the nervous system had its own mechanisms that could alter or block pain perception.[101]

Early Institute extramural researchers examined pain with other approaches. At the Temporomandibular Joint Research Center of the University of Illinois Medical Center in Chicago Dr. Daniel Laskin combined information from a variety of epidemiological, biochemical, psychological, and physiological studies to become the first investigator to indicate that facial muscle tension contributed to chronic pain. In the 1960s Laskin suggested that the pain resulted from a psychophysiological disorder. He found that the condition frequently responded to counseling and conservative treatment so that drastic, irreversible measures, such as surgery and occlusal repairs, could be avoided.[102]

Another extramural researcher, Dr. Barry Sessle of the University of Toronto, studied the brain stem and its relationship to pain. He showed how neural injury in certain structures within the brain stem could produce chronic pain in the teeth and mouth. In a long-term project that the Institute began supporting in the 1960s Sessle explored the brain stem's neurophysiological processes involved in pain transmission and control.[103]

Meanwhile, organized dentistry and Driscoll, with the support of the Institute, tried to arouse interest in pain research and control. In 1963 and 1965 the American Dental Society of Anesthesiology sponsored workshops on the issue but failed to persuade American dental schools to set standards for teaching pain control. The society tried again with a workshop cosponsored in 1970 with the American Association of Dental Schools, the ADA, and other organizations. Driscoll also delivered speeches urging others to engage in pain research. In 1970 the Institute formed a committee to consider the situation and make recommendations reflecting the potentially significant progress in clinical pharmacology and anesthesiology.[104]

Fear of pain, the Institute committee concluded, kept so many people away from essential dental care that more effective pain controls were deemed essential for dental patients. Moreover, in the committee's view, solutions only could emerge through basic and clinical research. Committee members acknowledged the paucity of research and education in curbing suffering and recommended NIDR support to remedy the situation through funding of trainees and of training centers. Institute administrators consequently proposed a five-year plan for the 1970s for basic and clinical research on the body's pain mechanisms, anxiety about dental treatment, and local and general anesthesias in dentistry.[105]

Both the research and education in the United States were so inadequate on intravenous use of amnesic, sedative, and general anesthetic agents to relieve pain that by the early 1970s more than fifty American general practitioners traveled to London to take courses in intravenous administration of anesthetics. According to an Institute appraisal, the British were considerably ahead of the United States in both research and clinical application of these techniques.[106]

There were also disturbing implications in professional attitudes on anesthesia in the United States. An Institute-sponsored survey showed that 60 percent of oral surgeons who were questioned preferred use of general anesthesia, a choice Driscoll considered less desirable than that of local anesthesia. He blamed the situation on inadequate research and urged the Institute to encourage increased extramural research in local and general anesthesia, including funding oral research in the Harvard and Washington pain control centers.[107]

Both the ADA and the Institute by 1971 encouraged the nation's dental schools to give more instruction on curtailing pain. The ADA adopted guidelines for teaching that subject in the dental schools, an action the Institute committee considered a milestone, although a "belated effort." To strengthen pain control curricula, the Institute announced national competition for academic awards to improve curricula and promote academic careers in that subject area. To stimulate the extramural effort, Dr. Aaron Ganz, a pharmacologist by training, was appointed chief of the Institute's extramural program for pain control research. In another astute move to nudge the nation's dental schools, the Institute formed another committee in 1972 to pass judgment on the earlier committee's recommendations. While the first committee included scientists and clinicians, the second consisted of deans, faculty members, science administrators, and several eminent investigators. The second group "quickly reaffirmed . . . with little debate" the parent group's proposals for a national program, including support for curricula in dental schools, academic awards, training, and pain control centers.[108]

During this period a team of Institute scientists headed by Driscoll continued to investigate more sophisticated methods of easing suffering. The group was among the first to test the safety and efficacy of intravenous sedation of patients who remained conscious during dental surgery. In 1972 the Driscoll clinicians concluded that intravenous administration of a local anesthetic with a memory-erasing drug made the patients more relaxed and cooperative and caused fewer irregular heartbeats than the anesthetic alone. By then a survey by the American Society of Oral Surgery showed that some oral surgeons were starting to use that method, also known as conscious sedation, instead of general anesthesia, still the predominant technique.[109]

Until the late 1970s clinical investigators at the Institute evaluated intravenous sedation primarily as an alternative to general anesthesia for dental outpatients. The clinicians tried two commonly used sedative drug combinations and found that, although each was equally effective in controlling pain, one combination caused respiratory and transient cardiovascular depressions.[110]

Meanwhile, the Institute had moved forward in the early 1970s with the initiation of basic research in pain by Dr. Ronald Dubner, a dentist who had joined the Public Health Service in 1958 and the Institute in 1961. The Public Health Service had sent Dubner to the University of Michigan in Ann Arbor for doctoral studies in neurophysiology for the next four years. After Dubner had completed his doctorate, NIDR had established a neurophysiology laboratory in 1965 to study neural mechanisms in the mouth and face. Attracted to pain research by 1970, Dubner had taken a one-year work-study assignment in London with a British pain expert, Patrick D. Wall, a university professor and one of the originators of the Gate Control Theory of Pain. Upon his return to the Institute in 1971, Dubner and his group had concentrated on pain research.[111]

In 1974 Dubner evaluated the use of acupuncture in pain control during a trip to China. Visiting Chinese hospitals, Dubner witnessed acupuncture applications, the ancient Chinese practice of inserting fine needles at certain body sites to relieve pain. The NIDR scientist traveled as a member of the Acupuncture-Anesthesia Study Group, sponsored by the Committee on Scholarly Communication with the People's Republic of China. The visit was influenced by the journey of President Richard M. Nixon to China and the Nixon administration's encouragement of better United States relations with China.

While Dubner agreed with other scientists that acupuncture could be "relatively effective" in anesthetizing patients for certain kinds of surgery, he did not recommend its use for routine dental services, including extractions. Dubner sided with the American Dental Association's stand that acupuncture in dentistry should be regarded as experimental.[112]

During the NIDR reorganization in 1974 Dubner's basic neurobiology program merged with Driscoll's clinical anesthesiology work into the Neurobiology and Anesthesiology Branch with Dubner as chief. Basic research in the branch correlated neurophysiology and neuropharmacology with anatomical studies and also neurophysiology with behavior. In a peer review of the branch's work in 1975, the evaluating committee praised the experimenters and their work. "The members of the review group were unanimous in their favorable impressions," reported Dr. Frederick W. L. Kerr, a committee member and professor of neurosurgery and neuroanatomy of the Mayo Clinic of Rochester, Minnesota.[113]

Institute influence in pain research spread internationally by 1975 when the Institute researchers and other prominent pain researchers, including Bonica, helped establish the International Association for the Study of Pain and the First World Congress on Pain. The international pain research community asked the Institute to serve as a focal point for standardizing terminology to evaluate, diagnose, and treat clinical pain syndromes.[114]

Originally a psychology graduate student in Dubner's branch, Richard Gracely found that pain could be measured in humans through a verbal judgment by the sufferer. By 1978 Gracely, who then had his doctorate, and his colleagues had devised and validated a word test for adults to rank degrees of pain. In the early experiments the Gracely team used physicians or college students as subjects and applied easily controlled electrical stimulation and cold temperatures to cleaned-out tooth cavities. The word scores and degrees of stimulation were consistent and matched each other. With later modifications the Gracely pain scales quantified the intensity of pain by "weak," "mild," "moderate," and "intense" and the unpleasantness by "annoying," "unpleasant," and "distressing." In later work the Institute researchers developed verbal and nonverbal pain measurements for children, including a range of faces with smiles to frowns, and scales that allowed patients to assess the amount of pain in other ailments. Dubner regarded the establishment of objective pain assessment a major clinical breakthrough. Subsequently, Institute scientists used the Gracely scales to test the effectiveness of pain-relieving drugs.[115]

In the meantime, the extramural program funded a long-range project proposed by Bonica. Under his leadership the University of Washington initiated an epidemiological study on dental and orofacial pain mechanisms, behavior, and modulation.[116]

The branch's clinical program also produced additional information on both nonpharmacological and pharmacological means of reducing pain. Studying a technique known as TENS (transcutaneous electrical nerve stimulation), the clinicians found that in certain nerve injuries electrical stimulation of the skin suppressed some pain. Other research revealed that the brain's naturally occurring peptides, such as beta-endorphin, were potent in quelling pain impulses.[117]

By the beginning of the 1980s the basic researchers in Dubner's branch had achieved significant progress in understanding how the body transmitted pain signals. The scientists acquired that knowledge by locating and studying brain cells involved in pain transmission. The NIDR investigators were among the first to examine the function and structure of the substantia gelatinosa—part of the spinal cord's dorsal horn in the medulla—research that led a Dubner team to identify specific brain neurochemicals involved in pain transmission. Scientists in Dubner's laboratory also were among the first to identify specialized receptors existing in skin that responded exclusively to tissue damage and noxious stimuli.[118]

The accomplishments of the NIDR pain researchers encouraged the NIH administration to fulfill a commitment repeatedly delayed since 1979—the establishment of a pain clinic on the Bethesda campus. In 1983 the NIH opened the first multidisciplinary pain clinic in the nation exclusively concerned with research. This new clinic was placed under the management of NIDR and located in the Clinical Center's Ambulatory Care Research Facility (ACRF). Physicians and dentists referred patients to the clinic to serve as voluntary subjects for research to improve diagnosis, measurement, and treatment for acute and chronic dental, cancer, arthritic, and diabetic pain.[119]

Research continued as before, but now expanded under the Pain Clinic. Under the new organization clinicians evaluated various pharmacologic approaches to curbing acute dental pain and tested the

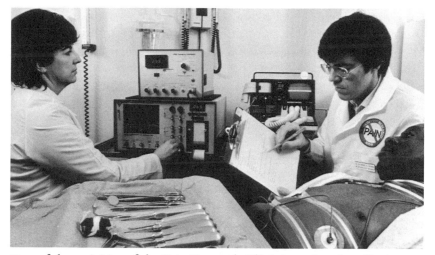

One of the activities of the Pain Research Clinic is testing the effectiveness of various drugs in the relief of pain and anxiety. Here Dr. Raymond Dionne and nurse Peggy Wirdzek measure an oral surgery patient's responses to an intravenous sedative.

safety of dental anesthetics. Dr. Raymond Dionne and others determined that epinephrine included in the administration of local anesthesia contributed toward increases in the heart rate and the amount of blood pumped by the heart. These findings prompted dentists to reevaluate epinephrine doses, particularly for patients with cardiovascular problems.[120]

Both intramural and extramural clinical researchers extensively used an oral surgery model for the study of pain that included removing impacted wisdom teeth. Through studies with oral surgery patients having wisdom tooth extractions, Dionne developed drug combinations that suppressed the onset of postoperative pain and reduced side effects. During the clinic's first three years, scientists employed the model to measure patients' beta-endorphin levels after administration of certain drugs or placebos.[121]

During the 1980s Dr. Kenneth Hargreaves and a Pain Clinic team established that the stress of oral surgery and subsequent postoperative pain caused the release of beta-endorphin from the pituitary gland into the blood. The increased levels of beta-endorphin were accompanied by less postoperative pain. In a study of fifty-two patients, they observed that when a local anesthetic was administered, the beta-endorphin levels decreased but increased after the drug wore off when the patient felt pain. Animal studies provided similar findings. These investigations supported the hypothesis that the body has a pain-suppressing system and demonstrated the important role of the oral surgery model in research for improving treatment of human pain.[122]

An extramural researcher, Dr. Jon Levine of the University of California at San Francisco, and his group also used the oral surgery model to study the relationship between opiate analgesics and a particular kind of antidepressant drug. That work showed that the postoperative administration of the antidepressant prolonged the effects of morphine analgesia. These findings suggested that clinical pain management could be improved while reducing the amount of morphine analgesia needed for effective pain control.[123]

While pain research advanced on the scientific front, supporters of the investigative efforts worked to gain additional help politically, financially, and administratively. Congress considered legislation on alleviating pain. During the hearings, witnesses emphasized the need for individuals scientifically trained to understand pain. In 1984, only a year after the clinic opened, Congress passed the Compassionate Pain Relief Act. Also following the creation of the Pain Clinic, the neuroscience and pain research share of NIDR extramural funds rose from 3.7 percent, a level that had existed for several years, to 5.7 percent—an increase from slightly more than $2.7 million to $4.1 million. The increased neuroscience and pain research funding share continued in 1987.[124]

The Institute and NIH also took other steps to strengthen the field of pain studies. The NIDR Long-Range Research Plan for Fiscal Years 1985-1989 recommended expanding training for pain researchers. Later, NIH Director Dr. James Wyngaarden appointed Dubner as the NIH representative on a committee to draft a mission and plans for an interagency committee on pain and analgesia. In 1985 the Institute asked for proposals to establish an extramural orofacial pain research center that would serve in addition as a training facility for pain investigators. The Institute funded the first center in 1986 at the University of California at Los Angeles (UCLA) where research was under way on the jaw opening reflex.[125]

In addition, the safety of anesthesia and sedation in the dental office aroused sufficient interest to induce the Institute and NIH to sponsor a consensus development conference on the subject in 1985. Representatives from both the dental and medical communities participated in discussions of future research needs relating to safety. Although the meeting's panel concluded that the outpatient safety record indicated no problems, they observed that their conclusion lacked supporting data. From those findings, the conference framed a collaborative protocol sponsored by the Institute to obtain reliable statistics on the various drug combinations used for dental outpatients. Collection and analysis of data on one thousand patients began afterwards to acquire the first reliable estimate of the safety of intravenous sedation in the United States.[126]

Meanwhile, extramural research grants had grown from twenty-two in 1973 to seventy-seven in 1987. The 1987 studies covered a range from epidemiological surveys of a specific facial disorder to six clinical evaluations of efficacy and safety of drugs, including intravenous premedications. Pain anatomy and physiology received the largest attention with thirty-six grants funded at $3 million.[127]

Much of the extramural pain research by 1987 was conducted at seven universities in the United States, including the University of Washington, UCLA, the University of California at San Francisco, Rutgers University, the University of North Carolina, Columbia University, and the University of Pittsburgh. One of the centers in the forefront of the field was the University of Washington, where Bonica had fathered American pain research. Following Bonica's retirement Dr. John Loeser headed the university's pain clinic, and Dr. Samuel Dworkin took over as principal investigator of the university's epidemiological study of dental and orofacial pain. In 1988 Dworkin received the IADR Behavioral Sciences Group Distinguished Senior Scientist Award for contributions to understanding psychophysiological and behavioral aspects of acute and chronic pain as well as the treatment of such pain.[128]

Social and Behavioral Sciences and Dentistry

Prior to federal government support of social and behavioral sciences in dentistry, few scientific behavioral publications appeared that related to dentistry. With the onset of government interest, social scientists by the mid-1950s discussed a range of issues from psycho-physiological aspects of oral functions and disease, such as nocturnal teeth grinding, to self-care behavior, utilization of professional services, and the fluoridation issue.[129]

The world's first systematic program of behavioral science research in dentistry was established in the 1950s by the Division of Dental Health of the Public Health Service. The division supported primarily studies on fluoridation issues, dental service utilization, education of dental professionals, and dental care systems research. To create a supply of persons trained in dentistry and social-behavioral research, both the division and the Institute financially supported students combining those disciplines. In the 1960s the Institute funded post-doctoral training for social psychology at the University of Houston and for physiological psychology at the University of Pittsburgh.[130]

The Institute role in social and behavioral sciences grew in 1976, supported by the appointment of Dr. Lois K. Cohen as a special assistant to the director to advise on the relationship of dental health to the social and behavioral sciences. Cohen had served with the Division of Dentistry and the former Division of Dental Health as both an intramural research sociologist and as a science administrator for the support of research grants and training in the social and behavioral sciences. During her first year at the Institute Cohen developed a strategy statement for the support of its intramural and extramural social and behavioral research programs. She and Dr. Patricia Bryant, who became the Institute's extramural health science administrator for those areas, later explained that the Institute's behavioral and social science program goals were aimed at determining how behavioral, social, cultural, and economic factors influenced oral health, including dental diseases and conditions. To stimulate research in such fields as psychology, social psychology, sociology, cultural anthropology, economics, political science, and health education, Cohen served as a consultant to national and international associations, ranging from the American Dental Association to the International Association for Dental Research and the World Health Organization.[131]

Healthy People, the 1979 surgeon general's report on health promotion and disease prevention, steered the Department of Health and Human Services in a new direction that focused on the relationship between behavior and health. That statement confirmed the relationship between behaviors and disease. The climate for an increased portfolio on the behavioral sciences was strengthened—enabling the Institute to increase its support of behavioral studies. That same year the Institute supported a National Research Conference on Oral Health Behavior to bring together social and behavioral scientists to discuss ways of developing, testing, and disseminating strategies to turn American oral health behavior toward preventive methods.[132]

Most of the Institute's extramural behavioral research grants funded pragmatic studies to help improve oral health behavior through educating individuals, groups, and communities. The awards supported studies of nonbiological effects of oral disease and surveys to determine reasons that kept individuals from seeking dental treatment. Some of the earliest extramural social and behavioral grants went to Dr. Barbara Melamed of the University of Florida, a specialist in studying the relationship between children's fears and anxieties and dental treatment, and Dr. Susan Reisine at the University of Connecticut, who assessed the social, psychological, and economic impacts of dental disease. By 1983 investigations suggested that a person's perception of the need for dental care most strongly influenced the decision to seek dental services. This finding indicated to NIDR administrators that critical intervention strategy should focus on converting an unmet clinically defined need into an effective demand for both self-care and professional service.[133]

In 1983 the Institute called for proposals to establish oral health and behavior research centers concentrating on social epidemiology and intervention strategies to promote oral health practices. The recommendations for such centers emerged from the NIDR long-range planning effort for 1985 through 1989, *Challenges for the Eighties,* which proposed funding to "encourage higher levels of interdisciplinary communication by creating centers of excellence" for introducing and sustaining such work. The Institute staff viewed the combination of behavioral and social researchers committed to oral health as a critical need. Yet budget requirements delayed consideration of center proposals. At least eight institutions applied, but none received priority scores sufficient for funding. Instead, Bryant sifted out the most meritorious parts of the proposals and advised that they be submitted for consideration as individual grants.[134]

NIDR enhanced its social and behavioral sciences operations during the 1980s. In 1983 Cohen was promoted to the positions of assistant director for international health and chief of the Office of Planning, Evaluation, and Communications. From 1985 to 1987 the Institute expanded its intramural social and behavioral sciences staff. In 1985 the Office of Planning, Evaluation, and Communications added a dentist-sociologist to lead an evaluation of Institute research. During the next two years social scientists joined the Epidemiology and Oral Disease Prevention Program to assess treatment needs and cost implications and to conduct research in oral health promotion. Adding to the stature of the NIDR efforts, the IADR Behavioral Sciences Group honored Cohen in 1987 by recognizing her with its first Distinguished Senior Scientist Award.[135]

By 1987 behavioral research remained as a small part of the NIDR budget. Funding increased only slightly in the 1983 to 1987 period. Behavioral research received 3.4 percent, or $2.3 million, of the 1983 NIDR budget, and 3.9 percent in 1987, amounting to $4.3 million. From 1983 to 1987 behavioral research accounted for 3.7 percent, or $18.3 million, of the total NIDR budget. Research into behavior and pain represented 46 percent of this amount and behavior and nonpain research 54 percent.

Most of the social and behavioral research supported by the NIDR between 1983 and 1987 was concentrated in three major areas:

- psychosocial and psychophysiological aspects of pain assessment, pain disorders, and related oral-motor behaviors ($7.8 million);

- behavioral and social factors influencing oral disease prevention ($2.5 million); and

- behavior of dental professionals and the dentist-patient interaction ($2.3 million).[136]

Commentary

A noteworthy aspect about the NIDR-sponsored research was its considerable diversity, a characteristic that resulted from several circumstances.

First, the government itself encouraged such a variety of work. Because Congress gave it responsibility for resolving dental health problems, the Institute became patron and promoter for much of the dental research in the nation. To carry out the congressional mandate, the Institute's directors gave wide latitude to intramural scientists in selecting investigative projects as long as those choices related to oral science. Their selections consequently involved the Institute in such specialties as dental genetics and pain studies.

In the extramural sector government actions outside the Institute's own jurisdiction also led to its assumption of additional research fields. Thus, the Institute increased support of restorative materials studies as a result of a shift of some of the financial responsibility from the National Bureau of Standards to the Institute. Later the Institute also included social and behavioral sciences in its intramural and extramural programs after another dental division in the Public Health Service relinquished those areas to NIDR.

The growth, finances, and multidisciplinary policy followed by the Institute in administering the extramural system also fostered diversity in research proposals. In the craniofacial anomalies program, for instance, the National Advisory Dental Research Council advocated multidisciplinary approaches to deal with that subject. The NADRC recommendation led to the first craniofacial anomalies center funded by the Institute.

The complexities of oral diseases, too, necessitated Institute backing of a variety of approaches. The course of the research on localized juvenile periodontitis exemplified the effectiveness of such a strategy. In that case epidemiological, basic, and clinical investigations complemented each other: the epidemiological survey indicated the prevalence of the disease; the basic research provided clinicians with techniques for studying it; and the clinical investigations clarified the nature of the condition and led to the development of effective treatment.

Further, the very position of the Institute as the nation's forerunner in the oral sciences led it to persuade other institutions to engage in new and/or less developed areas of research. For instance, because few dental schools initially offered courses in dental genetics and conducted little pain research, NIDR administrators successfully encouraged an expansion of these fields in the nation's dental schools.

Consequently, by supporting a variety of scientific, social science, and behavioral areas and disciplines in dental research, the Institute contributed toward better understanding, diagnosis, and treatment of such problems as periodontal diseases, craniofacial anomalies, and dental pain.

CHAPTER TEN

From the Past to the Future

Who controls the past controls the future. Who controls the present controls the past.

GEORGE ORWELL, *1984*

A product of the post-World War II era, the National Institute of Dental Research opened with a congressional mandate to work toward the eradication of dental diseases and malfunctions. The Institute got off to a strong start with its first major task of completing fluoridation research initiated by its predecessor unit. Those fluoridation study results helped revolutionize the practice of dentistry everywhere. Yet the Institute exerted influence in other areas of dentistry and science as well through its support of research within and outside the federal government. Since its inclusion in the American scientific community, the National Institute of Dental Research over forty years directed its activities toward the reduction of dental disease and stimulated the rise of dental research to improve general oral health. During the fortieth anniversary year NIDR and the nation's dental community commemorated these accomplishments with ceremonies at Grand Rapids, Michigan; Bethesda, Maryland; and Washington, D.C., and with exhibits at the National Library of Medicine; the NIH DeWitt Stetten, Jr., Museum of Medical Research; and the Smithsonian Institution Museum of American History.

Among the better known results of Institute intramural and extramural investigations during that period were the findings that:

- Fluoridated drinking water reduced dental decay.

- Dental caries was an infectious disease induced by bacteria, including *Streptococcus mutans*.

307

The staff of the National Institute of Dental Research in 1987.

Dr. Harald Löe, NIDR director, speaking during the "Thank You Grand Rapids" ceremony. Also taking part are (L to R) Dr. James B. Wyngaarden, director of NIH; Gerald R. Helmholdt, mayor of Grand Rapids; Dr. Willard B. VerMuelen, Grand Rapids dentist and former president of the West Michigan Dental Society; and Dr. Herschel S. Horowitz, fluoride researcher.

Dr. John S. Greenspan, president of the American Association for Dental Research.

Dr. William D. McHugh, President of the International Association for Dental Research.

(L to R) Dr. James A. Saddoris, president of the American Dental Association; Dr. Harald Löe, director of the National Institute of Dental Research; Dr. James B. Wyngaarden, Director of the National Institutes of Health.

NIDR ANNIVERSARY BANQUET MAY 25, 1988

(L to R) NIDR Director Dr. Harald Löe, American Dental Association, President Dr. James A. Saddoris, and Mr. Burton C. Borgelt, 1987-88 American Dental Trade Association chairman of the board, at the official opening of "Dental Science for Dental Health"—a joint exhibit of the NIDR and the Smithsonian, on display at the National Museum of American History during October and November 1988.

- Certain antibacterial substances could curtail periodontal diseases.

- Particular responses in the body's immune system occurred in progressive periodontal disease.

- A vaccine prevented herpes simplex virus type 1 in laboratory animals.

- Dental postoperative pain could be alleviated through use of certain drug combinations.

- Certain composite resins provided a more natural appearance than amalgams for filling primary molars.

These contributions affected dentistry positively and paved the way toward improved dental health around the world as well as in the United States.

International Impact

The NIDR emerged in a post-World War II period of international cooperation. Such an atmosphere, coupled with the growth of dental science, fostered the international collaboration that made possible the Institute's influence on world dentistry. The consequences were impressive.

For thousands of years dentistry concentrated on treatment of dental ailments; in the four decades of the NIDR's operation dentistry changed to an emphasis on prevention of disease. Along with the efforts of foreign and American dental scientists as well as organized dentistry, the Institute's efforts worked to raise the status of dental science. NIDR financial and moral support and scientific accomplishments guided and filled gaps in dental research and elevated the stature of dental science in the biomedical and behavioral science communities.

The Institute achieved renown for its work that led to fluoridation of public drinking water supplies to control tooth decay. Fluoridation triggered the major change in world dentistry to attention on prevention both in dental practice and in dental research. Scientifically proven effective and safe by the Institute, fluoridation proved to be the most effective and efficient method known for reducing dental caries. By operating the fluoridation studies, Dean, the NIDR's first director, conducted the most thorough epidemiological examinations ever made by the Public Health Service by the mid-twentieth century. After the studies confirmed a significant drop in tooth decay, Surgeon General William H. Stewart called fluoridation "one of the great disease prevention measures of all time."

So it happened that almost twenty years before Secretary of Health, Education and Welfare Joseph A. Califano established prevention as the nation's 1970s and 1980s health objectives, the Institute implemented its own policy of promoting disease prevention. By 1982 studies in nine western countries showed that in two decades the prevalence of tooth decay had decreased as much as 30 to 50 percent. These independently produced studies generally agreed on the reduction, which appeared sharpest in the 1970s. Analysts attributed the change to the extension of fluoride availability in several forms— including drinking water, dentifrices, topical application, and mouthrinses—to most of the western nations, especially in the decade of the 1970s.[1]

More than two dozen countries had installed fluoridated public drinking water supplies by 1986. Countless spin-offs emerged from the discovery that fluoridated water could arrest dental decay. Private industry developed means of using fluorides in other forms such as dentifrices; by 1986 90 percent of all toothpastes contained fluoride.[2]

Scientific progress fostered international cooperation in important ways. NIDR scientists benefited from advances by foreign scientists in such areas as cleft palate treatment and administration of anesthesia. In turn, research sponsored in the United States by the Institute affected worldwide dental practice. Institute testing of the high-speed drill, for instance, indicated that tooth pulp could withstand the rapid drilling but that the use of cooling materials was necessary to counter the heat. NIDR-supported scientists developed more cosmetically pleasing composite resins for filling primary molars, better cements, improved bonding materials, and tooth sealants containing fluoride that gave teeth 100 percent protection from decay. Clinical research by Institute and non-Institute supported scientists demonstrated the primary roles of oral hygiene in curtailing periodontal diseases. NIDR financing of research on cleft palate, for instance, resulted in the development of more effective surgical techniques and the revelation that corrective surgery in infancy was the most effective approach.

Achievements in basic and clinical research likewise strengthened ties between dental scientists in the United States and other countries. In the 1950s European work in dental research and with gnotobiotic animals helped Institute scientists conduct significant experiments on the involvement of bacteria in periodontal disease and dental caries. In turn, Institute-sponsored inquiries inspired foreign scientists to probe in certain areas. Some examples included the *Streptococcus mutans* investigations on dental caries and electron microscopy studies of tooth structure that led foreign researchers and other American scientists to take up such work. In another case the NIDR's collagen chemistry effort spread from the Institute to Germany, Belgium, and England.

The epidemiological arm, responsible for the fluoridation discovery, served especially as a goodwill symbol for the United States. Institute scientists identified dental disease and proposed some solutions to health officials in other countries. Within a decade of its establishment the Institute's epidemiologists, headed by Dr. Albert L. Russell, were collaborating with the WHO by surveying the inci-

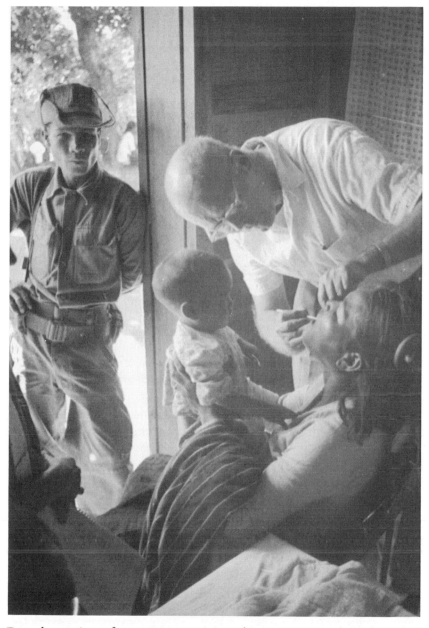

Dental examiners from NIDR participated in nutrition studies where they collected data on the relation between diet and oral diseases in several foreign countries, including Vietnam in 1960.

dence of dental disease in North America and South America, Europe, Southeast Asia, and the Middle East. Moreover, Russell's teams examined the relationship of nutrition to dental health. In the process, Russell connected sugar-sucking habits among some groups with excessive tooth decay and loss. To reduce dental caries among the young, Russell recommended fluoridating public drinking water supplies.[3]

The NIDR itself gave encouragement to dental research at home and abroad through training and research funding. With the establishment in 1968 of the John E. Fogarty International Center for Advanced Study in the Health Sciences, the National Institutes of Health increased emphasis on international health sciences cooperation.[4] Created as a memorial to the late congressman, a champion of health research and the dental institute, the Fogarty Center grew along with a discernible increase in international activities undertaken by the dental institute. The Fogarty Center support enabled foreign scientists to work in the United States and researchers from the United States to conduct studies abroad in their specialized fields.

Expansion in international cooperation by the Institute itself occurred primarily through research support mechanisms. As a result of visiting scientist programs from 1949 through 1986 over three hundred foreign dental scientists spent a year or more at the NIDR laboratories in Bethesda. Drs. Poul O. Pedersen and Marie Ussing (later Nylen) were among the earliest participants. The visiting scientist program grew from an average of five per year from 1962 to 1972, to twelve per year from 1973 to 1978, to thirty-seven per year from 1979 through 1985. Fifty-eight foreign scientists worked in the Institute laboratories during the 1987 fiscal year.

Worldwide, the NIDR led all other acknowledged sources of support for dental research from Fiscal Years 1976 through 1980. The Institute's extramural program supported 69 percent of all the dental research projects listed in the Smithsonian Science Information Exchange (SSIE). Because not all private industry sources cooperated with the survey compilers, the reports might not have accurately reflected the contribution of private industry to dental research. Nevertheless, during the same period United States government agencies, foundations, universities, and private industry sponsored 91 percent of the projects reported.[5]

The Institute also helped to foster dental research on an international scale. Annually, NIDR mailed its *Abstracts from NIDR Scientists* to over 150 foreign investigators. From Fiscal Years 1970 through 1980 it supported the annual publication of dental research projects by the SSIE. The first two years covered the United States and Canada; the reports for Fiscal Years 1973 through 1975 added Great Britain, and the lists for Fiscal Years 1976 through 1980 expanded by including other countries reporting dental research. After 1981 the SSIE was discontinued because of budget cuts—thus curtailing the NIDR's ability to monitor easily international dental science literature through this medium.

Along with these efforts the NIDR pursued the policy of encouraging international collaboration. From 1978 on, for example, Institute scientists collaborated with researchers at such institutions as the Max Planck Institute in Munich and the Tokyo Medical and Dental University. In cooperation with other American and foreign agencies, the NIDR Microbial Systematics Section worked to establish a worldwide data bank on human oral microbiota in 1981. Also during the 1980s the NIDR underwrote an annual survey begun in Norway in 1969 and in Sri Lanka in 1970 to assess progression of periodontal disease among a group of tea laborers. Institute Director Löe, who started the study at the The Royal Dental College, Aarhus, Denmark, continued to monitor the project after arriving at the Institute.

The WHO also recognized the pivotal role of the NIDR in international dental research. In 1980 the WHO designated the NIDR as a WHO Collaborating Center for Research in the Prevention of Dental Caries and Periodontal Diseases. Seven years later the WHO chose the Institute as the WHO Collaborating Center for Epidemiology, Prevention and Treatment of Oral Diseases and Conditions.[6]

Meanwhile, the NIDR supported a variety of international studies and conferences. The Institute's assistant director for international health, Dr. Lois Cohen, codirected a WHO collaborative study on dental manpower systems in relation to oral health status in ten nations; that work was completed in 1985. A new study of both industrialized and middle-income developing nations was launched with WHO in 1986 and 1987. It examined the relative contributions of lifestyle, environmental, and dental services system factors on oral health. The NIDR assisted the WHO and the IADR in planning a conference in Lagos, Nigeria, in 1982 on promoting a WHO International Collaborative Center for Dental Research and Oral Health in

Africa. The center was officially established in Nigeria in 1987.[7]

Moreover, the Institute provided leadership to international scientific organizations. The IADR elected six NIDR officials, including each director, as presidents. In 1981 that association installed as its first woman president Dr. Marie Nylen, also the Institute's first woman director of a laboratory and of both the intramural and extramural programs. In addition, Institute directors served as members of the WHO's Oral Health Research Advisory Group and the FDI's Commission on Oral Research and Epidemiology.[8]

In the 1980s the Institute continued to promote the free exchange of scientific information through visits of scientists between the United States and other countries and through support of international meetings and activities. In Fiscal Year 1987, for example, the NIDR sent 111 staff scientists to participate in seventy-five international meetings in nineteen countries. The Institute also supported four foreign research grants and one foreign contract that year. During that same period NIDR sponsored special projects with Mexico, India, and Italy as well as with the WHO, the FDI, the IADR, the ADA, and other organizations committed to international oral health collaboration.

The cost of the NIDR's international activities was small when compared to the goodwill and health improvements that followed. As budget examinations showed, a miniscule amount of the Institute's budgets funded its international activities. Grants to foreign scientists from 1979 to 1983, for instance, amounted to less than 1 percent of the Institute's budget, and expenses for all Institute international activities for the 1987 fiscal year took up less than 2 percent of the Institute's budget.[9] No monetary value, of course, could be assigned to the obvious benefits received by both the United States and other nations involved in such exchanges.

National Impact

When Secretary of Health and Human Services Margaret Heckler visited the National Institutes of Health in 1983, she questioned the continuation of dental research there because of the successful control of tooth decay. Heckler's remarks sent shock waves rippling through the dental science community. An alarmed Dr. John Hein, director of the Forsyth Dental Center in Boston, assured Heckler that dental diseases remained widespread throughout the world. Heckler, of course, did not abolish the Institute, but her suggestion revealed just how much change had occurred in dental health in the nation since the Institute's establishment.[10]

CHANGES IN THE NATION'S DENTAL HEALTH, 1960-1980

Indeed, surveys conducted in the 1960s, the 1970s, and 1979-1980 had indicated that the largest reductions by 1980 in children's tooth decay had occurred in the decade of the 1970s. During that period the NIDR had conducted the National Caries Program's intensive campaign to rid society of dental caries, particularly through the use of fluorides for the six- through seventeen-year-olds in the nation. Institute analysts estimated that the decrease in tooth decay had saved a total of some $2 billion in the nation's dental bill in 1981 alone.[11]

Institute scientists, perhaps too modestly, had refrained from taking credit for this progress. Nevertheless, the American dental science community undoubtedly played a major role in bringing about the changes. Such improvements emerged concurrent with scientific advances funded principally by the Institute and encouraged publicly by the ADA and the AADR, both of which lobbied consistently for NIDR's budgets. Obviously, fluoridated drinking water and fluoridated products, including toothpastes, tablets, and mouthrinses, especially contributed toward healthier teeth in children. Except for the promotion of dental hygiene and possibly increased use of antibiotics in childhood, no other factor, including any alteration of national eating habits, seemed to figure in the reduction of new dental caries. Despite widespread publicizing by the NIDR and health-conscious organizations that certain carbohydrates, notably refined sugar, contributed toward tooth decay, Institute researchers could find no evidence of any decrease in sugar consumption per capita during the period.[12]

THE COURSE OF DENTAL RESEARCH

Congressmen and ADA officials did envision such practical results when they created the Institute after learning that the appalling dental conditions of World War II recruits ranked as the number one cause for service rejection. Of equal importance, Congress and the ADA recognized the necessities of strengthening dental research manpower and assuring support for fundamental and applied studies to improve dental health.

One of the first challenges was to build a corps of dental science researchers in the United States to undertake these essential investigations. Leaders in dental research, such as Drs. Joseph Volker, George Paffenbarger, and H. Trendley Dean, provided evidence of the dearth of dental scientists at the Institute's inception. The dental research grant situation initially presented a sad picture as well. Of the 1,042 new research grants awarded by the National Institutes of Health in 1948, only seven went to dental scientists. In 1948 a total of eighteen institutions in the United States, not all of them with dental schools, conducted dental research with NIH funding. Yet American membership in the IADR also suggested that most of the world's dental scientists lived in the United States. In 1948 the IADR listed 507 United States members among its membership of 610.

In 1985 an NIDR survey showed the impact of its training support on dental research manpower in the United States. From the start of Institute training grants in 1957 through Fiscal Year 1982, almost 2,200 individuals had received some postdoctoral training support from the Institute. That assistance influenced the composition and activities of the nation's dental schools. Former Institute trainees made up 9.5 percent of the 4,587 full-time faculty in the fifty-seven United States dental schools for the 1983-1984 school year. The survey indicated that the greater proportion of faculty members spending at least 20 percent of their time in research were former Institute-supported trainees. Those former trainees with doctor of philosophy degrees tended to engage more in research than those with master's or dental degrees alone.[13]

The growth of extramural funding and those changes in dental school faculties undoubtedly stimulated the rise in dental research and numbers of investigators in the four decades. Extramural dental research grants increased by a factor of fifty-seven and the number of American dental scientists grew at least sevenfold. In 1985 the Institute awarded 398 dental research grants, or over 2 percent of the research projects granted that year by the National Institutes of Health. Simultaneously, the American membership in the IADR increased by a factor of eight from the 507 members of 1948 when it reached 4,260 by 1986, or almost 59 percent of the association membership. Along with that increase in dental researchers, the number of institutions in the United States that received extramural funds for dental research took a gigantic leap from 18 in 1948 to 181 in Fiscal Year 1986.[14] Clearly, the Institute succeeded in boosting both the amount of dental research and the numbers of dental researchers during its first four decades of operation.

During the same period the Institute extramural program funded a substantial portion of dental research undertaken in the United States. (Again, an approximate percentage of Institute support was difficult to determine because complete private industry expenditures were not available. Nevertheless, certain studies backed up the impression that NIDR appropriations made up a major share of dental research support.) For Fiscal Year 1950, for example, the Institute provided approximately 60 percent of dental research grants for extramural investigators; other government departments added another 30 percent, and private foundations and national organizations contributed about 10 percent. The total of almost $314,000 spent that year contrasted with $1.5 million of the Institute's direct operations budget that included the costs of both government intramural research and administration of extramural grants. By Fiscal Year 1980 the NIDR supported almost 66 percent of all reported dental research projects sponsored by United States sources.[15]

From the 1940s through the 1980s the emphasis shifted in dental research. In the extramural program for the first three years in which NIH dental research grants were awarded, 37 percent went for caries, fluoride, and restorative materials; 10 percent each for periodontal disease and nutrition; and 8 percent for craniofacial anomalies. With the exception of restorative materials, a National Bureau of Standards area, the intramural research of the Institute reflected a similar pattern: two-thirds of the 1948 publications concerned dental caries, fluorides, and tooth enamel, and the rest dealt with nutrition, bacteriology, and saliva.

By Fiscal Year 1985 extramural research showed drastic changes. Though it had been barely studied in the 1940s, periodontal and soft tissue disease research commanded 34 percent of the extramural funding in Fiscal Year 1985—the largest share. Caries and restorative material studies received 28 percent; 27 percent went to craniofacial development, pain, and behavioral science research.

The intramural program publications for Fiscal Year 1985 bore little resemblance to the dozen scientific articles on the 1948 list; some 180 articles dealt primarily with basic and clinical research in such areas as microbiology and immunology, developmental biology and anomalies, pain, oral medicine, mineralized tissue and bone, and the social sciences. Mineralized tissue and bone were subjects of almost 22 percent of the intramural papers that year.[16]

For all research programs, including intramural and extramural, NIDR monetary obligations for 1981 through 1987 indicated both a change in emphasis and a considerable broadening of the scope of dental research since the 1940s. Whereas dental caries had acquired the most intramural and extramural attention in the 1940s, in the 1980s periodontal diseases, with 20.9 percent of the NIDR obligations, led the research categories. For this fourth NIDR decade, dental caries investigations followed with 19.3 percent and congenital craniofacial anomalies with 11.2 percent. Nutrition, which had received 10 percent of the 1940s extramural grants, was the lowest of fourteen research areas in the 1980s, with less than 1 percent of all NIDR research obligations. Such topics as tooth implants, replants, and transplants, acquired craniofacial defects; behavioral studies; and pain, either absent or rarely mentioned in the 1940s, ranked among the top twelve subjects for NIDR obligations during the 1980s. (See chart "Distribution of NIDR Obligations by Research Area.") Clearly, in the forty-year interim both the revolutions in science, especially in molecular biology, and the changes in Americans' dental health altered the kind of extramural and intramural research supported by the Institute.

The most notable change in dental research since 1948 was the move toward more basic studies, a shift that would have warmed the hearts of such early advocates as Gies and Dean. The two individuals most responsible for that transformation at the Institute were Dean, the dreamer and architect of a basic research institute for dentistry, and Kreshover, the builder who as scientific director and as director made Dean's concept a reality. The transition was clearly evident in the types of journals publishing articles by NIDR scientists. Of approximately eighty papers by Institute researchers published in nongovernment journals between 1948 and 1953, over 64 percent appeared in dental publications and 36 percent in biomedical science

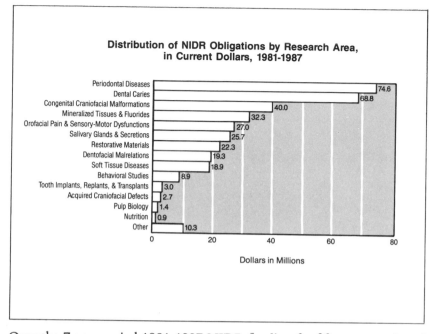

**Distribution of NIDR Obligations by Research Area,
in Current Dollars, 1981-1987**

Periodontal Diseases — 74.6
Dental Caries — 68.8
Congenital Craniofacial Malformations — 40.0
Mineralized Tissues & Fluorides — 32.3
Orofacial Pain & Sensory-Motor Dysfunctions — 27.0
Salivary Glands & Secretions — 25.7
Restorative Materials — 22.3
Dentofacial Malrelations — 19.3
Soft Tissue Diseases — 18.9
Behavioral Studies — 8.9
Tooth Implants, Replants, & Transplants — 3.0
Acquired Craniofacial Defects — 2.7
Pulp Biology — 1.4
Nutrition — 0.9
Other — 10.3

Dollars in Millions

Over the 7-year period 1981-1987 NIDR funding for fifteen categories of research totaled $356 million. Twenty-one percent of the total, $74.6 million, was obligated for research related to periodontal diseases, followed closely by caries research (19.3 percent, or $68.8 million). Both the relative share of research funds and the categories of research can be expected to change in the decades ahead in light of new challenges (e.g., AIDS research) and opportunities (e.g., biotechnology; oral health promotion/disease prevention research).

journals. By 1970 almost a complete reversal took place. That year a distinct shift occurred with 68 percent of the intramural papers in nondental publications, such as the *Journal of Biological Chemistry*, and 32 percent in dental journals. That trend continued through 1974. Following the 1974 reorganization of the Institute, the proportion of intramural articles in nondental journals in comparison to dental periodicals again rose in 1975. By 1978 extramural scientists published 77 percent of their papers in biomedical and pure science journals, a percentage that continued through 1984.[17]

By the 1970s the same preference for nondental science subjects prevailed generally for all NIDR-supported research published by intramural scientists and extramural grantees. Although limited information was available, NIH data bases furnished sufficient data to show the trends in published studies in which NIDR funded the research. The BID-MEDLINE, the computerized data base for NIH, for example, covered only 6 dental and about 240 core biomedical journals for the 1973 to 1984 period, but the publications included were the most influential. While not reflecting the complete output of NIDR-supported articles because so few dental journals appeared in the data base, the BID-MEDLINE identified approximately 6,000 intramural and extramural scientists' papers published from 1973 to 1984. Of that total, approximately 5,000 articles represented dental science research that was solely extramural; almost 650 came from intramural laboratories, and 410 resulted from collaboration between intramural and extramural researchers. A computer analysis of the 6,000 reports by Computer Horizons, Incorporated showed that 33 percent dealt with dental science and 66 percent with other biomedical sciences, with biochemistry and molecular biology as the leading fields.

The NIH-MEDLINE, another data base, provided enough data for the Computer Horizons analysts to show a difference in general scientific preference between intramural and extramural researchers. The NIH-MEDLINE represented 25 dental journals and approximately 1,200 biomedical science journals from 1981 to 1984 and reported on more than 3,400 published papers produced by NIDR-supported intramural and extramural scientists during that period. This data base indicated that more scientists in the intramural than extramural programs published principally on nondental topics. From 1981 through 1984 over 66 percent of the papers by extramural researchers concerned nondental topics in comparison to some 75 percent of the articles by intramural scientists.[18]

Yet the Institute gave strong support to papers accepted by the world's most prestigious dental journals. In a separate compilation from the NIH-MEDLINE that covered only articles acknowledging support, statistics for 1985 showed that the Institute led all other sources in funding research for such papers in the twenty-five leading English-language dental science journals. Of the 425 articles in the list published by United States institutions in the field of dental science, the NIDR was the sole financier of the research for 203 of those papers and shared support for the investigations in 50 other publications. A breakdown by percentage of funders of the research for those articles gave a minimum estimate and suggested the major sources of dental research funding in the United States for the 1980s (the total exceeded 100 percent because more than one institution frequently supported the research for an article):

National Institute of Dental Research	60
Other National Institutes of Health units	14
Other government agencies	12
Foundations	12
Universities	11
Private industry	10
Miscellaneous sources	6[19]

As the publication records indicated, from the 1940s to the 1980s dental science rose in scope and stature in the biomedical science community. The NIDR played a primary role in that ascent. From a staff of less than 50 with expertise in half a dozen fields in 1948, the Institute grew by 1982 to 430 with specialties in more than a dozen fields. Further, the ultimate approval for construction of Building 30, the Institute's main laboratory building, fostered the upsurge in such research by providing the space and facilities that the Institute needed to broaden its research. Other dental research facilities outside the NIH expanded their activities concurrently. With the multidisciplinary centers established in the late 1960s to attract scientists to dental research, a number of experts in a variety of fields entered into dental scientific investigations for the first time—so many that a 1977 RAND corporation study of such centers considered the NIDR's program one of the more successful at the NIH.[20]

In these four decades NIDR and NIDR-supported scientists also gained recognition from their biomedical and dental science peers. In 1972, for instance, over a dozen of the Institute's scientists served on the editorial boards of nine biomedical and six dental journals. National and international scientific organizations recognized over two dozen of the Institute's scientists with awards for their research between 1948 and 1988. Nine of those scientists received honors from institutions unconnected with the dental community. Non-NIDR scientists with extramural support also won prizes for their research. In 1985 the ADA presented its first Gold Medal Award for Excellence in Dental Research to one of them, Dr. Irwin Mandel, an expert in saliva research and professor at the Columbia University School of Dentistry.[21]

Institute administrators also recognized the importance of the relationship of the social and behavioral sciences to oral health. Consequently, the addition of those disciplines in the 1970s integrated those fields with biomedical research so that all factors could be considered to improve the nation's oral health care.

Despite the successes and peer recognition, a dark side emerged in dental research. The maintenance of an adequate researcher pool appeared in jeopardy, primarily because of economic reasons. Other occupations, particularly in business, led more college graduates to go into more lucrative occupations than dentistry and dental research by the 1980s. Fluoridation and improved oral health care had changed dental practice, particularly for juveniles, from restorative to the less profitable preventive dentistry. The results appeared in the declining numbers of dental school applicants and the consequent closure of several dental schools in the 1980s. In addition, practicing dentists could still earn considerably more than dental researchers. Inadequate government funding of oral health care and health professions education during this time undoubtedly played its part as well.

The NIDR's extramural budget did not keep pace with inflation in the 1970s and 1980s. While most of the institutes in the NIH showed growth concurrent with inflation from Fiscal Year 1977 to Fiscal Year 1986, the Institute was one of three that fell behind in extramural funding. In turn, the increases in extramural grant awards ranged from 34 to 213 percent for nine institutes, but the NIDR experienced the next to lowest growth of 10 percent.

Moreover, the Institute's training support from 1972 to 1982 dropped from 22 percent to 7 percent of its extramural budget. The Institute of Medicine of the National Academy of Sciences observed that there was a need for dental clinical researchers but a significant shortage of them in the nation in the 1980s. Advances in dental science and changes in dental practice necessitated a significant increase in dental school faculty members experienced in dental research. The NIDR was virtually the only source of financial support for such academic training. To attract candidates, NIDR introduced new career programs, such as the Dentist Scientist Award, after 1984.[22]

Several explanations come to mind for such a lag in the Institute's extramural research support: (1) the shift that Dr. Charles A. McCallum, vice president for health affairs and director of the University of Alabama Medical Center, traced back to the late 1960s of a federal preference for patient care over education and research; (2) the knowledge that dental research did not involve life-or-death matters; and (3) the realization that dental research in the twentieth century had made such great strides in improving public dental health.[23] Nevertheless, dental research was about to take some new turns in the 1980s as Institute scientists planned for the future.

Meeting the Challenges of the 1980s

The oral health problems and increasing average age level of American society had changed over the four decades since 1948. If the Institute was to survive as a solid research organization, it had to adapt to changing times and readjust its priorities to cope with the years ahead.

THE LONG-RANGE RESEARCH PLAN

To organize future NIDR activities, the National Affairs Committee of the AADR urged Dr. David B. Scott to initiate the Institute's long-range research plan for the 1980s. The planning was carried out under Löe. Subsequently, over one hundred scientists from outside the Institute, the members of the NADRC, and the Institute's staff spent almost three years developing the plan. Representatives of the AADR, the IADR, the ADA, and the NADRC sat on a coordinating committee that prepared the plan's structure. This second long-range research plan produced by the NIDR (the first occurred in the 1970s under Director Kreshover) appeared in 1983 as *Challenges for the Eighties. National Institute of Dental Research Long-Range Research Plan FY 1985-89.* The plan explained the state of the science for each major dental condition category and proposed research strategies for acquiring understanding of and solutions to oral diseases and disorders. *Challenges* called for collaboration and cooperation between the

NIDR and other institutions, both public and private. To achieve the plan's goals, the Institute required adequate funding for basic, applied, and clinical research and the training of dental researchers for the future.[24]

Challenges planners anticipated and gauged both the needs and potentials in dental research for the 1980s. Basic research took up two-thirds of all the plan's proposed research objectives, and applied research was covered in another one-quarter of the goals. Planners had in mind projects such as controlled clinical trials of new preventive approaches or treatments and new drug or instrumentation development.[25]

Priorities in the plan reflected most of the major oral problems of the 1980s—taking into account the growing concern for the dental health of older citizens. The plan stressed prevention for both dental caries and periodontal disease and the need to continue the quests for the perfect filling, adhesive, and other restorative materials. The planners emphasized the importance of improving methods of mechanical and chemotherapeutic plaque control and producing a safe, effective vaccine for herpes simplex. (Before the *Challenges* plan was published, Notkins of NIDR and Moss of NIAID developed a herpes simplex vaccine. See pages 255-56.) Further, as the plan also pointed out, other dental problems, such as disfiguring facial defects like cleft palate, remained and required a combination of fundamental and clinical research.[26]

The plan took up special areas of concern as well, including the lack of current epidemiological data on major oral health problems. *Challenges* planners thought it necessary to measure the prevalences of and social factors involved in periodontal diseases, dental caries, and craniofacial anomalies to help develop and test hypotheses, guide research planning, and establish bases for monitoring change.

In addition, *Challenges* committees recognized the significance of behavior in preventing oral diseases. Thus, the planners asked for investigations into behavioral factors affecting both dissemination and acceptance of preventive methods.[27]

RAMIFICATIONS OF THE PLAN FOR THE 1980s

Concurrent with developing this plan for the future, the NIDR administrators assumed responsibilities for other new ventures. One of the more important ones addressed the problems of an aging population in the nation. Beginning in 1981 under Scott and continuing under his acting successor, Dr. John F. Goggins, the Institute negotiated with the National Institute on Aging (NIA) for joint support of problems affecting the elderly. The Institute leadership strengthened attention on geriatrics by appointing Dr. Bruce Baum, who had been with the NIA, as the new clinical director in 1983. In 1984 the cooperation extended to the Veterans Administration (VA) when Director Löe started serving as a consultant on dental care for VA beneficiaries.[28]

The NIDR also established ties with nongovernment groups in the 1980s. In February 1985 the Institute held a special two-day conference at NIH with over 160 deans and other senior officials from virtually every dental school in the United States and Canada to foster dental research in those establishments. The NIDR officials scheduled the meeting to enhance the academic community's understanding of Institute programs and priorities and to increase NIDR appreciation of academic problems. The following year the Institute formed a task force to consider Institute relations with private industry. At a meeting called by the NIDR in May 1986, Institute scientists discussed the potential for collaborative efforts with representatives from the private sector.[29]

Challenges for the Eighties confronted the issue of maintaining an adequate dental researcher pool as well. The decline of dental researcher trainees during the 1970s matched a similar trend among physicians choosing research studies. Upon his assumption of the NIDR's directorship, Löe, who had just left a position as a dental school dean, vowed to turn the trend upward for the number of dentists seeking careers in clinical and basic research. The Institute soon introduced the Dentist Scientist Award in 1984 to encourage such training in basic and clinical research. Also concerned about the situation, the Institute of Medicine of the National Academy of Sciences predicted that from 1985 through 1990 the nation's dental schools would need annually at least 210 new full-time clinical scientists. To attain such an objective, the NIDR would have to support between 320 and 400 postdoctoral trainees per year. NIDR records showed that the main trainee support programs enrolled from 157 to 184 trainees between the 1981 and 1985 fiscal years. Consequently, to maintain viable dental research in the future, the NIDR, sole source for supporting such trainees, sought to obtain additional training funds and inaugurated the Dentist Scientist Institutional Award and the Physician Scientist Award for Dentists.[30]

Much of the NIDR intramural and extramural work, especially the basic research, already complied with the long-range plan published in *Challenges*. Envisioned by the planners, new developments, including those with potential for the future, emerged while the plan was in formulation as well as after *Challenges* was issued.

Imaginative devices for restorative dental treatment resulted from progress in computer technology. By 1986 at the University of Minnesota School of Dentistry, for instance, Drs. William Douglas and Ralph DeLong, NIDR grantees, had produced a computerized mechanical mouth for research purposes. Fitted with human teeth, this "mighty mouth" physically simulated both the chewing activities and the environment of a human mouth. "Mighty mouth" could demonstrate in a few weeks the effects of several years of wear on dental materials. This device thus allowed researchers to conduct faster, less expensive testing of dental materials.[31]

The following year a Massachusetts firm started designing a computerized system to produce precise restorations. NIDR supported this project with a small business innovation grant. Intended to fit on a table top in a dental office, this device captured a three-dimensional geometric profile of a single tooth and provided a suitable color for restorations such as crowns.[32]

Diagnostic researchers also took advantage of progress in computerized tomography (CT), the technique of X ray reconstruction of a selected plane in the body. By the mid-1980s computer advances enabled Dr. Richard L. Webber, chief of the NIDR Diagnostic Systems Branch, and his team to extend CT theory to the point of modeling a medical CAT (computerized axial tomography) scan. Webber's system demonstrated the integration of sophisticated data sampling and three-dimensional image interpretation techniques to identify early signs of periodontal and soft tissue diseases. The same system was shown to be useful for comparing dental X ray images exposed at different times on a selected dental region of the mouth. Moreover, the system could reduce the radiation exposure to less than that received in an ordinary dental radiograph. Whereas conventional dental X ray pictures could show only two dimensions and thus could miss minute changes occurring in the third dimension of dental tissue, this prototype "tomosynthetic" system could reveal dental problems undetected with standard equipment. To be implemented fully, this system required a new kind of X ray source that could be steered by computer, a special X ray detector that could produce signals intelligible to a computer, and more than $1 million for fabrication expenses. With such technology within the state of the art but limited by the NIDR budgets, the Institute shared the costs of technical development for the "tomosynthetic" dental X ray system with the National Institute of Standards and Technology, formerly the NBS.

This modest progress by the federal government was supplemented by less ambitious alternatives in the private sector. In 1988 private industry developed a closed circuit television system to facilitate the use of conventional dental X ray components in computerized dental radiography.[33]

As *Challenges* also anticipated, in the 1980s NIDR researchers and grantees continued research on both antibacterial agents and vaccines. Several investigators, including Dr. Dale Mirth of NIDR, sought to improve administration of tetracycline, an antibiotic frequently prescribed by dentists to treat periodontal diseases. In 1986 Mirth designed and started laboratory testing of a controlled-release tetracycline pellet that could be fitted in the mouth. The following year researchers at the University of Texas Health Science Center in San Antonio observed an immune response in animals injected with a vaccine that could neutralize bacteria contributing to periodontal disease. In 1988 this vaccine was in the laboratory stage of research. Meanwhile, Dr. Lorne Golub, a grantee at the State University of New York at Stony Brook, synthesized a new tetracycline analogue, chemically modified tetracycline (CMT), that inhibited the collagen-destroying enzyme, collagenase. Under clinical and laboratory study in 1988, CMT had the added virtue of lacking the properties that could induce bacterial resistance to the antibiotic.[34]

Further, NIDR implemented the special area recommendations of the long-range plan. For the behavioral sciences NIDR administrators added social scientists to the intramural staff and supported appropriate research in the extramural program to improve self-care and disease prevention. In 1987 grantees engaged in a variety of behavioral research projects concerned with preventing dental disease. With regard to epidemiology, before the Institute celebrated its fortieth anniversary in 1988, NIDR had completed major epidemiological studies that had been proposed in *Challenges*.[35]

The National Dental Health Surveys, 1985-1987

In fulfilling an important recommendation in the long-range research plan for the 1980s, NIDR directed two nationwide dental health surveys, one for adults and the other for children. The surveys were initiated to provide bases for research, assess the state of dental health in the nation, and identify areas where research was needed. In both projects the Institute trained the dentist examiners to set standards for descriptions of conditions in the reports.[36]

The first study, the National Survey of Oral Health of Employed Adults and Older Americans, was the most comprehensive of its kind yet done. The collection of information took a year and ended in March 1986. In addition to seeking data on the state and care of adult dental health in the nation, the NIDR Epidemiology and Oral Disease Prevention Program staff designed the study also to determine the prevalences of coronal and root surface caries and periodontal destruction, to detect changes in the future by geographic region, and to identify differences within five-year age intervals.

To obtain information on the nation's approximately 100 million employed adults and 4 million elderly, NIDR specialists selected representative samples from seven geographic regions in the contiguous forty-eight states. Subsequently, the project's teams performed oral examinations of 15,132 employed persons aged eighteen to sixty-four at eight hundred business establishments and 5,686 individuals over age sixty-five enrolled at two hundred senior citizen centers.[37]

The most striking result of the adult survey was the finding that, compared to statistics from earlier surveys, toothlessness had greatly decreased in employed adults below sixty-five years of age. In a 1960-1962 survey of adults in the same age group 14 percent were edentulous (toothless), but in the 1985-1986 survey only 4 percent of the employed adults examined had no teeth. Yet the 1986 study also showed that toothlessness continued to be a major problem for those over sixty-five years of age, with 41 percent missing all their teeth and only 2 percent retaining all twenty-eight teeth (third molars were not counted in the survey). Nevertheless, even the latter finding indicated progress over the 1960-1962 period when surveyors determined that 54.8 percent of those over sixty-five were edentulous.

While the survey recorded little difference among age groups with respect to coronal caries, the examinations also revealed that over 92

NIDR conducted a National Survey of Adult Dental Health between February 1985 and April 1986. This participant receives an oral exam in a mobile dental examination unit.

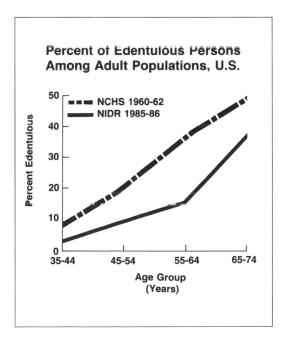

A comparison of two national surveys of adult oral health reveals a gradual and significant decrease in edentulousness at every age interval over the past twenty-five years. Sources: NCHS Series 11, No. 223, 1981, and NIH Pub. No. 87-2868.

percent of the coronal cavities had been filled. That result caused the NIDR compilers to note that both the employed and senior groups appeared to have "a very high level of restorative care for coronal caries."

Conversely, root caries turned out to be a significant problem for the elderly. Measured nationally for the first time in 1985 to 1986, root caries affected 63 percent of the senior subjects and 21 percent of the employed in the survey. In only about half of these cases had lesions been restored.

Moreover, the 1985-1986 adult survey identified periodontal diseases as prevalent among both groups but showed this family of illnesses inflicting more extensive damage with advancing age. Over three-quarters of the survey subjects exhibited some form of periodontal disease. More than 50 percent of the employed adults and 86 percent of the older group had at least one site with gingival recession. Meanwhile, more severe periodontal destruction appeared in 24 percent of the younger and 68 percent of the older participants.[38]

In 1986 and 1987 NIDR directed another survey of approximately forty thousand students aged five to seventeen throughout the United States. The NIDR staff selected sample populations to represent close to 43 million of the nation's schoolchildren.[39]

Released in 1988, this survey's results showed a dramatic decline in decay among United States schoolchildren over childhood dental caries observed in the previous decade. Examiners found no decay in the permanent teeth of 49.9 percent; in the 1979-1980 study 36.6 percent had been free of dental caries; and in the 1970s only an estimated 28 percent had no cavities. Even those youngsters in the 1986-1987 survey with decay showed fewer cavities in permanent teeth than children examined in 1979 and 1980. The earlier study found that each youth with dental caries averaged almost 5 decayed, missing, or filled surfaces out of a possible 128 surfaces on a full set of permanent teeth. This average dropped to only 3 decayed, missing, or filled tooth surfaces out of a maximum of 128 surfaces available per child for the 1986-1987 subjects.

The 1986-1987 survey led NIDR experts to conclude that decay was vanishing on the smooth surfaces of the teeth and on the surfaces between adjoining teeth. Between 1980 and 1987 the prevalence of caries decreased 32 percent on exposed smooth surfaces and on chewing surfaces of teeth and 54 percent on surfaces between teeth.

Percent of Children Caries-Free in Two National Surveys

Age	1979-80	1986-87
5	95.4	97.3
6	89.7	94.4
7	76.5	84.2
8	58.6	75.0
9	50.6	65.5
10	37.9	55.7
11	33.7	45.0
12	26.9	41.7
13	21.1	34.0
14	19.6	27.7
15	14.9	21.8
16	11.8	20.0
17	10.7	15.6
All Ages	**36.6**	**49.9**

Evidence that one of two children is caries-free comes from the National Survey of Oral Health in US Schoolchildren: 1986-1987, a follow-up to a similar survey conducted in 1979-1980. The new study reports that children have 36 percent less dental caries now than at the beginning of the decade. Source: NIH Pub. No. 82-2245, 1981.

Like the adult survey, the 1986-1987 study showed a high percentage of dental care among the participants. Examiners found that the group of youngsters with decayed, missing, or filled teeth had 82 percent of the cavities filled, 13 percent of the teeth decayed, and 4 percent of the teeth missing.[40]

Both the adult and juvenile surveys of the middle 1980s fulfilled the objectives of assessing progress and of suggesting areas for research. The studies revealed a continuation of trends in the United States toward better dental health and care of teeth, especially in the control of tooth decay on smooth surfaces and surfaces between teeth. At the same time results of the surveys supported shifts in dental

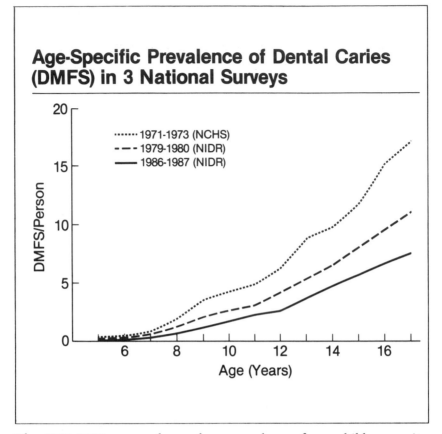

Age-Specific Prevalence of Dental Caries (DMFS) in 3 National Surveys

The 1986-1987 survey shows that not only are fewer children getting cavities today, but those who do are getting less. In 1980 children had an average of almost five decayed, missing, and filled surfaces (DMFS) on their permanent teeth. In 1987 they had an average of only three. With increased use of available preventive measures, the downward trend in dental caries seen since the early 1970s is expected to continue. Sources: NIH Pub. No. 82-2245, 1981, and DHHS Pub. No. (PHS) 81-1673.

research to make periodontal diseases a leading target and to devote more attention to dental problems affecting the elderly. Further, the two surveys provided baseline data for future studies necessary to monitor the effects and needs of dental research. Thus, as important as the surveys were in showing progress, they also served as bases for planning NIDR research for the future.

AIDS

While the 1980s plan covered virtually every imaginable angle of dental problems, the unpredictable burst into the carefully designed scenario. A new menace, AIDS, emerged as a dental problem after the Institute had published its long-range research plan for the 1980s. In AIDS, first noticed in homosexuals, the disease destroyed the body's immune system; no immediate cure or prevention appeared in sight.

Although the National Institutes of Health first investigated AIDS in 1981, the dental institute involvement started later after researchers found AIDS patients with numerous oral infections. Next, in 1983 and 1984 Drs. Sharon Wahl and Philip Smith of the NIDR Laboratory of Microbiology and Immunology identified an unhealthy monocyte, a specific defect in the immune system, that they associated with AIDS. Research showed that the human immunodeficiency virus (HIV) and the cytomegalovirus, a cause of pneumonia, could invade monocytes, immune cells normally involved in locating and destroying infectious agents in the body. Infected monocytes lost much of their regular defense functions and left the body more susceptible to the development of AIDS-related infections. During that time NIH scientists suspected that "intimate contact and presumably blood-to-blood transmission" served as routes of AIDS transmission; Dr. Robert Gallo and his National Cancer Institute team and Dr. Luc Lamontagnier and his Institut Pasteur group in France identified the retrovirus HTLV-III (later called HIV) as the cause.

The "blood-to-blood" transmission brought NIDR into the investigator safety aspect of AIDS research. The danger to those in health care and research had led the Centers for Disease Control to issue recommendations for protective measures to be taken by the nation's health care workers when handling AIDS cases. Along with other organizations such as the ADA which issued guidelines for the nation's dentists, NIDR also took precautions in clinical research. Following the advice of the Institute's dental clinic researchers, the NIDR clinic established rigid precautions in the form of protective garb for its dentists working with AIDS patients.

Meanwhile, AIDS research became part of the NIDR extramural program. By 1985 Institute grantees, including some in San Francisco, showed that several infections and Kaposi's sarcoma in the mouth frequently appeared with AIDS. One NIDR-sponsored investigation indicated that an unusual oral lesion, hairy leukoplakia, might serve as an indicator of AIDS as early as thirty-three months before AIDS detection.[41]

NIDR also assumed administrative responsibilities in the AIDS battle. After the Public Health Service designated AIDS as the chief health priority, in 1985 Dr. James B. Wyngaarden, director of the NIH, established the NIH AIDS Executive Committee and appointed Institute Director Löe to serve as a member. That same year the NADRC unanimously recommended that the NIDR give high priority to AIDS research in both its intramural and its extramural programs. An Institute AIDS task force, composed of scientists and administrators, advised Löe on research which by 1987 was under way throughout the Institute's intramural program. With $2.7 million allocated for Institute AIDS research during the 1987 fiscal year, NIDR scientists collaborated with the Food and Drug Administration to develop research on anti-invasive treatment of Karposi sarcoma; the Walter Reed Army Institute of Research for an epidemiological study; and the National Institute of Allergy and Infectious Diseases researchers to seek more clues, a cure, and the easing of pain associated with AIDS. In March 1988 NIDR, an officially designated WHO Collaborating Center, acted as host at a meeting to foster international collaboration on research and education related to oral manifestations and HIV infection in AIDS. Meetings of all the directors of WHO collaborating organizations involved in the oral manifestations of HIV infection subsequently met twice to organize themselves to implement the recommendations of the March meeting.[42]

In 1988 NIDR scientists made additional progress on AIDS research. By then the NIDR Clinical Investigations and Patient Care Branch had launched a pursuit for the identity of a component or components in saliva that inhibited the AIDS virus. In this effort Dr. Philip Fox and his team followed up on a 1986 report by another researcher that whole saliva from a chimpanzee and human inactivated the HIV. The NIDR group tested the AIDS virus mixed with whole saliva and with secretions collected from the major salivary glands from both healthy and AIDS-infected individuals. Fox and his colleagues found that the HIV was blocked by whole saliva and by secretions from two of the major salivary glands, the submandibular and sublingual (taken together because of the difficulty of separating them). Conversely, the investigations disclosed that secretions from the third major gland, the parotid, provided little protection against the AIDS virus.

In the larger of two studies the team tested samples from thirty-four people, including healthy men, women, and children and nine men with AIDS. Samples from twenty-eight of the subjects completely inactivated the HIV, and some anti-AIDS virus action appeared in samples from all the subjects. This research thus provided further evidence that the HIV probably was not transmitted through the salivary secretions. Yet identifying the anti-AIDS virus factor or factors remained as a challenge for the investigators.[43]

The Future

By 1988 the NIDR had moved closer to providing the means to eliminate major oral diseases and to correct troubling dental conditions. Among the successful applications produced through NIDR support were:

- Laminin, the intramural development helpful to laboratory research on nerve regeneration and wound healing;

- Bone morphogenic protein, isolated by an extramural grantee, that induced bone growth;

- Osteogenin, a bone-inducing substance discovered in an intramural laboratory and in clinical use in Boston to form new bone in patients with craniofacial defects;

- Cloning of tooth enamel genes by extramural and intramural teams with potential for contributing toward restoration of tooth enamel;

- A vaccine to prevent herpes simplex, in the animal experimentation stage at NIH;

- Pilocarpine, under Institute clinical testing to relieve "dry mouth";

- Improved composite resins and adhesive materials for tooth restoration, under development by grantees at the National Bureau of Standards; and

- A prototype computerized "tomosynthetic" dental X ray system producing more accurate images for earlier disease diagnosis and with less radiation exposure than standard dental X rays.[44]

In addition, investigations with promise for the future included studies that could:

- Lead to the creation of vaccines to prevent periodontal diseases and dental caries;

- Develop a new technique to reverse the effects of advanced stages of periodontal diseases—a method based on a concept of oral bacterial management to regenerate connective tissue and bone supporting the teeth in order to restore the tooth's attachment; and

- Map all the genes in the tooth to isolate and clone all genes essential to formation of dental hard tissues—research that could help devise new ways to inhibit or cure dental diseases and promote successful tooth implants.[45]

Further, to track the course of dental health in the nation, new surveys were scheduled. In 1988 a census under way included an oral health component in the 1988-1993 National Health and Nutrition Examination Survey. At the same time another kind of investigation of dental health in the United States was planned as part of a multinational study and social and environmental analysis of the oral health status of children and adults. NIDR administrators coordinated these epidemiological activities with extramural projects on risk factors in contracting oral diseases.[46]

In its fortieth anniversary year the Institute initiated preparations for a major research plan for the 1990s. This effort stressed dental disease prevention for all ages as well as goals to facilitate oral health by the year 2000. As Director Löe explained the new emphasis, the preventive program necessitated broadening because the elderly and "a lost generation" of middle-aged adults had missed out on previous projects aimed at the young.[47]

The plan for the 1990s was especially necessary because of the significant imprint dental research already had made on dentistry. Success had diminished the demands for certain specialties. Concerns arose about an excessive number of dentists in the United States. By the middle 1980s the number of dental schools in the nation had decreased. Such established dental colleges as those at Georgetown and Emory Universities either had closed or planned to go out of existence. Almost all dental schools in the nation had curtailed enrollments as well. Indeed, dental science had altered the very nature of the profession that so ardently had supported the assumption of dental research by the federal government.

More change was likely in the future, for research and education would indicate different needs. Löe predicted that except for orthodontists and maxillofacial surgeons the demands for specialists would diminish and the dental school curriculum would be modified for a new generation of general practitioners. Advances in research would contribute toward inclusion in the dentist's course of study such basic sciences as immunology, genetics, neurobiology, and cell and molecular biology and such clinical fields as internal medicine and oncology. This broadened education would prepare dentists to recognize and treat most conditions affecting the oral soft and hard tissues.[48]

Moreover, the decline in the prevalence of dental caries meant that preventive regimens instead of restoration would be the mainstay of future general practitioners and dental hygienists, whose roles would be enlarged. Restorations and repairs would still be necessary, but less frequently. Improved synthetic resins and bonding agents would enable dentists to make aesthetically pleasing, tooth-conserving repairs and to seal small caries lesions in both anterior and posterior teeth.[49]

Advanced diagnostic procedures such as computerized tomography would allow dentists to identify and treat dental caries and periodontal disease lesions at earlier stages. Family dentists would diagnose and treat cancerous and precancerous lesions, chronic orofacial pain, and sensory-motor disorders affecting taste, smell, speech, chewing, and swallowing.[50]

NIDR Director Löe foresaw a time when dental caries, periodontal diseases, and edentulousness would be rare. Dentistry would become a biomedical specialty, stomatology, just as dental research had developed into an accepted part of biomedical research. In Löe's view, these dentists of a later day would become "physicians of the mouth."[51] Like the National Institute of Dental Research, the "physician of the mouth" would be integrated into the biomedical world of the future.

H. Trendley Dean,
D.D.S.
Director, 1948-1953

*Directors of The
National Institute of
Dental Research*

Francis A. Arnold, Jr.,
D.D.S.
Director, 1953-1966

David B. Scott,
D.D.S.
Director, 1976-1981

Seymour J. Kreshover,
D.D.S., M.D., Ph.D.
Director, 1966-1975

Harald Löe,
D.D.S., Dr. Odont.
Director, 1983-present

Appendices

Appendix A

Calendar No. 1635

80th CONGRESS
2d Session
H. R. 6726

AN ACT

To amend the Public Health Service Act to provide for, foster, and aid in coordinating research relating to dental diseases and conditions, and for other purposes.

June 9 (legislative day, June 1), 1948
Read twice and ordered to be placed on the calendar

[PUBLIC LAW 755—80TH CONGRESS]

[CHAPTER 621—2D SESSION]

[H. R. 6726]

AN ACT

To amend the Public Health Service Act to provide for, foster, and aid in co-ordinating research relating to dental diseases and conditions, and for other purposes.

Be it enacted by the Senate and House of Representatives of the United States of America in Congress assembled, That this Act may be cited as the "National Dental Research Act".

PURPOSE

SEC. 2. The purpose of this Act is to improve the dental health of the people of the United States through the conduct of researches, investigations, experiments, and studies relating to the cause, diagnosis, and treatment of dental diseases and conditions; assist and foster such researches and other activities by public and private agencies; provide training in matters relating to dental diseases and conditions; and promote the coordination of all such researches and activities and the useful application of their results, with a view to the development and prompt widespread use of the most effective methods of prevention, diagnosis, and treatment of dental diseases and conditions.

RESEARCH AND TRAINING

SEC. 3. (a) The heading of title IV of the Public Health Service Act (42 U. S. C., ch. 6A), as amended, is amended to read "TITLE IV—NATIONAL CANCER, HEART, AND DENTAL INSTITUTES".

(b) Title IV of such Act is further amended by adding immediately after section 415 the following new part:

"PART C—NATIONAL INSTITUTE OF DENTAL RESEARCH

"ESTABLISHMENT OF INSTITUTE

"SEC. 421. There is hereby established in the Public Health Service a National Institute of Dental Research (hereafter in this part referred to as the 'Institute').

"DENTAL DISEASE RESEARCH AND TRAINING

"SEC. 422. In carrying out the purposes of section 301 with respect to dental diseases and conditions the Surgeon General, through the Institute and in cooperation with the National Advisory Dental Research Council (hereafter in this part referred to as the 'Council'), shall—

"(a) conduct, assist, and foster researches, investigations, experiments, and studies relating to the cause, prevention, and methods of diagnosis and treatment of dental diseases and conditions;

"(b) promote the coordination of researches conducted by the Institute, and similar researches conducted by other agencies, organizations, and individuals;

"(c) provide fellowships in the Institute from funds appropriated or donated for the purpose; .

"(d) secure for the Institute consultation services and advice of persons from the United States or abroad who are experts in the field of dental diseases and conditions;

"(e) cooperate with State health agencies in the prevention and control of dental diseases and conditions; and

"(f) provide training and instruction and establish and maintain traineeships, in the Institute and elsewhere in matters relating to the diagnosis, prevention, and treatment of dental diseases and conditions with such stipends and allowances (including travel and subsistence expenses) for trainees as he may deem necessary, the number of persons receiving such training and instruction, and the number of persons holding such traineeships, to be fixed by the Council, and, in addition, provide for such training, instruction, and traineeships through grants, upon recommendation of the Council, to public and other nonprofit institutions.

"ADMINISTRATION

"SEC. 423. (a) In carrying out the provisions of section 422 all appropriate provisions of section 301 shall be applicable to the authority of the Surgeon General, and grants-in-aid for dental research and training projects shall be made only after review and recommendation of the Council made pursuant to section 424.

"(b) The Surgeon General shall recommend to the Administrator acceptance of conditional gifts, pursuant to section 501, for study, investigation, or research into the cause, prevention, or methods of diagnosis or treatment of dental diseases and conditions, or for the acquisition of grounds or for the erection, equipment, or maintenance of premises, buildings, or equipment of the Institute. Donations of $50,000 or over for carrying out the purposes of this part may be acknowledged by the establishment within the Institute of suitable memorials to the donors.

"FUNCTIONS OF THE COUNCIL

"SEC. 424. The Council is authorized to—

"(a) review research projects or programs submitted to or initiated by it relating to the study of the cause, prevention, or methods of diagnosis and treatment of dental diseases and conditions, and certify approval to the Surgeon General, for prosecution under section 422 (a) hereof, of any such projects which it believes show promise of making valuable contributions to human knowledge with respect to the cause, prevention, or methods of diagnosis and treatment of dental diseases and conditions;

"(b) collect information as to studies which are being carried on in the United States or any other country as to the cause, prevention, or methods of diagnosis or treatment of dental diseases and conditions, by correspondence or by personal investigation of

3 [Pub. Law 755.]

such studies, and with the approval of the Surgeon General make available such information through appropriate publications for the benefit of health agencies and organizations (public or private), physicians, dentists, or any other scientists, and for the information of the general public;

"(c) review applications from any university, hospital, laboratory, or other institution, whether public or private, or from individuals, for grants-in-aid for research projects relating to dental diseases and conditions, and certify to the Surgeon General its approval of grants-in-aid in the cases of such projects which show promise of making valuable contributions to human knowledge with respect to the cause, prevention, or methods of diagnosis or treatment of dental diseases and conditions;

"(d) recommend to the Surgeon General for acceptance conditional gifts pursuant to section 501 for carrying out the purposes of this part;

"(e) make recommendations to the Surgeon General with respect to carrying out the provisions of this part; and

"(f) review applications from any public or other nonprofit institution for grants-in-aid for training, instruction, and traineeships in matters relating to the diagnosis, prevention, and treatment of dental diseases and conditions, and certify to the Surgeon General its approval of such applications for grants-in-aid as it determines will best carry out the purposes of this Act.

"OTHER AUTHORITY WITH RESPECT TO DENTAL DISEASES AND CONDITIONS

"SEC. 125. This part shall not be construed as superseding or limiting (a) the functions or authority of the Surgeon General or the Service, or of any other officer or agency of the United States, relating to the study of the causes, prevention, or methods of diagnosis or treatment of dental diseases and conditions; or (b) the expenditure of money therefor.

"SEC. 426. There is hereby authorized to be appropriated the sum of $750,000 for each fiscal year, beginning with the fiscal year ending June 30, 1949, for the purpose of carrying out the provisions of this part."

NATIONAL ADVISORY DENTAL RESEARCH COUNCIL

SEC. 4. (a) Section 217 of such Act is amended by adding at the end thereof the following new subsection:

"(g) The National Advisory Dental Research Council shall consist of the Surgeon General or his representative, the chief medical officer of the Veterans' Administration or his representative, the Surgeon General of the Army or his representative, the Surgeon General of the Navy or his representative, who shall be ex officio members, and twelve members appointed without regard to the civil-service laws by the Surgeon General with the approval of the Administrator. The twelve appointed members shall be leaders in the fields of fundamental sciences, medical sciences, education, or public affairs; six of such twelve shall be selected from leading dental, medical, or scientific authorities who are outstanding in the study, diagnosis, or treatment of dental diseases and conditions, and at least four of such six shall be dentists. Each appointed member of the Council shall hold office for a term of four years except that any member appointed to fill a vacancy occurring prior to the expiration of the term for which his predecessor was appointed shall be appointed for the remainder of such term, and except that, of the members first appointed, three shall hold office for a term of three years, three shall hold office for a term of two years, and three shall hold office for a term of one year, as designated by the Surgeon General at the time of appointment. None of such twelve members shall be eligible for reappointment until a year has elapsed since the end of his preceding term. Every two years the Council shall elect one member to act as chairman for the succeeding two-year period."

(b) Subsection (b) of section 217 of such Act is amended to read as follows:

"(b) The National Advisory Health Council shall advise, consult with, and make recommendations to, the Surgeon General on matters relating to health activities and functions of the Service. The Surgeon General is authorized to utilize the services of any member or members of the Council, and where appropriate, any member or members of the National Advisory Cancer Council, the National Advisory Mental Health Council, the National Advisory Heart Council, or the National Advisory Dental Research Council, in connection with matters related to the work of the Service, for such periods, in addition to conference periods, as he may determine."

(c) The heading of section 217 of such Act is amended to read "National Advisory Health, Cancer, Mental Health, Heart, and Dental Research Councils."

(d) Subsection (e) of section 208 of such Act is amended to read as follows:

"(e) Members of the National Advisory Health Council, members of the National Advisory Mental Health Council, members of the National Advisory Cancer Council, members of the National Advisory Heart Council, and members of the National Advisory Dental Research Council, other than ex officio members, while attending conferences or meetings of their respective Councils or while otherwise serving at the request of the Surgeon General, shall be entitled to receive compensation at a rate to be fixed by the Administrator, but not exceeding $50 per diem, and shall also be entitled to receive an allowance for actual and necessary traveling and subsistence expenses while so serving away from their places of residence."

(e) Paragraph (d) of section 301 of such Act is amended to read as follows:

"(d) Make grants-in-aid to universities, hospitals, laboratories, and other public or private institutions, and to individuals for such research projects as are recommended by the National Advisory Health Council, or, with respect to cancer, recommended by the National Advisory Cancer Council, or, with respect to mental health, recommended by the National Advisory Mental Health Council, or, with respect to heart diseases, recommended by the National Advisory Heart Council, or, with respect to dental diseases and conditions, recommended by the National Advisory Dental Research Council;".

(f) Paragraph (g) of such section 301 is amended to read as follows:

"(g) Adopt, upon recommendation of the National Advisory Health Council, or, with respect to cancer, upon recommendation of the

5 [Pub. Law 755.]

National Advisory Cancer Council, or, with respect to mental health, upon recommendation of the National Advisory Mental Health Council, or, with respect to heart diseases, upon recommendation of the National Advisory Heart Council, or, with respect to dental diseases and conditions, upon recommendations of the National Advisory Dental Research Council, such additional means as he deems necessary or appropriate to carry out the purposes of this section."

RESEARCH FACILITIES

SEC. 5. There is hereby authorized to be appropriated a sum not to exceed $2,000,000 for the erection and equipment of suitable and adequate buildings and facilities for the use of the National Institute of Dental Research in carrying out the provisions of this Act. The Federal Works Administrator is authorized to acquire, by purchase, condemnation, donation, or otherwise, a suitable and adequate site or sites, selected on the advice of the Surgeon General of the Public Health Service, in or near the District of Columbia for such buildings and facilities, and to erect thereon, furnish, and equip such buildings and facilities. The amount authorized to be appropriated in this section shall include the cost of preparation of drawings and specifications, supervision of construction, and other administrative expenses incident to the work: *Provided*, That the Federal Works Agency shall prepare the plans and specifications, make all necessary contracts, and supervise construction.

GENERAL PROVISIONS

SEC. 6. (a) Section 2 of the Public Health Service Act, as amended, is amended by striking out the word "and" at the end of paragraph (m), by striking out the period at the end of paragraph (n) and inserting in lieu thereof "; and", and by inserting after paragraph (n) the following new paragraph:

"(o) The term 'dental diseases and conditions' means diseases and conditions affecting teeth and their supporting structures, and other related diseases of the mouth."

(b) Section 633 (b) of such Act is amended by striking out "$25" and by inserting in lieu thereof "$50".

Approved
June 24 1948

Harry S. Truman

Appendix B
NIDR and NIH Appropriations, FY 1948-1988, in Current Dollars

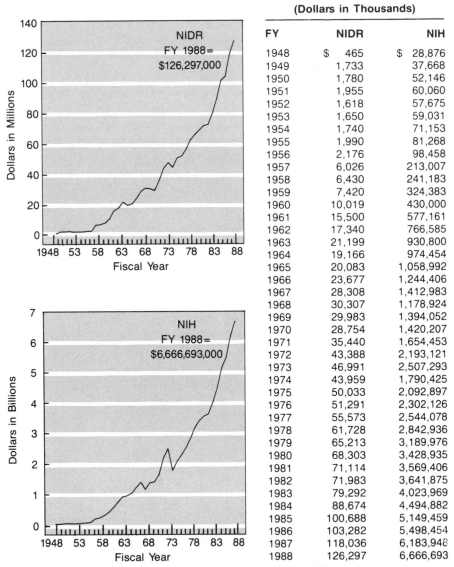

(Dollars in Thousands)

FY	NIDR	NIH
1948	$ 465	$ 28,876
1949	1,733	37,668
1950	1,780	52,146
1951	1,955	60,060
1952	1,618	57,675
1953	1,650	59,031
1954	1,740	71,153
1955	1,990	81,268
1956	2,176	98,458
1957	6,026	213,007
1958	6,430	241,183
1959	7,420	324,383
1960	10,019	430,000
1961	15,500	577,161
1962	17,340	766,585
1963	21,199	930,800
1964	19,166	974,454
1965	20,083	1,058,992
1966	23,677	1,244,406
1967	28,308	1,412,983
1968	30,307	1,178,924
1969	29,983	1,394,052
1970	28,754	1,420,207
1971	35,440	1,654,453
1972	43,388	2,193,121
1973	46,991	2,507,293
1974	43,959	1,790,425
1975	50,033	2,092,897
1976	51,291	2,302,126
1977	55,573	2,544,078
1978	61,728	2,842,936
1979	65,213	3,189,976
1980	68,303	3,428,935
1981	71,114	3,569,406
1982	71,983	3,641,875
1983	79,292	4,023,969
1984	88,674	4,494,882
1985	100,688	5,149,459
1986	103,282	5,498,454
1987	118,036	6,183,948
1988	126,297	6,666,693

When plotted in current dollars over 40 years both NIDR and NIH show steep growth rates. The NIDR appropriation increased from $465,000 in 1948 to $126,297,000 in 1988.

Appendix C

Major Components as Percents of Total NIDR Appropriation

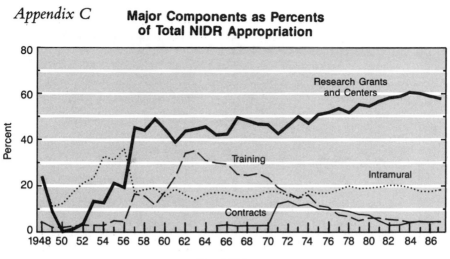

NIDR extramural support of individual research investigators, program projects, and research centers accounts for about 60 percent of NIDR appropriations, a proportion that has been stable for the past 5 years. Research training awards have fallen from highs of 30 to 35 percent in the 1960s to a level of 4 to 5 percent today. Contract support also has fallen and presently accounts for a little under 5 percent of appropriations. Intramural research has been maintained at a level between 18 and 20 percent over the last decade. (Percents do not add to 100 since research management and support are not included.)

NIDR Obligations for Research Training, Fellowships, and Career Development Awards in Current Dollars

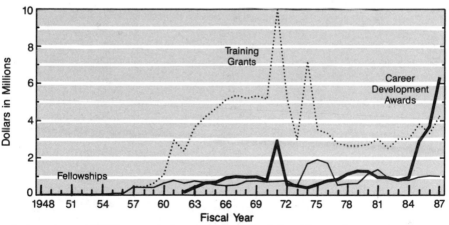

A closer look at NIDR support of research training, fellowships, and career development awards shows dramatic changes over time. From 1948 through 1956 individual fellowships were the only mechanism for research training. Institutional training grants were begun in 1957 and saw great growth in the late 1960s and early 1970s. National Research Service Awards (NRSA) were begun in 1975 and by 1978 all fellowship (F) and training (T) awards were implemented through the NRSA mechanism. Career development awards were begun in 1962 and showed slow growth until 1985 and the advent of the Dentist Scientist Award program.

Appendix D

Percent of NIDR Obligations for Research Grants, Career Development Awards, and Contracts by Performing Institution

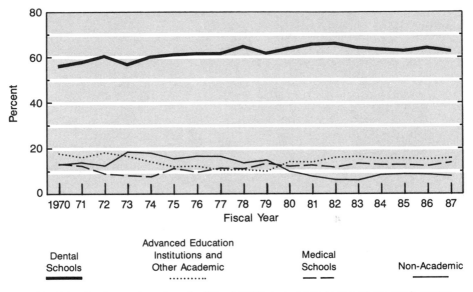

| Dental Schools | Advanced Education Institutions and Other Academic | Medical Schools | Non-Academic |

Dental schools receive close to 2/3 of NIDR support in terms of research grants, contracts, and career development awards. Advanced education and other academic institutions (e.g., graduate schools, schools of engineering, pharmacy, public health) receive about 15 percent of NIDR funding in these areas; medical schools about 13 percent, and non-academic organizations (including private industry, non-university hospitals, some government agencies; and private professional organizations) about 8 percent of funds.

Appendix E

ADA-NIDR Research Fellows

Dr. E. G. Hampp	1942-1969
Dr. Robert Omata	1949-1952
Dr. John Folk	1952-1960
Dr. Tetsuo Shiota	1955-1960
Dr. Stuart Narrod	1955-1960
Dr. George Martin	1960-1962
Dr. Frances Kendrick	1961-1963
Dr. Charles Wittenberger	1961-1969
Dr. Richard Evans	1963-1967
Dr. E. G. Miller	1963-1967
Dr. A. J. Steffek	1964-1970
Dr. Jack London	1967-1969
Dr. A. C. Verrusio	1968-1970

Source: American Dental Association Council of Dental Research Files.

Appendix F

National Institute of Dental Research Lectures
(Seymour J. Kreshover Lectures)

1983	Dame Honor B. Fell Strangeways Laboratories, England	"The Promotion and Inhibition of Collagen Breakdown in Synovial Tissue"
1984	Dr. Roy Curtiss, III Washington University, St. Louis	"Genetic Analysis of the Virulence of Streptococcus Mutans: Prospects for an Anti-Caries Vaccine"
1985	Dr. Robert J. Genco State University of New York, Buffalo	"Molecular Factors Influencing Neutrophil Defects in Periodontal Disease"
1986	Dr. Irwin D. Mandel Columbia University, New York	"The Role of Saliva in Maintaining Oral Homeostasis"
1987	Dr. Harold C. Slavkin University of Southern California, Los Angeles	"Gene Regulation in the Development of Oral Tissues"
1988	Dr. Ronald J. Gibbons Forsyth Dental Center Boston, Massachusetts Harvard School of Dental Medicine, Cambridge, Massachusetts	"Bacterial Adhesion to Oral Tissues: A Model for Infectious Diseases"

Appendix G

Major Departmental, National, and International Awards to NIDR Personnel, 1948–1988

Over the years NIDR personnel have been the recipients of hundreds of awards, honorary degrees, and honorary memberships. To make the list manageable, it has been limited to the highest departmental awards for civil service employees and commissioned officers, as well as national and international awards. The departmental awards are those awarded by the Public Health Service (PHS), and the Department of Health and Human Services (DHHS) as well as its predecessors, the Department of Health, Education and Welfare (DHEW) and the Federal Security Agency (FSA). From 1919 to 1931 dental scientists served in the Dental Corps of the PHS and from 1931 to 1948 in the Dental Section of the National Institutes of Health. Data for this list was obtained from the NIDR Information and Personnel offices. Every attempt was made to compile as complete and accurate a list as possible from the information available.

Service	Name	Award	Contribution
1907–1953	Elvove, Elias	FSA Award for Superior Service	Fluoride research: developed methods for the determination of the fluoride content of water & the removal of fluoride from water
1921–1953	Dean, H. Trendley	Gorgas Medal Association of Military Surgeons John M. Goodell Prize, American Water Works Association	Epidemiology and leadership in fluoride research

Appendix G (continued)

Service	Name	Award	Contribution
		Lasker Award, American Public Health Association	
		Distinguished Service Medal, American Association of Public Health Dentists	
		Miller Prize, Fédération Dentaire Internationale	
1936–1966	McClure, Frank J.	Award for Basic Research in Oral Therapeutics, International Association for Dental Research (hereafter IADR)	Fluoride research
		H. Trendley Dean Award, IADR	
		DHEW Superior Service Award	
1937–1966	Arnold, Francis A.	William John Gies Award, American College of Dentists	Dental research administration; fluoride research

		H. Trendley Dean Award, IADR	
		Special award for contributions to health of children, National Fluoridation Assembly	
1942-1969	Hampp, Edward G.	Academy Award in Biological Sciences, Washington Academy of Sciences	First to isolate Borrelia Vincenti in pure culture making possible new approaches to the study of spirochetes
1944-1965; 1976-1981	Scott, David B.	Arthur S. Flemming Award, U.S. government	Mineralized tissue research; electron microscopy; forensic dentistry
		Award for Research in Mineralization, IADR	
		Special recognition for pioneering work in modern forensic dentistry, American Academy of Forensic Sciences	
1948-1969	Fitzgerald, Robert J.	Albert Joachim International Prize, Fédération Dentaire Internationale	Caries research: established infectious nature of experimental caries and the cariogenic potential of *streptococcus mutans*
		Award for Dental Caries Research, IADR	

Appendix G (continued)

Service	Name	Award	Contribution
1948-1976	Larson, Rachel H.	DHEW Superior Service Award	Caries & animal research
1948-	Rogosa, Morrison	Bergey Award, American Society of Microbiology	bacterial toxonomy: lactobacilli research
1949-1950; 1955-	Nylen, Marie U.	Award for Basic Research in Biological Mineralization, IADR	Mineralized tissue research; electron microscopy
		Federal Woman's Award	
		Issac Schour Memorial Award in Anatomical Sciences	
		Lucy Hobbs Taylor Award, American Association of Women Dentists	
		DHEW Superior Service Award	
		DHEW Distinguished Service Award	
1949-1966	Russell, Albert L.	H. Trendley Dean Award	Oral pathology; epidemiology and caries research

1949; 1953-1968	Stanley, Harold R.	Gorgas Odontological Society Award	Oral pathology; research in human dental pulp
1952-1982	Piez, Karl A.	T. Duckett Jones Memorial Award, Helen Hay Whitney Foundation	Collagen research
1953-1979	Driscoll, Edward	Horace Wells Club Award Heidbrink Award Monheim Award Research Recognition Award, American Association of Oral and Maxillofacial Surgeons DHEW Superior Performance Award	Anesthesiology; pain research
1953-1970	Fullmer, Harold M.	Fulbright Award—research scholar, University of Adelaide	Histochemistry and microchemistry of tissues, bone, and teeth; experimental pathology
1955-1981	Keyes, Paul H.	Albert Joachim International Prize, Fédération Dentaire Internationale Award for Caries Research, IADR	Caries research: established infectious nature of experimental caries and the cariogenic potential of *streptococcus mutans*

Appendix G *(continued)*

Service	Name	Award	Contribution
1956-1975	Kreshover, Seymour J.	Pierre Fauchard Medal, Pierre Fauchard Academy	Dental pathology; leadership in dental science research
		PHS Distinguished Service Award	
1958-	Mergenhagen, Stephan E.	Award for Basic Research in Oral Science, IADR	Microbiology; immunology
		U.S. Senior Scientist Award, Alexander von Humboldt Foundation, West Germany	
		Basic Research and Periodontal Disease Award, IADR	
		DHEW Superior Service Award	
1958-1972	Scherp, Henry W.	DHEW Superior Service Award	Oral microbiology
1959-	Dubner, Ronald	Carl A. Schlack Award, Association of Military Surgeons of the U.S.	Pain research

1959-1988	Martin, George R.	Award for Basic Research in Oral Science, IADR DHHS Distinguished Service Award U.S. Senior Scientist Award, Alexander von Humboldt Foundation, West Germany Doerenkamp-Zbinden Foundation Award	Collagen research; basement membrane research
1960-	Notkins, Abner L.	David Rumbough Scientific Award, Juvenile Diabetes Foundation Paul E. Lacy Research Award in Diabetes Paul Ehrlich and Ludwig Darmstaedter Prize, West Germany DHHS Distinguished Service Award	Research in autoimmune diseases; diabetes; herpes simplex vaccine
1960-1985	Kakehashi, Samuel	Jack D. Robertson Dental Award	Clinical research: as scientist, administrator, and teacher

Appendix G *(continued)*

Service	Name	Award	Contribution
1961-1988	Brown, Kenneth S.	Kenneth S. Brown Ectodermal Dysplasia Research Award, established by National Foundation for Ectodermal Dysplasias	Research in the genetics, biology, and biochemistry of birth defects of craniofacial structures
1961-	Eanes, Edward David	Award for Basic Research in Biological Mineralization, IADR	Mineralized tissue research
1963-1967; 1969-1972	Malone, Thomas	DHEW Superior Service Award	Leadership in fostering research grants & research training
1965-1977	Brocard, Tula	DHEW Superior Service Honor Award	Planning & directing the program to disseminate NIDR scientific findings
1966-1976	Greulich, Richard	DHEW Superior Service Award	Dental research administration
1966-1971	Lavender, Dick R.	Edward J. Hatton Award, IADR	Calcification research
1966-1971	Miller, Edward	Award for Basic Research in Oral Science, IADR	Collagen research

1967-	Carlos, James	PHS Superior Service Award	Epidemiology; dental research administration
1968-	Hand, Arthur R.	ORCA-Rolex Prize, European Organization for Caries Research	
		Award for Basic Research in Oral Science, IADR	Salivary and related exocrine gland research
1970-	Termine, John	Award for Basic Research in Biological Mineralization, IADR	Bone research
1971-1987	Horowitz, Herschel S.	Carl A. Schlack Award, Association of Military Surgeons of the U.S.	Epidemiology; caries research
		H. Trendley Dean Award, IADR	
1972-	Valega, Thomas	Society of Biomaterials Award	Biomaterials research
1973-1982	Bowen, William H.	Award for Dental Caries Research, IADR	Caries research: developed and used primate model in caries research
1975-	Hascall, Vincent	PHS Superior Service Award	Connective tissue research
1975-1985	Kemp, Christopher W.	Edward H. Hatton Award, IADR	Reported quick technique for determining percentage of living bacteria in samples of dental plaque

Appendix G (continued)

Service	Name	Award	Contribution
1975-	Kleinman, Hynda	Doerenkamp-Zbinden Foundation Award	Development of basement membrane gel assay that rapidly tests invasiveness of tumor cells
1976-	Cohen, Lois K.	Distinguished Senior Scientist Award, IADR Behavioral Sciences Group	Helped to establish behavioral and social sciences as an integrated part of dental research
		PHS Superior Service Award	
1977-	Small, John S.	Distinguished Service Award, Assoc. of State & Territorial Dental Directors	Fluoridation promotion
1978-1985	Cole, Michael P.	Award for Basic Research in Oral Science, IADR	Caries research
1980-	Kleinman, Dushanka	PHS Outstanding Service Medal	Epidemiology; effects of smokeless tobacco
1982-	Baum, Bruce	Carl A. Schlack Award, Association of Military Surgeons of the U.S.	Clinical research: oral physiology & salivary dysfunction

1983- Löe, Harald

Honorary Professorship, Medical Sciences University, Beijing, China

Alpha Omega Achievement Medal Award

Award for Basic Research in Periodontics, IADR

American Society of Preventive Dentistry International Award

William J. Gies Award, American Academy of Periodontology

International Lecturer of the Year Award, Academy of International Dental Studies

Norwegian Dental Association 75th Anniversary Prize

Gold Medal, University of Ghent, Belgium

Honored by Her Majesty the Queen of Denmark (Knight of Danebrog)

Periodontal research; leadership in dental science research

Appendix G (continued)

Service	Name	Award	Contribution
1983-	Löe, Harald *(continued)*	Swedish Dental Societies International Prize	
1985-1987	Albini, Adriana	Doerenkamp-Zbinden Foundation Award	Development of basement membrane gel assay that rapidly tests invasiveness of tumor cells
1986-1987	Iwamoto, Yukihide	Doerenkamp-Zbinden Foundation Award	Development of basement membrane gel assay that rapidly tests invasiveness of tumor cells

Appendix H

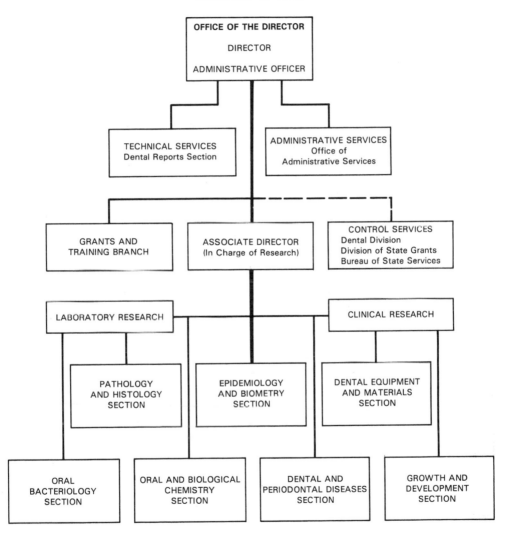

**NATIONAL INSTITUTE OF DENTAL RESEARCH
November 7, 1949**

OFFICE OF THE DIRECTOR

DIRECTOR

ADMINISTRATIVE OFFICER

TECHNICAL SERVICES
Dental Reports Section

ADMINISTRATIVE SERVICES
Office of
Administrative Services

GRANTS AND
TRAINING BRANCH

ASSOCIATE DIRECTOR
(In Charge of Research)

CONTROL SERVICES
Dental Division
Division of State Grants
Bureau of State Services

LABORATORY RESEARCH

CLINICAL RESEARCH

PATHOLOGY
AND HISTOLOGY
SECTION

EPIDEMIOLOGY
AND BIOMETRY
SECTION

DENTAL EQUIPMENT
AND MATERIALS
SECTION

ORAL
BACTERIOLOGY
SECTION

ORAL AND BIOLOGICAL
CHEMISTRY
SECTION

DENTAL AND
PERIODONTAL DISEASES
SECTION

GROWTH AND
DEVELOPMENT
SECTION

Appendix H

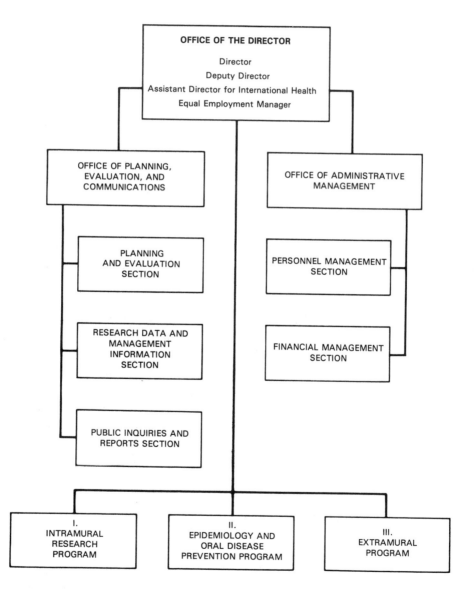

NATIONAL INSTITUTE OF DENTAL RESEARCH
November 7, 1988

OFFICE OF THE DIRECTOR

Director
Deputy Director
Assistant Director for International Health
Equal Employment Manager

OFFICE OF PLANNING, EVALUATION, AND COMMUNICATIONS

OFFICE OF ADMINISTRATIVE MANAGEMENT

PLANNING AND EVALUATION SECTION

PERSONNEL MANAGEMENT SECTION

RESEARCH DATA AND MANAGEMENT INFORMATION SECTION

FINANCIAL MANAGEMENT SECTION

PUBLIC INQUIRIES AND REPORTS SECTION

I. INTRAMURAL RESEARCH PROGRAM

II. EPIDEMIOLOGY AND ORAL DISEASE PREVENTION PROGRAM

III. EXTRAMURAL PROGRAM

Appendix H (continued)

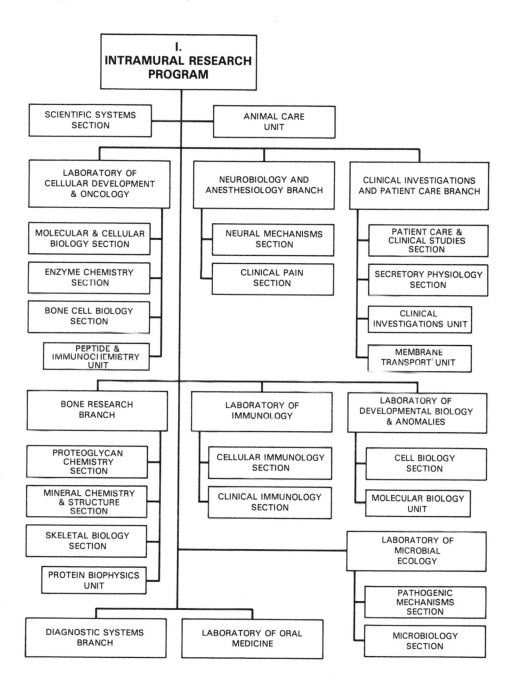

Appendix H (continued)

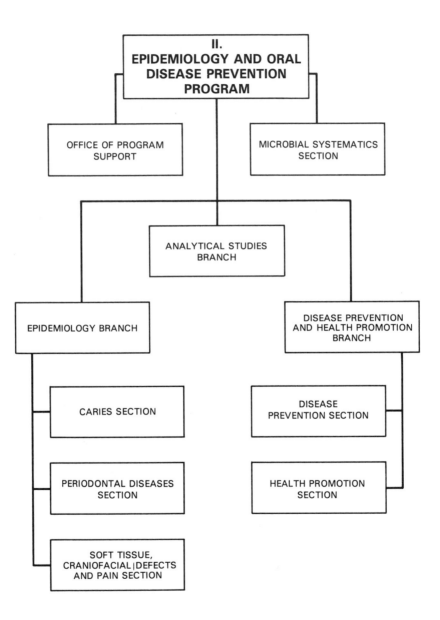

Appendix H (continued)

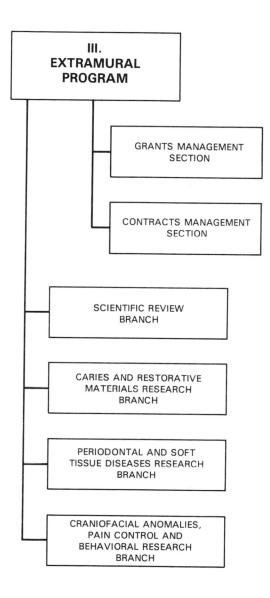

Appendix I

NIDR Fortieth Anniversary Commemoration Chronology for 1988

February 22	H. J. Res. 465 to honor the fortieth year of NIDR is introduced by Reps. Steny Hoyer and Constance A. Morella of Maryland and Mervyn M. Dymally of California.
March 9	"Dental Science-Dental Health: New Frontiers," a symposium sponsored by NIDR, is held at the AADR and American Association of Dental Schools annual meeting in Montreal, Canada.
April 10-12	The Annual Dental Research Students Conference is hosted by NIDR to acquaint eighty-one outstanding dental students with opportunities in dental research. Sponsors are the ADA, Warner-Lambert Oral Health Products Group, and participating dental schools.
April 21	At Grand Rapids, Michigan, scene of the first fluoridation study, NIDR Director Dr. Harald Löe and NIH Director Dr. James B. Wyngaarden lead ceremonies recognizing the citizens of that city for their "outstanding contributions to the dental health of the United States and the entire world."
May 2	Löe addresses the Boston section of AADR on "NIDR: Past, Present and Future" at the Forsyth Dental Center.
May 24	"A Century of American Dental Research," an exhibit commemorating the fortieth anniversary of NIDR, opens at the National Library of Medicine for viewing until mid-October.
	Dr. Jens Pindborg delivers a lecture and slide show on "Dentistry in the Arts" at NIH.
May 25	The "H. Trendley Dean Conference Room" in Building 30 is dedicated to honor the first NIDR director.

NIDR sponsors "Dental Science-Dental Health: The Status of American Oral Health," a symposium on dental health surveys of children and adults and plans for a national oral health campaign.

AADR sponsors a cocktail reception and dinner at the Shoreham Hotel in Washington, D.C., to honor the fortieth anniversary of NIDR. Congresswoman Morella is the keynote speaker.

June 22   Dr. George R. Martin, chief of the NIDR Laboratory of Developmental Biology and Anomalies, delivers the G. Burroughs Mider Lecture at NIH on "Basement Membranes: Key Determinants of Differentiation and Their Role in Cancer Mestastasis."

June 24   NIDR holds a picnic on the grounds of Bethesda Naval Hospital to commemorate the day forty years before that President Harry Truman signed the Dental Research Act establishing NIDR.

September 26   Dr. Ronald Gibbons, associate director of the Forsyth Dental Center, delivers the sixth annual Seymour J. Kreshover Lecture at NIH on "Bacterial Adhesion to Oral Tissues: A Model for Infectious Diseases."

October 8-11   The NIDR fortieth anniversary celebration is included in the joint meeting of the ADA and FDI in Washington, D.C., with a tour of NIDR laboratories and NIH; a lecture on dentistry in stamps by Dr. Alan Drinnan of SUNY, Buffalo, with a companion exhibit at the NIH Clinical Center; and a U.S. Postal Service cancellation booth at the ADA registration area.

October 9   "Dental Science-Dental Health," a symposium for the ADA-FDI meeting, is sponsored by NIDR.

               "Dental Science for Dental Health," an eighty-foot exhibit on NIDR contributions to dental science, opens at the Smithsonian Institution Museum of American History with a special reception sponsored by the ADA for two thousand persons.

Notes

CHAPTER ONE. *Dentistry: From Magic to Science*

1. Hermann Prinz, *Dental Chronology. A Record of the More Important Historic Events in the Evolution of Dentistry* (Philadelphia: Lea & Febiger, 1945), 15.

2. Vincenzo Guerini, *History of Dentistry from the Most Ancient Times until the End of the 18th Century* (New York: Lea & Febiger, 1909), 35. Despite its age, this work was the most scholarly history of dentistry available.

3. Mark W. Allen, "A Tooth, a Horse-pill, and a Little Black Bag," *Medical Affairs* (September 1966): 4-7, 50-51; Guerini, *History of Dentistry*, 20-22, 25, 29-30; Tom Harney, "1,000 Year-old Skull Indicates Dentistry Is Not a New Skill," *Biomedical News* (July 1970).

4. M. D. K. Bremner, *The Story of Dentistry. From the Dawn of Civilization to the Present. With Special Emphasis on the American Scene* (New York: Dental Items of Interest Publishing Company, 1954), 50, 445. Although Bremner wrote a lively account, he did not provide any documentation in this work. Despite its title this book did not include the most important milestones in twentieth century dental history in the United States.

5. Bremner, *Story of Dentistry*, 48; Guerini, *History of Dentistry*, 103-4.

6. Tom Harney, "1,000 Year-old Skull."

7. Bremner, *Story of Dentistry*, 77, 446.

8. Bernhard Wolf Weinberger, *An Introduction to the History of Dentistry: With Medical & Dental Chronology & Bibliographic Data*, 2 vols. (St. Louis: C. V. Mosby Company, 1948), 1:221. Weinberger's work was well documented and covered much of the same time period as Guerini.

9. *The New Encyclopaedia Britannica Macropaedia*, 15th ed., s.v. "dentistry."

10. Bremner, *Story of Dentistry*, 86-87; *The New Encyclopaedia Britannica*, s.v. "dentistry"; *Columbia Encyclopedia*, 1967 ed., s.v. "van Leeuwenhouk, Antonie." Van Leeuwenhouk's first name also has been spelled as "Antony."

11. Bremner, *Story of Dentistry*, 446; Guerini, *History of Dentistry*, 263.

12. Bremner, *Story of Dentistry*, 97-106, 446; Francis Arnold, Jr., "Dental Research: Past-Present-Future," 5, "Speeches," NIDR Information Office Files (hereafter NIDR IO).

13. Bremner, *Story of Dentistry*, 305-9, 337-42.

14. Fauchard's works were not translated into English until the twentieth century.

15. Bremner, *Story of Dentistry*, 120; *Columbia Encyclopedia*, s.v. "Hunter, John."

16. Bremner, *Story of Dentistry*, 446.

17. Bremner, *Story of Dentistry*, 122-24; *Encyclopedia of American History*, s.v. "population and immigration."

18. Bernhard Wolf Weinberger, *An Introduction to the History of Dentistry in America. Washington's Need for Medical and Dental Care. Houdon's Life Mask versus His Portraitures*, 2 vols. (St. Louis: C. V. Mosby Company, 1948), 2:143-50. Despite the title, this work was not a history of dentistry in America but was instead a series of vignettes of prominent dentists up to the end of the eighteenth century. Again, as in vol. 1, this work was carefully documented. Gardette's essay appeared in vol. 7, 266-68, of *The American Museum*.

19. Bremner, *Story of Dentistry*, 128-29.

20. Dr. Samuel L. Mitchell, M.D., to Dr. Thomas Charles Hope, M.D. and adjunct professor of chemistry, University of Edinburgh, October 10, 1796, in *American Journal of Dental Science* 1, no. 2 (1851): 79-85; William Frederick Norwood, *Medical Education in the United States before the Civil War* (New York: Arno Press & The New York Times, 1971), 31, 113-14.

21. Bremner, *Story of Dentistry*, 135; Isaac Sissman, *75 Years of Dentistry—University of Pittsburgh: A History of the School of Dental Medicine* (University of Pittsburgh, 1971), 14-15; Charles W. Ballard, "Dental Education," *American Journal of Dental Science* 1 (October 1851): 59-71; *Encyclopedia of American History*, s.v. "population and immigration."

22. Bremner, *Story of Dentistry*, 306, 434; Walter Hoffman-Axthelm, *History of Dentistry* (Chicago: Quintessence Publishing Company, 1981), 401; Levi Spear Parmly, *A Practical Guide to the Management of the Teeth Comprising Discovery of the Origin of Caries on Decay of the Teeth* (Philadelphia: Collins and Croft, 1819), 76, 79, 83-84.

23. Earl G. Jones, "Bainbridge . . . Cradle of Dentistry," *Ohio Dental Journal* (December 1969); *75 Years of Dentistry*, 16-17; George H. Callcott, *A History of the University of Maryland* (Baltimore: Maryland Historical Society, 1966), 89.

24. Bremner, *Story of Dentistry*, 137-39.

25. Bremner, *Story of Dentistry*, 141-44.

26. Bremner, *Story of Dentistry*, 154, 166-68; Sissman, *75 Years of Dentistry*, 17-18; Ben Robinson, "A Synoptic History of the American Dental Association, Part 1, 1859-1896," *Journal of the American Dental Association* (hereafter *JADA*) 58 (June 1959): 22.

27. R. W. McCluggage, *A History of the American Dental Association* (Chicago: ADA, 1959), 67-88, 121; Bremner, *Story of Dentistry*, 154-55; Robinson, "Synoptic History," 21-25. An excellent, carefully documented, and interesting work, the McCluggage book also included a history of organized dentistry in the United States. As McCluggage noted, the National Dental Association of 1897 was renamed the American Dental Association in 1922. Dr. David B. Scott described the 1866 to 1869 organization of dental colleges in his unpub-

lished manuscript, "The History of the Association of Colleges of Dentistry," which he prepared in 1943 at the Baltimore College of Dentistry.

28. Sissman, *75 Years of Dentistry*, 17; Robinson, "Synoptic History," 21-22.

29. Howard L. Ward, "The Development of Dental Curriculum," *Journal of the American College of Dentists* (April 1972): 107; Bremner, *Story of Dentistry*, 346.

30. Sissman, *75 Years of Dentistry*, 17; Ward, "Dental Curriculum," 106-7; Bremner, *Story of Dentistry*, 346.

31. Sissman, *75 Years of Dentistry*, 18-19; Bremner, *Story of Dentistry*, 161.

32. Prinz, *Chronology*, 138; Bremner, *Story of Dentistry*, 378; *Dental Hygiene* 54 (March 1980): 116.

33. Bremner, *Story of Dentistry*, 177-205.

34. P. M. C. James, "One Hundred Years of Dental Public Health," *British Dental Journal* 151 (1981): 20; McCluggage, *History of American Dental Association*, 208.

35. Bremner, *Story of Dentistry*, 235, 307-8; Francis Arnold, "Highlights of American Dentistry in the Field of Research," *International Dental Journal* 10 (March 1960): 18; F. E. Rodriguez, "Studies in the Specific Bacteriology of Dental Caries," *Military Dental Journal* 5 (December 1922): 200.

36. Bremner, *Story of Dentistry*, 209, 228, 262-63, 299-300, 448; *Bulletin of the History of Dentistry* 7 (April 1959).

37. Bremner, *Story of Dentistry*, 248-50, unnumbered photograph page.

38. Gardner P. H. Foley, "Periodical Literature—Key in the Progress of Dentistry, 1901-1920," *JADA* 84 (March 1972): 501-2.

39. Leonard D. White, *The Jacksonians: A Study in Administrative History, 1820-1861* (New York: University of Chicago, MacMillan Company, 1954), 482.

40. Weinberger, *History of Dentistry in America*, 273-74, 277, 279-80.

41. Ralph Chester Williams, *The United States Public Health Service, 1798-1950* (Commissioned Officers Association of the United States Public Health Service, 1951), 23-31; McCluggage, *History of the American Dental Association*, 143-46. Williams's work provided useful background material on both the Public Health Service and National Institutes of Health.

42. White, *The Jacksonians*, 499-501.

43. White, *The Jacksonians*, 500; James, "One Hundred Years of Dental Public Health," 20.

44. Leonard D. White, *The Republican Era. 1869-1901: A Study in Administrative History* (New York: Macmillan Company, 1958), 246, 243; *Encyclopedia of American History*, s.v. "population and immigration."

45. Stewart M. Brooks, "The Key to Secession," *CAL* (December 1966): 1-3.

46. McCluggage, *History of American Dental Association*, 143-45; "In the Days of

Appomattox," "History of Dentistry and Medicine (2)," NIDR IO; Robinson, "Synoptic History," 19; Brooks, "Key to Secession," 3.

47. Brooks, "Key to Secession," 1-3; McCluggage, *History of the American Dental Association*, 144; Col. George F. Jeffcott, *United States Army Dental Service in World War II* (Washington: Office of the Surgeon General, Department of the Army, 1955), 1.

48. This is the judgment of Wyndham Miles, author of an excellent history of the National Library of Medicine. Citation follows.

49. Wyndham Davies Miles, *A History of the National Library of Medicine: The Nation's Treasury of Medical Knowledge* (NIH Publication No. 85-1904, 1982), iii, 45, 54; Surgeon-General, U.S. Army, *Index-Catalogue of the Library of the Surgeon General's Office, U. S. Army*, vols. 1, 2, 4, 5, 7, 9, 10, 14.

50. James A. Shannon, "The Development of the Federal Role in the Support of Medical Research," *Bulletin of the New York Academy of Medicine*, 2d ser., 37 (January 1961): 7; *Annual Report of the Supervising Surgeon of the Marine-Hospital Service of the United States for the Fiscal Year 1873* (Washington: GPO, 1873), 9, 12, 13; H. Trendley Dean, "Some General Epidemiological Considerations," *Dental Caries and Fluorine*, 2. An essential source for any Public Health Service history, the annual Marine-Hospital Service reports became the *Public Health Service Reports* in 1902. Those reports of the 1870s referred to the "Marine Hospital Bureau" in discussing the service's yearly work. The text of *Dental Science in a New Age* uses "Marine Hospital Service" to avoid confusing the reader.

51. *Annual Report of the Supervising Surgeon-General of the Marine-Hospital Service of the United States for the Fiscal Years 1874*, 54, and *1881*, 44, 49, 54, 60, 64, 69, 74, 79.

52. "History of the United States Public Health Service, 1798-1948," May 1948 manuscript, 7, "History, NIH and PHS," Brent Jaquet's Files, NIDR IO; A. M. Stimson, *A Brief History of Bacteriological Investigations of the United States Public Health Service*, Supplement No. 141 to the *Public Health Reports* (Washington: GPO, 1938), 2-5.

53. "Minutes of August 7, 1885," *Transactions of the American Dental Association at the Twenty-Fifth Annual Session*, 26-28. McCluggage, *History of the American Dental Association*, 211. These *Transactions*, actually annual reports, provided a fruitful source of information on dental history in the United States.

54. Robert H. Wiebe, *The Search for Order, 1877-1920*, American Century Series (New York: Hill and Wang, 1968), 111, 115; Harold U. Faulkner, *The Quest for Social Justice, 1898-1914* (Chicago: Quadrangle Books, 1959), 177; McCluggage, *History of the American Dental Association*, 209-10.

55. "Minutes of the August 6, 1897, Meeting of the National Dental Association," *Transactions of the American Dental Association*, Session of 1897, 16-20.

56. Col. P. M. Ashburn, *A History of the Medical Department of the United States Army* (Boston: Houghton Mifflin Company, 1929), 209-10.

57. Harold L. Faggart, "The First Century, 1898-1922," *JADA* 58 (June 1959): 32-33, and Francis J. Garvey, "Dentistry and the Legislative Process," *JADA* 40 (June 1950): 744-59; Walter D. Love, "Army Dentistry Forty Years Old," *JADA* 42 (March 1951): 313-14; "Fiftieth Anniversary, The United States Naval Dental Corps," *JADA* 65 (August 1962): 228-29.

58. Norman F. Gerrie, "Dental Public Health," *JADA* 40 (June 1950): 751.

59. "Agreement between the Thomas W. Evans Museum and Institute Society and the Trustees of the University of Pennsylvania," June 15, 1912, and the Will of Dr. Thomas W. Evans, loaned by the University of Pennsylvania School of Dental Medicine; Henry Rainey, *Dr. Thomas W. Evans, America's Dentist to European Royalty* (University of Pennsylvania School Library, 1952), 62; The Dental Research Advisory Committee, "The Field of Dental Research: Statement Prepared at the Request of the Chairman of the Medical Division of the National Research Council," April 1931, 11, "MED: Committee on Dental Research Advisory, 1928-1931," Central Files, National Academy of Sciences Archives (hereafter NAS); information from the University of Pennsylvania School of Dentistry librarian. The National Academy of Sciences Archives included unique and interesting material on the status of dental research in the United States.

60. The Dental Research Advisory Committee, "The Field of Dental Research: Statement Prepared at the Request of the Chairman of the Medical Division of the National Research Council," April 1931, 11, "MED: Committee on Dental Research Advisory, 1928-1921," Central Files, NAS; *American Dental Association Transactions*, 107th Annual Session, November 14-17, 1966, 72; *Transactions of the National Dental Association*, March 30-April 2, 1909, 116-19; W. A. Price to Rupert Blue, January 6, 1917, and Blue to Price, January 31, 1917, Record Group 90 (hereafter RG 90), Central File, 1897-1923, File 2111, National Archives and Records Administration (hereafter NARA). Although fragmentary, RG 90, records of the Public Health Service, contained significant material on the Public Health Service's relationship with dentistry in the twentieth century.

61. Faulkner, *The Quest for Social Justice*, 184; W. G. Ebersole to Walter Wyman, surgeon general, U.S. Public Health & Marine Hospital Service, October 25, 1911, RG 90, Central File, 1867-1923, File 1206, NARA; Arthur H. Merritt, "Mouth Hygiene and its Relation to Health," in *The Public Health Movement: The Annals of the American Academy of Political and Social Science* 37 (March 1911): 472-86.

62. Ebersole to Wyman, October 25, 1911; Ebersole to Dr. Rupert Blue, surgeon general, U.S. Public Health & Marine Hospital Service, August 15, 1912; W. Smith Frankland, chairman, Oral Hygiene Committee of the District of Columbia Dental Society, to Gen. Rupert Blue, June 24, 1912; Ebersole to Blue, November 23, 1912, and Blue to Ebersole, November 27, 1912, RG 90, Central File, 1897-1923, File 206, NARA.

63. Victoria Harden, *Inventing the NIH: Federal Biomedical Research Policy, 1887-1937* (Baltimore: The Johns Hopkins University Press, 1986), 42. Harden

provided an excellent scholarly, interesting history of the origins of the National Institute(s) of Health.

64. Frankland to Blue, June 24, 1912, and Blue to Frankland, June 28, 1912, RG 90, Central File, 1897-1923, File 1206, NARA; John S. Marshall, "Practical Hints on Office Sanitation," *Items of Interest* (October 1912): 765-75.

65. "Passed assistant surgeon" was a title given to a commissioned officer of the Public Health Service.

66. H. E. Hasseltine, "The Sterilization of Dental Instruments," *Hygienic Laboratory-Bulletin* no. 101 (August 1915): 53-69. Hasseltine referenced the Marshall speech to four western dental societies.

67. Frank C. Cady, "Indian Dental Service," *JADA* (June 1934): 1099; Frank J. McClure, *Water Fluoridation: The Search and the Victory* (Bethesda: NIDR, 1970), 13. The McClure work was a rich source for information on the federal government's role in fluoridation.

68. F. C. Cady, "Dental Health Organizations in State Departments of Health of the United States," *Public Health Bulletin* no. 251 (Washington: GPO, 1939).

69. American Expeditionary Forces, General Headquarters, Commander-in-Chief Reports, Appendix to Report of Commanding General S.O.S. Chief Surgeon, RG 120, Folder 319, NARA; Faggart, "1898-1922," 36-38.

70. U.S. *Statutes at Large* 40:1017.

CHAPTER TWO. *The Federal Government Moves Into Dental Research, 1919-1945*

1. *The First Fifty-Year History of the International Association for Dental Research* (Chicago: University of Chicago Press, 1973), 21-26.

2. William J. Gies, *Dental Education in the United States and Canada: A Report to the Carnegie Foundation for the Advancement of Teaching* (New York: Carnegie Foundation for the Advancement of Teaching, 1926), 157; Sissman, *75 Years of Dentistry*, 59, 70; files of NAS. Quotation was on p. 157 of the Gies report.

3. G. Burroughs Mider, "The Federal Impact on Biomedical Research," *Advances in American Medicine: Essays at the Bicentennial* 2 (Josiah Macy, Jr. Foundation, 1976), 824-30. An executive order of May 11, 1918, made the council a permanent body.

4. Dr. Thomas B. Hartzell to Dr. Henry A. Christian, chairman of the division of medical sciences, October 10, 1919, "MED: Committee on Dental Investigations, 1919-1923," Central Files, NAS.

5. Dr. Thomas B. Hartzell to Dr. V. C. Vaughan, division of medical sciences, November 8, 1921, "MED: Committee on Dental Investigations, 1919-1923," Central Files, NAS.

6. Dr. Henry A. Christian to Dr. W. S. Thayer, Johns Hopkins Hospital, May 13, 1920, "MED: Committee on Dental Investigations, 1919-1923," Central Files, NAS.

7. L. Hektoen to Capt. F. E. Rodriguez, January 27, 1925, "MED: Committee on Dental Investigations, 1924-1926," Central Files, NAS; *Transactions of the American Dental Association*, November 10-14, 1924, 99-100.

8. C. M. Jackson, chairman, division of medical sciences, to Dr. Thomas B. Hartzell, June 24, 1924; Hartzell to Capt. S. [sic] E. Rodriguez, November 15, 1924; and L. Hektoen, chairman, division of medical sciences, to Rodriguez, January 27, 1924, "MED: Committee on Dental Investigations, 1924-1926," Central Files, NAS.

9. Howard T. Karsner to Dr. Barrows, May 16, 1928, and Karsner to Dr. Arthur D. Black, June 13, 1928, "MED: Committee on Dental Research Advisory, 1928-1931," Central Files, NAS; *Fifty-Year History of the International Association for Dental Research*, 27; *Transactions of the Seventieth Annual Session of the American Dental Association*, August 20-24, 1928, 142, and "National Research Council Report of Committee on Dental Research," April 25, 1929, "MED: Committee on Dental Research Advisory, 1928-1931," Central Files, NAS. The other committee members were Dr. Lafayette B. Mendel, professor in the Department of Physiological Chemistry, Yale University; Dr. E. R. LeCount of the Department of Pathology, Rush Medical College, University of Chicago; Col. Charles F. Craig, a bacteriologist with the Army Medical School, Washington, D.C.; and Dr. Vilray P. Blair of Washington University, St. Louis, Missouri.

10. "National Research Council Report of Committee on Dental Research," April 25, 1929, and "The Field of Dental Research: Statement Prepared at the Request of the Chairman of the Medical Division of the National Research Council," April 1931, 95, "MED: Committee on Dental Research Advisory, 1928-1931, Central Files, NAS.

11. G. C. Paffenbarger and N. W. Rupp, "A History of the International Association for Dental Research Wilmer Souder Award in Dental Materials, with a Short Biography of Wilmer Souder," *Dental Materials* 2, no. 2 (1986): 50; C. G. Peters and W. H. Souder, "Some Physical Properties of Dental Materials," *Physical Review: A Journal of Experimental and Theoretical Physics* 13, ser. 2 (1919): 302-3; George C. Paffenbarger, John A. Tesk, and Walter E. Brown, "Dental Research at the National Bureau of Standards: How It Changed the Practice of Dental Health Service," *JADA* 111 (July 1985): 83; Wilmer Souder, "Dental Research at the National Bureau of Standards—Reminiscences," in *Dental Materials Research*, ed. George Dickson and James M. Cassel (NBS Special Publication 354, July 1972), 3.

12. Paffenbarger, Tesk, Brown, "Dental Research at the National Bureau of Standards," 84; "Past, Present and Future Plans of the Research Commission, *JADA* 35 (September 15, 1947): 402; *Transactions of the American Dental Association at the Sixty-Eighth Annual Session*, August 21-27, 1926; "Annual Report of the Secretary-Treasurer of the Scientific Foundation and Research Commis-

sion of the American Dental Association from July 1, 1925, to June 30, 1926,"
83; Lon W. Morrey, "A Synoptic History of the American Dental Association," *JADA* 58 (June 1959): 47; W. T. Sweeney, "Dental Materials Research
at the National Bureau of Standards—History and Individuals," *Dental Materials Research*, 8.

13. Paffenbarger, Tesk, Brown, "Dental Research at the National Bureau of Standards," 84, 88.

14. "Fernando E. Rodriguez," *JADA* (December 1932): 2195; McClure, *Fluoridation*, 13; F. E. Rodriguez, "Studies," 214. Rodriguez worked under the direction of Maj. Henry J. Nichols, assistant director of laboratories, and with the
assistance of the laboratory's Department of Bacteriology and Preventive
Medicine.

15. Rodriguez, "Studies," 199-214; James McIntosh, James Warwick, and P.
Lazarus-Barlow, *Lancet* 1 (London, 24, 1922): 1183-85.

16. *Military Dental Journal* 6 (June 1923): 96; C. Willard Camalier, Sr., *100 Years of
Dental Progress in the Nation's Capital* (Washington, May 1966), 125; *JADA*
(December 1932): 2195.

17. *Annual Report of the Surgeon General of the Public Health Service of the United States
for the Fiscal Year 1920*, 48; "The Work of the United States Public Health
Service during the World War," manuscript in the NIH Library, 153; Dr.
George A. Garrington, "A History of the Dental Corps of the United States
Public Health Service," manuscript, NIDR, 11-12.

18. Garrington, "History of the Dental Corps," 13, 17; *Annual Report of the Surgeon
General for the Fiscal Year 1920*, 256-57. The service continued to send some
professional dental personnel to the Veterans' Bureau until the act of June 7,
1924, which ended the detail of service personnel to the Veterans' Bureau.

19. Hartzell to Christian, October 10, 1919, "MED: Committee on Dental Investigations, 1919-1923," Central Files, NAS.

20. Resolution of July 19, 1922, RG 443, Box 196, Resolutions Folder, NARA.
The National Dental Association elected Hartzell president for a two-year
term in 1921. In 1922 the National Dental Association was renamed the
American Dental Association.

21. Messner biography in the District of Columbia Dental Society minutes in the
1928-1936 minutes binder, District of Columbia Dental Society Archives,
Washington, D.C.

22. Minutes, May 1936, District of Columbia Dental Society, Binder 1928-1936,
District of Columbia Dental Society Archives, Washington, D.C.; Garrington,
"History of the Dental Corps," 17; Memorandum Regarding Office Space of
the Dental Section by Clinton Messner, January 10, 1927, RG 90, Box 54,
District of Columbia and the States, 0245-H25 Washington, D.C., Dental
Clinic Folder, NARA; Messner to the surgeon general, July 6, 1927, RG 90,
Box 49, 0412 General Folder, NARA.

23. Henry L. Banzhaf to Gen. Herbert M. Lord, August 11, 1927, and Banzhaf to Surgeon General H. S. Cumming, August 11, 1927, RG 90, Box 159, 1950 ADA Folder, NARA.

24. Memorandum for the surgeon general (Attention: Dr. Stimson) from G. Mc-Coy, November 5, 1928, RG 90, Box 49, 0412 General Folder, NARA. The other participants included Dr. Rolla E. Dyer, assistant director of the laboratory, Claude S. Hudson of the Division of Chemistry, and Dr. William Charles White, tuberculosis expert in the Public Health Service; G. W. Mc-Coy to Professor Hudson, April 11, 1930, H. Trendley Dean Papers (hereafter Dean Papers), National Library of Medicine (hereafter NLM).

25. *Annual Report of the Surgeon General of the Public Health Service of the United States for the Fiscal Year 1931*, 47. The first epidemiological study will be discussed in the next chapter.

26. *Hearings Before a Subcommittee of the Committee on Commerce*, 70th Cong., 1st sess., S. 3391, April 25, 1928, 36-39.

27. Ibid.; 71st Cong., 2d sess., S. Rept. 102, Proposed National Institute of Health, 43-46.

28. Resolution, RG 90, Box 159, 1950 ADA Folder, NARA.

29. "The Field of Dental Research," April 1931, 94-95, "MED: Committee on Dental Research Advisory, 1928-1931," Central Files, NAS.

30. *Transactions of the Seventy-Fourth Annual Session American Dental Association*, September 12-16, 1932, 325-26; "The Fifty-Year Battle for Better Teeth," 5, Information Office Photographic File, Dr. Dean, NIDR IO.

CHAPTER THREE. *The National Institute of Health Initiates Dental Research*

1. Dental research was undertaken at the following universities: California, Louisville, Michigan, Minnesota, Northwestern, Harvard, Pennsylvania, Western Reserve, Illinois, and Rochester. The Forsyth Infirmary at Boston cooperated with the Harvard Medical School in research. In addition, the West Texas Dental Society investigated a disfiguring brown stain on teeth. For example, see *Transactions of the American Dental Association at the Sixty-Eighth Annual Session*, August 21-27, 1926, 70-71.

2. John Eager to the surgeon general, October 7, 1901, *Public Health Reports* (hereafter *PHR*) issued by the supervising surgeon-general, Marine-Hospital Service, vol. 16, Part 2, nos. 27-52 (Washington: GPO, 1902), 2576-77; Donald R. McNeil, *The Fight for Fluoridation* (New York: Oxford University Press, 1957), 10-11; McClure, *Fluoridation*, 2-3. Eager, who was not a dentist, also thought that the stained teeth were devoid of enamel, but that observation was incorrect. McNeil wrote a fascinating account of early fluoridation controversies in *Fight for Fluoridation*, the first published history on this subject.

3. McNeil, *Fight for Fluoridation*, 11-14; Grover A. Kempf and Frederick S. McKay, "Mottled Enamel in a Segregated Population," *PHR* 45 (November 28, 1930): 2923.

4. Rodriguez, as quoted in Frederick S. McKay, "An Investigation of Mottled Teeth," *Dental Cosmos* 58 (August 1916): 898-900.

5. McKay, "Investigation of Mottled Teeth," 904; Special Collection, Colorado College Library, information by telephone inquiry on December 3, 1986.

6. McKay, "Investigation of Mottled Teeth," 904; F. C. Smith, "Mottled Enamel and Brown Stain," *PHR* 31 (October 20, 1916): 2915-18.

7. McNeil, *Fight for Fluoridation*, 3-23.

8. David White, chairman, division of geology and geography, National Research Council, to Dr. G. W. McCoy, director, Hygienic Laboratory, February 4, 1927, Dean Papers, NLM.

9. F. W. Almond, M.D., director, State of Idaho Department of Public Health, Boise, to the surgeon general, November 5, 1923, and memorandum by G. W. McCoy, November 28, 1923, Dean Papers, NLM; McNeil, *Fight for Fluoridation*, 18-22, 200; Frederick S. McKay, "The Present Status of the Investigation of the Cause and of the Geographical Distribution of Mottled Enamel, Including a Complete Bibliography on Mottled Enamel," *Journal of Dental Research* 5:563. In reply to the Idaho health official, McCoy sent an abstract of the articles by McKay and Black on mottled enamel and brown stain.

10. McKay to Clark, December 7, 1925, and February 12, 1926, "Historical Items," John Small's Files, NIDR.

11. McKay to surgeon general, January 9, 1926, "Historical Items," John Small's Files, NIDR; A. M. Stimson, *Brief History of Bacteriological Investigations*, 72-73, 75; Harry F. Ferguson to Robert H. Lockwood, editor, *Water Works Engineering*, February 8, 1926; J. W. Bugbee to Lockwood, February 11, 1926, and Lockwood to the surgeon general with copies of Ferguson's and Bugbee's letters, December 20, 1926, "Historical Items," John Small's Files, NIDR.

12. Memorandum by G. W. McCoy, February 26, 1926; C. V. (Voegtlin) to Dr. McCoy, undated memorandum, accompanying memorandum of February 26, 1926, both sent to the surgeon general and to A. M. Stimson, assistant surgeon general, and "Memorandum: Regarding Letter from McKay on 'Mottled Enamel' of Teeth," February 25, 1926, by William Mansfield Clark, professor of chemistry, Hygienic Laboratory, "Historical Files," John Small's Files, NIDR; McClure, *Fluoridation*, 21, 25, 34.

13. Shortly after McKay had met with Clark, the surgeon general assigned Clark to duty in Europe and appointed Kempf to succeed Clark as chief of Child Hygiene Investigations. A. M. Stimson to Frederick S. McKay, February 12, 1926, "Historical Items," John Small's Files, NIDR; *Annual Report of the Surgeon General of the Public Health Service of the United States for the Fiscal Year 1926* (Washington: GPO, 1926), 41; Grover A. Kempf, Santa Fe, New Mexico, to the surgeon general, Washington, D.C., March 11, 1926, "Historical

Items," John Small's Files, NIDR. While in New Mexico, Kempf was puzzled by his discovery that some five hundred rural, poor New Mexican children in inferior general health had healthier than average teeth. He found that the "use of the toothbrush is practically unknown . . . no dental hygiene [is] practiced, and only six children had ever visited a dentist." Kempf wondered if a simple diet might be responsible for their superior oral health.

14. Kempf to Clark, April 26, 1927; Clark to Kempf, April 27, 1927; Kempf to McKay, May 17, 1927; McKay to Kempf, May 16, 1927, "Old Service Correspondence on Mottled Enamel," John Small's Files, NIDR; Memorandum by Clark, February 25, 1926, "Historical Items," John Small's Files, NIDR; McClure, *Fluoridation*, 21.

15. Kempf to McKay, November 12, 1926, "Old Service Correspondence on Mottled Enamel," John Small's Files, NIDR; McKay to Kempf, November 16, 1926, "Historical Items," John Small's Files, NIDR; McNeil, *Fight for Fluoridation*, 25-27; McKay to Kempf, January 12, 1927, "Historical Items," John Small's Files, NIDR; Kempf, McKay, "Mottled Enamel in a Segregated Population," 2923-40.

16. McNeil, *Fight for Fluoridation*, 27; H. V. Churchill, "Occurrence of Fluorides in Some Waters of the United States," *Industrial and Engineering Chemistry* 23 (September 1931): 996-98. In 1933 Lewis Clark Stubbins, consulting engineer for the Los Angeles Division of the California Taxpayers' Association, said that McKay asked Churchill to test the fluorine content of various domestic water supplies. McKay was present when Stubbins made that statement. See "Preliminary Report: Presence of Colorado River Water and Its Effect on Community Health," March 1, 1933, Dean Papers, NLM.

17. Churchill, "Occurrence of Fluorides," 998; McKay to Hugh S. Cumming, surgeon general, June 30, 1931, Wyndham Miles Folder, "Notes for History," National Library of Medicine History of Medicine Division (hereafter NLMHMD).

18. Minutes of the Meeting of the Research Commission, American Dental Association, October 8, 1929, and July 20 and 22, 1930, American Dental Association Archives, Chicago, Illinois (hereafter ADA Archives).

19. Typewritten biography, January 1953, in Dean Papers, NLM; "The Fifty Year Battle for Better Teeth," Information Office Photographic File, 4-6, NIDR IO; *Annual Report of the Surgeon General of the Public Health Service of the United States for the Fiscal Year 1932*, 43; Marjorie Dent Candee, ed., *Current Biography* (New York: W. H. Wilson Company, 1957), 30-31.

20. McKay to Hugh S. Cumming, surgeon general, June 30, 1931, Wyndham Miles Folder, "Notes for History," NLMHMD; Dean to McKay, June 30, 1931, Dean Papers, NLM.

20. "The Fifty Year Battle for Better Teeth," Information Office Photographic File, 4-6, NIDR IO; correspondence between Dean and McKay in Dean Papers, NLM.

22. "The Fifty Year Battle for Better Teeth," Information Office Photographic File, 5-6, NIDR IO.

23. Memorandum by Professor Claude Hudson, chemist, and Dean to the surgeon general, October 3, 1931; Dean to the surgeon general, December 7, 1931, Dean Papers, NLM.

24. Italics the author's. Dean to the surgeon general, February 6, 1932, Dean Papers, NLM; H. Trendley Dean, "Epidemiological Studies in the United States," *Dental Caries and Fluorine* (AAAS, 1946), 5-6.

25. *Annual Report of the Surgeon General of the Public Health Service of the United States for the Fiscal Year 1932*, 43; McClure, *Fluoridation*, 57, 60; Dean to Assistant Surgeon General L. R. Thompson, October 27, 1933, RG 90, Box 159, 1950 Folder, NARA. According to Dean's daughter, Ruth C. Dean, in a conversation with the author in February 1987, her father referred to his trips for the mottled enamel investigations as his "shoe leather surveys."

26. Memorandum by Dean to Assistant Surgeon General L. R. Thompson, October 27, 1933, RG 90, Box 159, 1950, ADA Folder, NARA.

27. *American Men of Science*, 9th ed., vol. 1, *Physical Sciences* (New York: R. R. Bowker Company, 1955), 542; Elias Elvove, "Estimation of Fluorides in Water," *PHR* 48 (October 6, 1933): 1219-22; Dr. Francis Arnold, interview no. 2 by Dr. Wyndham Miles, June 17, 1964, NLMHMD; McClure, *Fluoridation*, 63-64; Dean, "Epidemiological Studies," 7; Dean to McKay, November 6, 1935, Dean Papers, NLM.

28. McClure, *Fluoridation*, 61, 64; H. Trendley Dean and Elias Elvove, "Chronic Endemic Dental Fluorosis," *Journal of the American Medical Association* (hereafter *JAMA*) 107 (October 17, 1936): 1269-72.

29. Dean and Elvove, "Chronic Endemic Dental Fluorosis," 10; McClure, *Fluoridation*, 64, 63.

30. Claude S. Hudson to Dr. McCoy, June 26, 1936, RG 443, Box 182, Dental Studies, 1934-1936 Folder, NARA; L. R. Thompson to the chief clerk and administrative officer, September 24, 1940, RG 443, Box 81, Elvove, Elias Folder, NARA; Dean to the surgeon general, September 22, 1932, February 21 and May 25, 1933, Dean Papers, NLM; Dr. Frank McClure, interview by Dr. Wyndham Miles, May 20, 1964, NLMHMD; "Notes on Dr. Frank J. McClure—Answers to Questions," February 19, 1970, Information Office Photographic File, Dr. McClure, NIDR IO. From 1932 to 1933 the section on nutrition conducted rat and dog experiments with fluoride for Dean.

31. Dr. Francis Arnold, interview no. 1 by Dr. Wyndham Miles, June 10, 1964, Wyndham Miles files and tapes, NLMHMD; Francis A. Arnold to the surgeon general, September 22, 1937, RG 443, Box 76, Arnold, Francis A. (Jr.) Folder, NARA; Arnold to surgeon general, December 28, 1937, RG 443, Box 76, Arnold, Francis A. (Jr.) Folder, NARA; Dean to the surgeon general, February 3, 1938, RG 443, Box 182, Dental S4 1937-1938 Folder, NARA.

32. McClure, *Fluoridation*, 37-56.

33. H. T. Dean to F. S. McKay, October 3, 1940, Dean Papers, NLM.

34. Henry Klein and Carroll E. Palmer, "Dental Caries in American Indian Children," *Public Health Bulletin* 239 (December 1937): 37; Dean to McKay, Febru-

ary 7, 12, and 25, 1938, Dean Papers, NLM; H. Trendley Dean, "Endemic Fluorosis and Its Relation to Dental Caries," *PHR* 53, no. 33 (August 19, 1938): 1443-52; McClure, *Fluoridation*, 76, 78; Dean, "Epidemiological Studies," 6, 8.

Klein and Palmer wrote the following analysis:

> The southwestern area, which has the lowest caries attack rates of all the areas studied, is in general an endemic fluorosis area . . . This fact may have important implications and would seem to justify some discussion. Fluorides are well known as enzyme inhibitors . . . and it may be suggested that perhaps a measure of the responsibility for low caries attack rates in the southwestern area may be the result of the drinking of fluoride waters. Such water may provide an enzyme inhibitor which will operate to limit the chemical degradation of tooth impacted carbohydrates to organic acids, so reducing the production of local acidity about the teeth and so limiting an important vector in caries initiation. It may be mentioned in this connection that support for this concept is discernible in the literature.

Dean, however, did not cite Klein and Palmer nor give credit to them for that observation, which preceded his 1938 publication. Considering the close relationships in the National Institute of Health in the 1930s, one must surmise that Dean learned of the Klein and Palmer analysis and followed through with his own more substantive version.

35. Dean, "Endemic Fluorosis."

36. McKay to Dean, June 5, 1939, and Dean to McKay, June 26, 1939, Dean Papers, NLM.

37. McClure, *Fluoridation*, 109; Dean, "Epidemiological Studies," 8.

38. McClure, *Fluoridation*, 82-83, 106; Dean, "Epidemiological Studies," 7.

39. Dean, "Epidemiological Studies," 14, 16, 20, 29.

40. W. J. Pelton to Dr. Mountin, October 1, 1942; Dean to Pelton, October 9, 1942; and H. W. Streeter to director, National Institute of Health, October 16, 1942, RG 90, Box 45, 0412 General Folder, NARA. H. W. Streeter, the senior sanitary engineer, Office of Stream Pollution Investigations; C. T. Butterfield, principal bacteriologist; and C. C. Huchhoft, principal chemist, also participated in the meeting. In 1942 Dean and his colleagues used the terms "fluorine" and "fluorination."

41. W. J. Pelton to J. W. Mountin, November 11, 1942, "Historical Records," John Small's Files, NIDR.

42. J. W. Mountin, assistant surgeon general, States Relations Division, to Hon. Thomas C. Desmond, November 12, 1942, RG 90, Box 45, 0412 General Folder, NARA; W. J. Pelton to J. W. Mountin, November 11, 1942, "Historical Records," John Small's Files, NIDR; L. T. Hunt to H. T. Dean, November 9, 1942, and Dean to Hunt, November 12, 1942, "Historical Files," NIDR IO; McClure, *Fluoridation*, 122, 129; David Bernard Ast, "The Caries-Fluorine Hypothesis and a Suggested Study to Test Its Application," *PHR* 58 (June 4, 1943): 23. Mountin advised the New York legislator that the Public Health

Service thought it necessary to conduct additional studies first to insure the safety to humans before treating water with fluoride.

43. Arnold to C. R. Taylor, January 26, 1943, "Grand Rapids—Correspondence to and from the State Health Department (Dr. Fred Wertheimer)" (hereafter "Grand Rapids—Correspondence"), NIDR; National Institute of Health Weekly Report, May 1-8, 1943, RG 443, Box 107, General Records, 1950 231 Folder, NARA; Nicholas C. Leone, Michael B. Shimkin, Francis A. Arnold, Jr., Clyde A. Stevenson, Eugene R. Zimmerman, Patricia B. Geiser, and Jacob E. Lieberman, "Medical Aspects of Excessive Fluoride in a Water Supply," *PHR* 69 (October 1954): 925-36.

44. F. J. McClure and C. A. Kinser, "Fluoride Domestic Waters and Systemic Effects I. Relation to Bone-Fracture Experience, Height, and Weight of High School Boys and Young Selectees of the Armed Forces of the United States," McClure, and "II. Fluorine Content of Urine in Relation to Fluorine in Drinking Water," McClure and Kinser, Reprint no. 2588 from *PHR* 59, no. 48 (December 1, 1944), and no. 49 (December 8, 1944), respectively.

45. W. J. Pelton to J. W. Mountin, December 29, 1942, "Grand Rapids—Correspondence," John Small's Files, NIDR. The other cities Faust recommended were Bay City, with a population of 47,956 and a water supply from Lake Huron, and Muskegon Heights, with a population of over 16,000 and a Lake Michigan water source.

46. C. R. Taylor to Francis A. Arnold, Jr., January 21, 1943, "Grand Rapids—Correspondence," John Small's Files, NIDR.

47. As Faust described Grand Rapids, it had "one of the most stable populations of any city in Michigan." Dean to William R. Davis, June 7, 1944, "Grand Rapids—Correspondence," John Small's Files, NIDR; Davis to Dean, June 13, 1944, ibid.; Raymond J. Faust to Dean, July 7, 1944, ibid.; Leone et al., "Medical Aspects of Excessive Fluoride"; Dean to Davis, July 17, 1944, and Davis to Dean, July 24, 1944, "Grand Rapids—Correspondence," John Small's Files, NIDR.

48. Davis to Dean, July 24 and August 3, 1944; Walter H. Sack, city manager, to Dr. William DeKleine, n.d., "Grand Rapids—Correspondence," John Small's Files, NIDR; William DeKleine to Trendley Dear [sic], August 2, 1944, John Small's Files, NIDR; Michigan Department of Health Public Health News, 38-W 9/15/44, "Grand Rapids—Correspondence," John Small's Files, NIDR.

49. McClure, *Fluoridation*, 114.

50. Louis Schwartz, F. C. Makepeace, and H. T. Dean, "Health Aspects of Radium Dial Painting. IV. Medical and Dental Phases," *Journal of Industrial Hygiene* 15 (November 1933): 447-55.

51. *Annual Report of the Surgeon General of the Public Health Service for the Fiscal Year 1934*, 27.

52. F. C. Cady et al., *A Survey of Dental Activities of State Departments and Institutions of the United States, Public Health Bulletin*, no. 227 (Washington: GPO, 1936),

iii; H. S. Cumming to Dr. Stanley H. Osborn, Commissioner of Health, Hartford, Connecticut, February 27, 1935, RG 90, Box 49, 0412 General Folder, NARA; H. Trendley Dean and Francis A. Arnold, "Dental Research and the National Institute of Health. 1. Intramural Research," *JADA* 38 (January 1949): 15.

53. Cady et al., *A Survey of Dental Activities*, iv, 1; George B. Winter, "President's Address," *JADA* 23 (September 1936): 1617; F. C. Cady, *Dental Health Organizations in State Departments of Health of the United States, Public Health Bulletin*, no. 251 (Washington: GPO, 1939), 3.

54. Cady, *Dental Health Organizations*, v, 3.

55. L. R. Thompson to Dr. John A. Ferrell, Rockefeller Foundation, October 17, 1934, RG 443, Box 182, Dental Studies 1934-1936 Folder, NARA, and John McMullen, acting surgeon general, to the members of the National Advisory Health Council, November 5, 1934, RG 443, Box 182, Rockefeller Gift Folder, NARA.

56. C. T. Messner, W. M. Gafafer, F. C. Cady, and H. T. Dean, *Dental Survey of School Children, Ages 6-14 Years, Made in 1933-1934 in 26 States, Public Health Bulletin* no. 226 (Washington: GPO, 1936), 1-2.

57. Ibid.; Dr. Thomas Parran, surgeon general, to Mrs. Ralph Walton, Houston, Texas, March 19, 1938, RG 90, General Classified Records, Group IX-General Files, 1936-1944, 0412 Dentistry Folder, NARA.

58. Dean, "Endemic Fluorosis."

59. Dr. Thomas Parran, surgeon general, to the general counsel, Federal Security Agency, January 27, 1940, "Historical Files," NIDR IO; Dean to the surgeon general, February 3, 1938, RG 443, Dental S4 1937-1938 Folder, NARA; Parran to Daniel F. Lynch, secretary, Research Commission, July 11, 1939, RG 443, General Records 075A, American Dental Association Folder, NARA; Harden, *Inventing the NIH*, 173. In Title V Congress authorized an annual appropriation of $2 million for Public Health Service research into diseases and sanitation problems, but Congress never appropriated the full amount during the 1930s.

60. Winter, "President's Address," 1618; Garrington, "Dental Corps History," 19; Dr. H. E. Kelsey to the surgeon general, November 23, 1936, and Daniel F. Lynch to the surgeon general, August 31, 1937, RG 443, Box 31, General Records 075A, American Dental Association Folder, NARA.

61. See note 60 above.

62. For a discussion of Thompson and Parran, see Harden, *Inventing the NIH*, 170-71; Dr. Francis Arnold, interviews 1 through 5 by Dr. Wyndham Miles, June 10, June 17, September 16, October 4, and December 9, 1964, respectively; Dr. David B. Scott, interview by Ruth R. Harris, September 3, 1986, NIDR IO.

63. Carroll E. Palmer, passed assistant surgeon, Child Hygiene, to E. H. Bruening, chairman, Committee on Economics, ADA, September 8, 1937, RG 443, Box

31, General Records 075A, American Dental Association Folder, NARA; Dean and Arnold, "Dental Research and the National Institute of Health," 15.

64. Henry Klein, Carroll E. Palmer, and John W. Knutson, "Studies on Dental Caries. I. Dental Status and Dental Needs of Elementary School Children," *PHR* 53 (May 13, 1938): 751-65; "Significant Events in Division of Dental Health History," Chief Dental Officer, Public Health Service Files (hereafter CDO PHS); Palmer to Bruening, September 8, 1937, RG 443, Box 31, General Records 075A, American Dental Association Folder, NARA; Klein and Palmer, "Dental Caries in American Indian Children"; Knutson, "Studies on Dental Caries. IV. Tooth Mortality in Elementary School Children," *PHR* Reprint No. 1021 (June 24, 1938).

65. *American Dental Association Transactions*, July 17-21, 1939, 247-51.

66. Dean to the surgeon general, RG 443, Box 182, Dental S4 1937-1938 Folder, NARA; Francis A. Arnold, Jr., "The Production of Carious Lesions in the Molar Teeth of Hamsters *(C. auratus)*," *PHR* 57 (October 23, 1942): 1599-1604; Commission on the Survey of Dentistry in the United States, *The Survey of Dentistry: The Final Report* (Washington, D.C.: American Council on Education, 1961), 425.

67. Trench mouth is referred to also as ulcerative stomatitis, acute necrotizing ulcerative gingivitis (ANUG), and Vincent's infection.

68. *American Dental Association Transactions of the Eighty-First Annual Session*, July 17-21, 1939, 247-49; Thomas Parran, surgeon general, to Daniel Lynch, July 11, 1939, RG 443, Box 31, General Records 075A, American Dental Association Folder, NARA; L. R. Thompson, to Hugo Muench, Rockefeller Foundation, August 12, 1939, RG 443, NIH 1930-1948, Box 87, 1650 J-K, Knutson, John W. Folder, NARA; L. R. Thompson, director, NIH, to Dr. Daniel F. Lynch, secretary, Research Commission, ADA, May 9, 1941, RG 443, Box 31, General Record 075A, American Dental Association Folder, NARA.

69. Dean, Charles Armstrong, and L. R. Thompson to Dr. Daniel F. Lynch, September 16, 1941, RG 443, NIH 1930-48 General Records, Box 84, 1650 H, Hampp, E. G. Folder, NARA; *American Dental Association Transactions of the Eighty-Third Annual Session*, October 27-31, 1941, 204, 209-10; Dyer, Armstrong, and Dean to Dr. Daniel F. Lynch, February 5, 1942, RG 443, NIH 1930-48 General Records, Box 84, 1640 H, Hampp, E. G., NARA; Dean to the director, May 30, 1942, RG 443, Box 31, General Records 075A, American Dental Association Folder, NARA.

70. Dean to the Director, May 20, 1942, NIDR.

71. "Dr. Dean's Material" and Jane Stafford, "Trench Mouth Recovery Speeded by Immediate Scaling and Attention to Mouth Sanitation," October 5, 1944, Dean Papers, NLM; *American Dental Association Transactions of the Eighty-Fourth Annual Session*, August 24-26, 1942, 255; Alvin E. Strock to Dean, April 16, 1945, Dean Papers, NLM.

72. Dean to Senior Dental Surgeon David Cooper, Headquarters, U.S. Coast Guard, Washington, D.C., June 1, 1945, Dean Papers, NLM.

73. Dean to P. A. Dental Surgeon H. B. McCauley, U.S. Coast Guard Training Station, Atlantic City, New Jersey, October 19, 1945, Dean Papers, NLM.

CHAPTER FOUR. *Birth of the National Institute of Dental Research*

1. Derek J. de Solla Price, *Little Science Big Science* (New York: Columbia University Press, 1963), 1.

2. Harden, *Inventing the NIH,* 170-73.

3. John R. Steelman, *The Nation's Medical Research,* vol. 5, *Science and Public Policy. A Report to the President* (Washington: GPO, 1947), 59-60, 42-44.

4. The Reorganization Act of 1939 (P.L. 76-19, 53 Stat. L. 561); Dr. A. Packchanian to Dr. L. R. Thompson, director, NIH, May 3, 1939, and Packchanian to Dr. Thomas Parran, surgeon general; Dr. L. R. Thompson, director, NIH, to Dr. R. E. Dyer, chief, Division of Infectious Diseases, July 24, 1939, RG 443, Box 70, 1575 Folder, NARA. Because Packchanian's earlier draft contained no mention of a dental institute, possibly Dean persuaded Packchanian to include such an institute in the final version. Some of Packchanian's other suggestions that were later adopted included the establishment of a research hospital and a "National Institute of Infectious Diseases."

5. "Dr. C. Willard Camalier Dies, Former Dental Society Head," *Washington Post,* April 23, 1976, B12; C. Willard Camalier, Sr., *100 Years of Dental Progress in the Nation's Capital,* (Washington, D.C.: 1966), 175, 222, 225-28, 236.

6. *Biographical Directory of the American Congress 1774-1961,* (Washington: GPO, 1961), 1375. Murray's papers at the University of Montana Library were unavailable for research for this history.

7. S. 3607; H. T. Dean to the director, NIH, March 26, 1940, and Dean to Dean Basil G. Bibby, Tufts College Dental School, Boston, October 18, 1940, "Historical Files," NIDR IO; S. 194; U.S. Cong., House, *Research Relating to Dental Diseases: Hearing before a Subcommittee of the Committee on Interstate and Foreign Commerce . . . on S. 194,* July 14, 1941 (Washington: GPO, 1941). Dr. Frank Cady also urged the surgeon general to expand dental work in the service. See Cady to the surgeon general, March 19, 1941, RG 90, Box 45, 0412 Dentistry Folder, NARA.

8. Public Law 184, 57 Stat. 587; H.R. 7616, September 19, 1942, 77th Cong., 2d sess.; H.R. 649, January 6, 1943, 78th Cong., 1st sess.; S. 400, January 14, 1943, 78th Cong., 1st sess.; "Reorganization of United States Public Health Service Provides Rear Admiral for Dental Division," *JADA* 31 (January 15, 1944): 159-61; Sterling Mead to Sen. Lister Hill, May 13 and 25, 1944, Lister Hill Papers, Roll 1, Senate Related Papers, 1938-1946, NLMHMD.

9. Public Law 410; J. A. Trautman, senior surgeon, assistant chief, Division of Commissioned Officers, to Dean, June 26, 1945, RG 443, Box 80, Dean, Harold T. Folder, NARA.

10. Dr. Thomas Parran, surgeon general, "Elements of a National Health Program," (preliminary draft), RG 443, Box 122, 1973 General, Postwar Planning Folder, NARA.

11. "The Dental Status and Dental Needs of Young Adult Males, Rejectable, or Acceptable for Military Service, According to Selective Service Dental Requirements," "Historical Files," NIDR IO; "Report of the U.S. Army Medical Department Research and Development Program 1 January-31 March 1947," 161-66, NLM.

12. U.S. Cong., Senate, *Wartime Health and Education: Hearings before a Subcommittee of the Committee on Education and Labor . . . pursuant to S. Res. 74*, pt. 5, 78th Cong., 2d sess., July 10, 11, and 12, 1944 (Washington: GPO, 1944), 1649-54; Rear Adm. A. W. Chandler, Dental Corps, U.S. Navy, "Dental Education and Research in the Navy," *Military Surgeon* 102 (April 1948): 166-67. No explanation was available for the difference between the percentages of rejections for dental reasons reported in 1940 and on December 7, 1941. In both cases dental causes led the list of reasons for physical rejection for service.

13. U.S. Cong., Senate, *Dental Research and Dental Care: Hearings before a Subcommittee of the Committee on Education and Labor . . . on S. 190*, 79th Cong., 1st sess., June 26, 27, and 28, 1945 (hereafter *Hearings on S. 190*) (Washington: GPO, 1945), 62-63.

14. *Hearings on S. 190*, 10, 18, 21; "Statement on National Program for Dental Health Issued by Joint Committee of Three ADA Committees," *JADA* 32 (March 15, 1945): 498-503. The ratio of dentists to population was already changing before the United States entered the war. Between 1930 and 1940 there was 1 dentist for every 1,720 persons; by 1940 the country had but 1 dentist for every 1,865 individuals.

15. See note 14 above.

16. *Hearings on S. 190*, 6, 116.

17. Camalier, *One Hundred Years of Dental Progress*, 222; U.S. Cong., Senate, 79th Cong., 1st sess., S. 190, "Legislation Supporting and Establishing National Institute of Dental Research 1956-1947," NIDR IO.

18. "Statement of Hon. James E. Murray, United States Senator from Montana, on the Introduction of a Bill to Establish a National Institute of Dental Research," "Historical Files," NIDR IO.

19. *Hearings on S. 190*, 6, 146-47.

20. *Hearings on S. 190*, 116, 146-47.

21. *Hearings on S. 190*, 12-13, 35, 22.

22. *Hearings on S. 190*, 25, 33, 82-83.

23. *Hearings on S. 190*, 25, 47, 82-83.

24. *Hearings on S. 190*, 83.

25. *Hearings on S. 190*, 21, 33, 40-43, 109-14.

26. U.S. Cong., Senate, *National Institute of Dental Research Act, May 20 (legislative day, March 5, 1946)*, Report, 79th Cong., 2d sess., S. Rept 1363, 2; U.S. Cong., House, *National Institute of Dental Research: Hearing before the Committee on Interstate and Foreign Commerce . . . on H.R. 574, H.R. 4200, and S. 176*, 80th Cong., 2d sess., March 11, 1948 (hereafter *Hearing on S. 176*), 11.

27. National Institutes of Health Legislative Office, "Chronology of Legislation," April 10, 1985, 4.

28. David B. Scott, "The Support of Research by the American College of Dentists," *Journal of the American College of Dentists* 37 (1970): 201-5.

29. H. Trendley Dean, "The Personnel Problem in Dental Research: With Some Comments on USPHS Research Fellowships," *Journal of the American College of Dentists* 15 (June 1948): 52, 53.

30. H. T. Dean to Assistant Surgeon General W. T. Wright, Jr., Dental Division, May 29, 1946, "Historical Files," NIDR IO.

31. Review of the President's Secretary's File, Harry S. Truman Library, Independence, Missouri (hereafter PSF HSTL). White House Staff noted from 1945 through 1947 that Truman did not discuss any views on a prospective dental institute after the Senate passed S. 190 and sent it to the House.

32. Steelman, *The Nation's Medical Research*, 10-11, 75, 86, 88, 116. Quotation was on p. 88.

33. "Summary of the National Health Act of 1947 (S. 545)" and "Statement of Dr. Thomas Parran, Surgeon General, U.S. Public Health Service, on S-1320 and S-545 before the Subcommittee on Health of the Senate Committee on Labor and Public Welfare, July 9, 1947," RG 235, Box 50, 032.2 1947 Folder, NARA; "Legislative History of Public Law 755—80th Cong. (H.R. 6726)," Files of Office of the Director, Office of Program Planning and Evaluation, Division of Legislative Analysis, NIH. The bills introduced in 1947 were S. 545 by Taft; S. 176 by Murray, Pepper, Taft, Aiken, and Morse; H.R. 574 by Harris; and H.R. 4200 by Brehm. Taft's S. 545 was a national health bill that provided for a dental research institute. Parran thought that the Taft bill needed considerable amendment and did not endorse it. Brehm introduced H.R. 6470 and 6726 in 1948.

34. *Congressional Record*, Senate, July 24, 1947, 10165; "Legislative History of Public Law 755," 1.

35. *Hearing on S. 176*, 12-21. For Parran quotation see p. 13.

36. *Hearing on S. 176*, 29, 33, 39, 43, 55, and 58. The association witnesses included Dr. Carl Flagstad, chairman of the Legislative Committee; Dr. Harold Hillenbrand, the association's secretary and journal editor; Dr. Allen Gruebbel, executive secretary of the association's Council on Dental Health; Dr. Charles B. Hall, secretary of the association's Research Commission; and Dr. Sterling V. Mead, past president of the association. The International Association for Dental Research, represented by its president, Dr. Harold C. Hodge, and the American Association of Dental Schools, with Dr. Walter H. Wright as spokesman, also testified in favor of the dental research institute bill.

37. *Hearing on S. 176*, 8-10. Quotation on p. 10.

38. *Hearing on S. 176*, 16, 18, 38-39.

39. *ADA News Letter* 1 (May 15, 1948): 2, and (June 1, 1948): 1.

40. U.S. Cong., House, *Amending the Public Health Service Act to Provide for a National Institute of Dental Research*, Report No. 2158, 80th Cong., 2d sess., June 2, 1948, 2-3; *Congressional Record*, June 8, 1948, 7595; "Legislative History of Public Law 755," 1.

41. Undated memorandum on H.R. 6726, probably by Dean or Arnold, "National Institute of Dental Research—Administration, Save—Arnold," "Legislation—Supporting for National Institute of Dental Research 1956-1947 and Establishing of NIDR," NIDR IO; *Congressional Record*, Senate, June 12, 1948, 8115; *Congressional Record*, House, June 14, 1948, 8258.

42. Ewing to Hon. James E. Webb, June 16, 1948, and Staats to William Hopkins, the White House, June 24, 1948, Papers of Harry S. Truman, White House Bill File, HSTL; Bruce D. Forsyth to the President, June 17, 1948, "Notes for History," Wyndham Miles Files, NLMHMD; "Legislative History of Public Law 755." Dr. C. Willard Camalier arranged in advance with the White House staff for the president's signing in the presence of dental profession leaders. See Camalier to Matthew J. Connelly, June 14, 1948, Official File, File Folder "Dentists," 286-C, HSTL; *ADA News Letter* 1 (July 1, 1948): 2.

43. By 1948 the government used the term "fluoridation" instead of "fluorination."

44. *Annual Report of the Federal Security Agency 1948*, 261-66.
45. R. E. Dyer to the surgeon general, July 13, 1948, "Legislation—Save Arnold," NIDR IO.

46. General Circular No. 54, Organization Order No. 22, Federal Security Agency Serial No. 452, December 1, 1948, RG 443, Box 70, 1575 Folder, NARA; "Implementing Circular, Serial No. 470, Federal Security Agency, April 1, 1949," *The Division of Dental Public Health: Its Authorization, Functions, Objectives, Organization, Resources, Projects*, Division of Associated and Dental Health Profession, Dr. Thomas Louden's Files, PHS.

47. Staff meeting, July 20, 1948, transcript, "Legislation—Save Arnold," NIDR IO.

48. Ibid.

49. Dr. Masur to Dr. Dyer, August 6, 1946, "National Dental Institute," Files of the Office of the Director, National Institutes of Health (hereafter OD NIH); Carl O. Flagstad, D.D.S., chairman, Council on Legislation, "Statement of the American Dental Association Requesting an Appropriation to Support the Provisions of the National Dental Research Act," Notebook: ADA Statements 81st—1949-50, Files of the American Dental Association, Washington, D.C. (hereafter ADA DC).

50. General Circular No. 49, Serial No. 440, September 13, 1948, "Legislation Supporting for National Institute of Dental Research 1956-1947 and Establishing of NIDR," no. 3 of 4, NIDR IO.

51. Ibid.; recollection of Dr. David B. Scott; Dr. Rachel Larson Henry, interview by Ruth R. Harris, March 10, 1987; Dean to staff members, NIDR, November 9, 1948, "NIDR History," NIDR IO; Dr. Karl Piez, interview by Ruth R. Harris, December 29, 1986. Dr. David Scott, in an interview of September 3, 1986, made a similar statement.

52. Personnel Orders No. 198, October 22, 1948, and October 15, 1948, RG 443, Box 76, Arnold, Francis A. (Jr.) Folder, NARA; Personnel Orders No. 203, October 29, 1948, RG 443, Box 80, Dean, H. T. Folder, NARA; October 20, 1948, National Institute of Dental Research FY 1949 Civil Service Personnel and Commissioned Officers-Regular, "Historical Files," NIDR IO; director, NIH, to the surgeon general, June 22, 1949, RG 443, Box 76, Arnold, Francis A. (Jr.) Folder, NARA.

53. "No. 15 in a Series: Microscopic Studies on Teeth," *NIH Record* 1 (December 23, 1949): 2.

54. National Institutes of Health, Papers Submitted for Publication and Presentation during the Fiscal Year 1948 and Addendum to Papers Submitted during Fiscal Year 1948, RG 443, General Records, Box 105, 1680 168 Folder, NARA; "Proposed Dental Budget for FY 1949," "Legislation—Save Arnold," NIDR IO.

55. "Proposed Dental Budget for FY 1949," "Legislation—Save Arnold," NIDR IO; "NIDR Professional Staff Listing Back Issues, 1958-present," NIDR IO. The organizational chart was signed by Dean and Dyer on November 7, 1949; "National Advisory Dental Research Council Minutes of Meeting," January 10, 1949, 13-14, NIDR Library.

56. "Memorandum in Regard to Proposed Budget, Dental Research Institute, Fiscal Year 1949," June 11, 1949, "Notes for History," Wyndham Miles Files, NLMHMD.

57. National Advisory Dental Research Council, Minutes of Meeting, January 10, 1949, NIDR Library.

58. Ibid., 6, 7, 13, 14; "Extramural Research Support," 140, "Legislation Supporting for National Institute of Dental Research 1956-1947 and Establishing of NIDR," no. 3 of 4, NIDR IO.

59. R. E. Dyer through Dr. H. Trendley Dean to Dr. Robert M. Stephan, March 16, 1949, RG 443, Box 95, NIH 1930-1948, 1650 S-T, Stephan, R. M. Folder, NARA; memorandum by Dean, June 20, 1949, RG 443, Box 76, 1650A, Arnold, Francis A., Jr., Folder, NARA; National Advisory Dental Research Council, Minutes of Meeting, November 4, 1949, 6; "Extramural Research Support," 149; "Legislation Supporting for National Institute of Dental Research 1956-1947 and Establishing of NIDR," no. 3 of 4, NIDR IO. Officially started in June 1949, the Dental Research Specialty Board members were Drs. Robert M. Stephan, Isadore Zipkin, Edward G. Hampp, and Robert J. Fitzgerald, dental scientists in the Institute.

60. "Extramural Research Support," 140-51; Mary G. Munger, "Growth of the Extramural Programs of the National Institutes of Health (FY 1944 through

FY 1958)," February 19, 1960, "Historical Files," NIDR IO; Kenneth M. Endicott and Ernest M. Allen, "Trends in Public Health Service Research Grants 1946-1952," January 30, 1953, 5, RG 90, Box 88, 62A64, 5. Grants Program, 1956 Folder, Federal Records Center, Suitland, Maryland (hereafter FRC); "Statement of the American Dental Association to the Senate Appropriations Committee Seeking an Appropriation to Assist Local Communities to Fluoridate Water Supplies; and Construction Funds for the National Institute of Dental Research Building," May 15, 1951, Notebook: ADA Statements, 81st—1954-50 through 85th—1957-58, ADA DC.

61. National Advisory Dental Research Council, Minutes of Meeting, February 17, 1950, 1; National Institutes of the Health, "Report for the Fiscal Year July 1, 1950-June 30, 1951," 103.

62. Director, NIDR, to Dr. Bruce D. Forsyth, February 6, 1950, RG 443, Box 105, General Records, 1680 168 Folder, NARA; *NIH Record* 1 (December 2, 1949): 1.

CHAPTER FIVE. *Fluoridation: Success and Controversy*

1. F. A. Arnold, Jr., to Dr. C. Ray Taylor, Michigan Dept. of Health, Lansing, February 28, 1945; Dr. William R. Davis to Arnold, NIH, Bethesda, Maryland, March 9, 1945; Arnold to Davis, March 15, 1945, "Grand Rapids—Correspondence," John Small's Files, NIDR; H. W. Street, sanitary engineer, Sanitary Engineering Division, Public Health Service, Cincinnati, to Dr. H. T. Dean, August 6, 1945, and Dean to Street, July 16, 1945, "Historical Records," John Small's Files, NIDR.

2. Dr. Francis Arnold, interview no. 4 by Dr. Wyndham Miles, December 9, 1964. The tapes are available at NLMHMD and NIDR IO.

3. "Grand Rapids, Michigan—Fluoridation Project Background," "25th Anniversary of Fluoridation in 1970 (Quarter-Century Observances)," Brent Jaquet's Files, NIDR IO; U.S. Cong., House, *Chemicals in Foods and Cosmetics: Hearings before the House Select Committee to Investigate the Use of Chemicals in Foods and Cosmetics . . . Pursuant to H. Res. 74 and H. Res. 447*, pt. 3, 82d Cong., 2d sess. (hereafter Hearings on H. Res. 447) (Washington: GPO, 1952), 1497, 1509-10; "Our Grand Rapids Project: Research in Caries Control," *NIH Record* 3 (August 6, 1951): 4; Files of Biometry Section, NIDR; H. Trendley Dean, Frances A. Arnold, Jr., Philip Jay, and John W. Knutson, "Studies on Mass Control of Dental Caries through Fluoridation of the Public Water Supply," *PHR* 65 (October 17, 1950): 1403-8.

4. Arnold to chief, Division of Physiology, April 1, 1948, "Legislation Supporting for National Institute of Dental Research 1956-1947 and Establishing of NIDR," no. 3 of 4, NIDR IO; NIDR publications for calendar years 1948, 1949, 1950, and 1951, "NIDR Publications 1948-1960," NIDR IO; "Oral Health Activities Memorandum No. 4," April 17, 1950, "Dental Health

Memoranda January 1950 - December 1952," CDO PHS; U.S. Public Health Service, *Annual Report of the Federal Security Agency 1949* (Washington: GPO, 1949), 53.

5. F. J. Maier to Dr. John W. Knutson, August 22, 1946, Dean Papers, NLM; McClure, *Fluoridation*, 130; *Hearings on H. Res. 447*, 1640.

6. *Annual Report of the Federal Security Agency 1948*, 267.

7. Fred Wertheimer to Philip Jay, School of Dentistry, University of Michigan, Ann Arbor, January 19, 1948, "Grand Rapids—Correspondence," John Small's Files, NIDR.

8. J. F. Volker, H. C. Hodge, H. J. Wilson, and S. N. Von Voorhis, "The Absorption of Fluoride by the Enamel, Dentin, Bone, and Hydroxyapatite as Shown by the Radioactive Isotope," *Journal of Biological Chemistry* 184 (1940): 543, as summarized in McClure, *Fluoridation*, 184-89.

9. McClure, *Fluoridation*, 184-89; McNeil, *Fight for Fluoridation*, 69-70; Basil G. Bibby, "Effects of Topical Application of Fluorides on Dental Caries," *Fluorine in Dental Public Health: A Symposium at the Ninety-fourth Monthly Conference of the New York Institute of Clinical Oral Pathology . . .* October 30, 1944 (New York City: 1945), 36-39; Wertheimer to Jay, January 19, 1948, "Grand Rapids—Correspondence," John Small's Files, NIDR.

10. *Washington Post*, December 11, 1948; Wertheimer to Jay, January 19, 1948, "Grand Rapids—Correspondence," John Small's Files, NIDR.

11. U.S. Cong., House, *Hearings before the Subcommittee of the Committee on Appropriations*, Department of Labor-Federal Security Agency Appropriation Bill for 1949, pt. 2, 80th Cong., 2d sess., February 3, 1948, 165-79, 256-65, and *The Supplemental Federal Security Agency Appropriation Bill, Fiscal Year 1944*, H. Rept. 1821, 3-4.

12. Wertheimer to Jay, January 19, 1948, "Grand Rapids—Correspondence," John Small's Files, NIDR.

13. Jay to Wertheimer, January 13, 1968; Arnold to Wertheimer, January 29, 1948; Wertheimer to Arnold, February 4, 1948; Dean to Wertheimer, June 4, 1948, "Grand Rapids—Correspondence," John Small's Files, NIDR.

14. Garrington, "History of the Dental Corps," 135.

15. F. A. Bull, "Control of Dental Caries by the Addition of Fluorides to Public Water Supplies," *JADA* 41 (August 1950): 147-51; McNeil, *Fight for Fluoridation*, 44-50, 66-79.

16. *Annual Report of the Federal Security Agency 1948*, 263; H. T. Dean to W. A. Peirce, manager, Racine Water Department, September 28, 1948, and Dr. F. A. Bull to Dr. Frederick S. McKay, June 17, 1949, Dental Health Education Files, State Historical Society of Wisconsin, Madison (hereafter DHEF SHSW).

17. U.S. Public Health Service, *Annual Report of the Federal Security Agency 1949* (Washington: GPO, 1950), 52; "The Fluoridation of Public Water Supplies:

Statement of Recommended Policy and Procedure," *Journal American Water Works Association* 41 (July 1949): 575-79; H. T. Dean to Hon. Frank E. Keefe, House of Representatives, October 6, 1949, RG 443, Box 48, Ke Folder, NARA.

18. H. Trendley Dean, "The Advancement of Fluoridation," *Journal American Water Works Association* 43 (January 1951): 17-21; H. Trendley Dean, Francis A. Arnold, Jr., Philip Jay, and John W. Knutson, "Studies on Mass Control of Dental Caries through Fluoridation of the Public Water Supply," *PHR* 65 (October 27, 1950): 1403-8; U.S. Cong., House, *Hearings before the Subcommittee on Appropriations, Department of Labor-Federal Security Agency Appropriations for 1951, Public Health Service (Part 2)*, 81st Cong., 2d sess., 567.

19. McNeil, *Fight for Fluoridation*, 73-74; McClure, *Fluoridation*, 247-48; Bull, "Control of Dental Caries," 148-49.

20. "U.S.P.H.S. Recommends Public Water Fluoridation," *JADA* 41 (July 1950): 93-94; "Oral Health News Number 5," 1, "Dental Health Memoranda, January 1950-December 1952," CDO PHS; "Fluoridation Coming of Age," *Water & Sewage Works* (November 1950): 484; *ADA News Letter* 3 (June 1, 1950): 1.

21. McNeil, *Fight for Fluoridation*, 73-74; McClure, *Fluoridation*, 248; "Oral Health Activities Memorandums No. 6 and 7 (June-July)," 1, "Dental Health Memoranda January 1950-December 1952," CDO PHS; *Annual Report of the Federal Security Agency, Public Health Service 1950* (Washington: GPO, 1951), 18.

22. *Hearings on H. Res. 447*, 1487, 1694; "Fluoridation in the United States 1945-1965," "Fluoridation—News Clippings," John Small's Files, NIDR; "Oral Health News," issue no. 10, November 1950, 5, "Dental Health Memoranda January 1950-December 1952," CDO PHS.

23. McNeil, *Fight for Fluoridation*, 84-105.

24. An excellent account of research carried out on the toxicity and physiological effects of fluoride appears in McClure, *Fluoridation*, 47-56, 191-244.

25. Dr. Francis Arnold, interview no. 3 by Dr. Wyndham Miles, June 17, 1964, NLMHMD.

26. Topping to Dr. Robert F. Korns, May 17, 1951, in *Hearings on H. Res. 447*, 1679-80; Donald R. McNeil, "America's Longest War: the Fight over Fluoridation, 1950—," *Wilson Quarterly* 9 (Summer 1985): 147.

27. "Proceedings Fourth Annual Conference of State Dental Directors with the Public Health Service and the Children's Bureau, June 6-8, 1951, Washington, D.C.," John Small's Files, NIDR.

28. *Hearings on H. Res. 447*, 1483, 1488; Division of Medical Sciences, *Report of the Ad Hoc Committee on Fluoridation of Water Supplies*, Publication 214, 6; "National Institutes of Health, Report for the Fiscal Year July 1, 1950-June 30, 1951," 103, RA11.D6323 1951, National Institutes of Health Library (hereafter NIHL); "Fluoridation in the United States 1945-1965," "Fluoridation—News Clippings," John Small's Files, NIDR.

29. A. L. Russell and E. Elvove, "Domestic Water and Dental Caries. VII. A Study of the Fluoride-Dental Caries Relationship in an Adult Population," *PHR* 66 (1951): 1389, as reported in McClure, *Fluoridation*, 153-56. McClure noted that an English scientist, Robert Weaver, discussed the subject in a 1944 publication but was concerned with tooth mortality rates. Dr. Charles F. Deatherage of the Division of Dental Health Education, State Department of Health in Illinois, had done studies on men of draft age during World War II. Deatherage's results suggested that adults retained the dental benefits of fluoridation, but his surveys included only men through twenty-eight years of age. See McClure, *Fluoridation*, 90-93.

30. Wertheimer to Arnold, June 26, 1950; T. L. Vander Velde, chief, Section of Water Supply, Division of Engineering, to George Liddle, city manager, Muskegon, Michigan, April 3, 1951, and Liddle to Vander Velde, April 10, 1951, "Old Service Correspondence on Mottled Enamel," John Small's Files, NIDR; F. A. Arnold, Jr., R. C. Likins, A. L. Russell, and D. B. Scott, "Fifteenth Year of the Grand Rapids Fluoridation Study," *JADA* 65 (December 1962): 781.

31. McClure, *Fluoridation*, 143-47.

32. McNeil, *Fight for Fluoridation*, 180-81.

33. *Evening Star*, February 28, 1952, 1, *Hearings on H. Res. 447*," 1528-43. Taylor's quoted statement was on p. 1540. A literature search of scientific journals failed to show any publication on this work by Taylor—an indication that it was not subjected to review by his peers.

34. *Hearings on H. Res. 447*, 1353-1795. Knutson's statement appeared on p. 1497. From 1937 to 1939 the National Cancer Institute conducted field studies in ten metropolitan areas, including Denver, with about 1 ppm fluoride in its water supply, and San Francisco, where the water supply was fluoride free. The total cancer rates amounted to 518.2 cases per 100,000 for Denver and 525.9 per 100,000 at San Francisco. See H. Trendley Dean, "U.S.P.H.S. Position on Fluoridation and Public Water Supplies," *Journal American Water Works Association* 43 (September 1951): 673.

35. *Hearings on H. Res. 447*, 1353-1795; publications lists of the staff of the National Institute of Dental Research for 1948 through 1952, NIDR IO.

36. *Hearings on H. Res. 447*, 1602-26. Quotation was on p. 1626.

37. *Hearings on H. Res. 447*; Miller to the Editor, *Washington Post*, March 4, 1952.

38. U.S. Cong., House, *Investigation of the Use of Chemicals in Foods and Cosmetics, Report, Fluoridation of Public Drinking Water*, H. Rept. 2500, 82d Cong., 2d sess., July 10, 1952.

39. "Fluoridation in the United States, 1945-1965"; McNeil, *Fight for Fluoridation*, 142, 154.

40. McNeil, *Fight for Fluoridation*, 155-58; National Institute of Dental Research, "Dental Caries Reduction by Fluoridation of a Water Supply," Box 1, Sue Burrough's Fluoridation File, NIDR IO; McClure, *Fluoridation*, 233-37; Oveta Culp Hobby to Miller, April 2, 1954, RG 235, Box 238, 930 Folder, NARA.

41. Affidavit of Oscar R. Ewing, May 30, 1957; Mary Belle Walker to Editor, *The Progress Index*, n.d.; March 27, 1957, Statement by Leon E. Hickman, vice-president and general counsel for ALCOA, Box 17, "Fluoridation," Oscar Ewing Papers, HSTL. Hickman said that ALCOA produced little sodium fluoride because the firm needed its base, fluorospar, for its aluminum business. Because sodium fluoride could not compete economically with sodium silicofluoride, derived from phosphate rock and the preferred substance for fluoridating water supplies, ALCOA requested its distributors not to solicit sodium fluoride for water fluoridation, Hickman said.

42. "Lasker Awards," Tuesday, October 21, 1952, Cleveland, Ohio, 88th Annual Meeting, American Public Health Association, Dean Papers, NLM. After McKay retired to Colorado Springs in 1940, Dean continued consulting him on both mottled enamel and fluoridation matters. McKay, of course, avidly supported the fluoridation movement. That correspondence appeared in the Dean Papers.

43. WH 1, 2A512, "American Dental Association," Folder No. 2, NLM; H. Trendley Dean, "Some Reflections on the Epidemiology of Fluorine and Dental Health," pt. I, *American Journal of Public Health* 43 (June 6, 1953): 707-8; NIDR annual publications lists, NIDR IO.

44. Marjorie Dent Candee, ed., *Current Biography* (New York: H. W. Wilson Company, 1957), 29-31.

45. Italics the author's. Scheele to the administrator, Federal Security Agency, February 6, 1953, RG 235, Box 237, 930-1-7-53 Folder, NARA.

46. Letters, Box 24, "Fluoridation," Oveta Culp Hobby Papers, Dwight D. Eisenhower Library, Abilene, Kansas (hereafter DDEL); letters and John W. Knutson, assistant surgeon general, to Roswell B. Perkins, assistant secretary, Department of Health, Education and Welfare, July 26, 1954, RG 235, Box 238, 930 Folder, NARA; Hobby to Congressman Withrow, June 20, 1955, and Hobby to Mrs. Merlin Meythaler, May 5, 1955, Box 24, "Fluoridation," Oveta Culp Hobby Papers, DDEL; F. A. Arnold, Jr., director, NIDR, to Bethuel M. Webster, New York City, December 26, 1956, "Fluoridation—News Clippings," John Small's Files, NIDR.

47. Arnold to Webster, December 26, 1956, "Fluoridation—News Clippings," John Small's Files, NIDR; U.S. Cong., House, *Fluoridation of Water, Hearings before the Committee on Interstate and Foreign Commerce . . . on H.R. 2341*, 83d Cong., 2d sess. See also U.S. Cong., House, 84th Cong., 2d sess., 681-82; "Testimony of the Public Health Service . . . before the House Committee on Interstate and Foreign Commerce . . . on H.R. 2341," 1, NIDR IO. Quotation was taken from the last reference cited.

48. Dr. Francis Arnold, interview no. 4 by Dr. Wyndham Miles, December 9, 1964; Arnold to Webster, December 26, 1956, "Fluoridation—News Clippings," John Small's Files, NIDR.

49. "Presidential Support for Fluoridation," CDO PHS.

50. U.S. Cong., House, *Testimony of the Public Health Service before the House Committee on Interstate and Foreign Commerce in Connection with Hearings on H.R. 2341*,

83d Cong., 2d sess., May 25, 26, 27, 1954 (hereafter *Hearings on H.R. 2341*) (Washington: GPO, 1954), 36-45, 95-103, 151-65.

51. *Hearings on H.R. 2341*, 375-76, 8-15.

52. *Hearings on H.R. 2341*, 1-3.

53. *Hearings on H.R. 2341*, Sue Burrough's Fluoridation File, Box 1, "Fluoridation—Resource Material," NIDR IO.

54. Ibid., 6.

55. See note 47 above; Hobby to Miller, April 2, 1954, RG 235, Box 238, 930 Folder, NARA; "Progress Report, National Institutes of Health, Number 15: Studies on Fluoridation," April 1954, and *Hearings on H.R. 2341*, Sue Burrough's Fluoridation File, Box 1, "Fluoridation—Resource Material," NIDR IO; Nicholas C. Leone et al., "Medical Aspects of Excessive Fluoride in a Water Supply"; McNeil, *Fight for Fluoridation*, 190.

56. H. V. Smith to Mr. Robert J. Munch, Greenwich, Connecticut, September 17, 1954, in The Board of Health of the City of New York, *Report to the Mayor on Fluoridation for New York City*, October 24, 1955; Francis A. Arnold, Jr., H. Trendley Dean, Philip Jay, and John W. Knutson, "Effect of Fluoridated Public Water Supplies on Dental Caries Prevalence," *PHR* 71 (July 1956): 654-56; *Report to the Mayor on Fluoridation for New York City*, 42-45; Arnold to Webster, December 26, 1956, "Fluoridation—News Clippings," John Small's Files, NIDR.

57. *ADA News Letter* 7 (December 15, 1954): 1.

58. "Fluoridation in the United States, 1945-1965," NIDR IO.

59. McNeil, *Fight for Fluoridation*, 159-61.

60. Dr. Francis Arnold, interview no. 3 by Dr. Wyndham Miles, September 16, 1964.

61. S. Stephen Kegeles and Lois K. Cohen, "Role of Social Sciences in Dentistry," in *Social Sciences and Dentistry: A Critical Bibliography*, 2 vols., ed. N. D. Richards and L. K. Cohen (Fédération Dentaire Internationale, 1971), 1:368.

62. Bernard and J. L. S. Mausner, "A Study of the Anti-Scientific Attitude," *Scientific American* 192 (February 1955): 35-39; McNeil, "America's Longest War," 150; "The Nature of the Fluoridation Controversy in the United States," *Australian Dental Journal*, June 1959, 5-6.

63. Scheele to Willis Gradison (for Secretary Folsom), August 8, 1955, RG 235, Box 238, 930 Folder, NARA.

64. Expert Committee on Water Fluoridation, "First Report," World Health Organizational Technical Series No. 146 (Geneva: WHO, 1958). Quotation appeared on p. 21.

65. Dr. David B. Scott, interview by Ruth R. Harris, September 3, 1986.

66. Arnold et al., "Fifteenth Year of the Grand Rapids Fluoridation Study," 780-85; McClure, *Fluoridation*, 109-47; "Background State," n.d., received January

5, 1970, from Kent County Health Department, Grand Rapids, "25th Anniversary of Fluoridation in 1970 (Quarter-Century Observances)," Brent Jaquet's Files, NIDR.

67. See note 66 above.

68. Fédération Dentaire Internationale, "Fluoridation Round the World," "Fluoridation—News Clippings," John Small's Files, NIDR; "Fluoridation in the United States, 1945-1965."

69. *ADA News Letter* 13 (August 1, 1960): 1-2.

70. Director, NIDR, to director, NIH, December 13, 1960, "Weekly Reports," 1956-1962, vol. I, Files of the Chief, NIDR IO.

71. "Fluoridation Memorandum No. 21," January 21, 1963, and "DOH Memoranda," ADA, Bureau of Public Information, News Release of February 27, 1963, Sue Burrough's Fluoridation File, Box 1, untitled folder, NIDR IO; Arnold to Board of Trustees, Fredonia, New York, May 3, 1963, Dr. David B. Scott's "F" Files (hereafter Scott's F Files), Box 1, "Fluoridation Correspondence," NIDR; The National Institute of Dental Research, "Research on Fluorides and Fluoridation," March 14, 1966, Sue Burrough's Fluoridation File, Box 3, "Fluoride," NIDR IO; "The Fourth Great Public Health Measure," delivered at the National Dental Health Assembly, February 7, 1966, ADA Archives.

72. "Presidential Support for Fluoridation," CDO PHS; *ADA News Letter* 14 (December 1961): 1.

73. "Research on Fluorides and Fluoridation," 3-4; McClure, *Fluoridation*, 216-19.

74. "Research on Fluorides and Fluoridation," 2; McClure, *Fluoridation*, 158-61.

75. See note 74 above; see also H. S. Horowitz and S. B. Heifetz, "Effects of Prenatal Exposure to Fluoridation on Dental Caries," *PHR* 82 (1967): 297. In the early 1970s Heifitz and Horowitz joined NIDR when the division's epidemiological responsibilities were shifted to the Institute. For more details, see Chapter 6. The Institute hired Carlos in 1967. In the 1970s he headed the National Caries Program, discussed in Chapter 7.

76. "Research on Fluorides and Fluoridation."

77. Ibid.

78. Arnold to Dr. Thomas J. Kiernan, the Irish ambassador, March 3, 1963; Arnold to secretary, Department of Health, Custom House, Dublin, Ireland, May 31, 1963, and Arnold to K. W. Connolly, secretary, Department of Health, Dublin, Ireland, August 7, 1964, Scott's F Files, Box 1, "Fluoridation Correspondence," NIDR. In 1960 the Division of Dental Public Health and the Division of Dental Resources were merged to form the Division of Dental Health and Resources.

79. McClure, *Fluoridation*, 280-82; *Saturday Review*, December 7, 1963, 77-79; January 4, 1964, 85-94; February 15, 1964, 24, 58; J. Stewart Hunter to Norman Cousins, December 26, 1963, Sue Burrough's Fluoridation File, Box 2, NIDR IO.

80. "Comments on the Article 'Documenting the Case Against Fluoridation,' by John Lear, Science Editor, *Saturday Review*," January 4, 1964; "Comments on the Article 'The Real Danger of Fluoridation,' by John Lear, Science Editor, *Saturday Review*, December 7, 1963; Arnold to Dr. R. A. Connor, chief, Dental Health Division, Department of National Health and Welfare, Ottawa, Ontario, Canada, February 19, 1964, Sue Burrough's Fluoridation File, Box 2, NIDR IO.

81. Donald Galagan to the surgeon general, January 31, 1964, and February 19, 1964; Galagan to W. Howard Chase, New York, New York, February 27, 1964; and J. Stewart Hunter to the chief dental officer, April 3, 1964, Sue Burrough's Fluoridation File, Box 2, "*Saturday Review* Articles on Fluoridation, Lear and Steve, February and May 1969," NIDR IO.

82. Sarah S. Hirakis and Franklin M. Foote, "Statewide Fluoridation: How It Was Done in Connecticut," *JADA* 75 (July 1967): 174-78; "Status of Fluoridation in the Nation's Fifty Largest Cities," November 1965, "Fluoridation—News Clippings," John Small's Files, NIDR; Howard A. Rusk, "The War on Tooth Decay," *New York Times*, August 27, 1967. Los Angeles had a small amount of natural fluoride, less than 1 ppm, in its water supply.

83. Howard A. Rusk, "The War on Tooth Decay," *New York Times*, August 27, 1967; Alvin F. Gardner, dental officer, Office of Drug Surveillance, Bureau of Medicine, Food and Drug Administration, to director, Bureau of Medicine, December 30, 1966; and McClure to director, NIDR, January 5, 1967, Sue Burrough's Fluoridation File, Box 3, "Fish Protein Concentrate Studies," NIDR IO; "FDA to Give Approval of Fish Flour Thursday," *Washington Post*, January 31, 1967; McClure, *Fluoridation*, 181-82. In 1965 the Division of Dental Public Health was renamed the Division of Dental Health.

84. *Congressional Record—Extension of Remarks*, March 10, 1969, E1810-14; National Institutes of Health, PS, CPB-8, February 1969, "Use of Fluoridated Water in Hemodialysis." An autopsy on one patient showed accumulations of fluoride that ultimately might have intensified bone abnormalities already associated with kidney failure. Yet the examiners could not determine if the individual had already retained more than the usual amounts of fluoride in her vertebrae before she underwent hemodialysis or whether the accumulation resulted from dialysis with fluoridated water. Tests on other hemodialysis patients showed that two had higher concentrations of fluoride in bone tissue while three did not. The examiners suggested that the fluoride actually could have been beneficial rather than harmful to the patients' bone tissue. Announcing that the safe amount of fluoride in water used for hemodialysis "has not been finally determined," the National Institute of Arthritis and Metabolic Diseases noted that fluoride might be harmful in dialysis but that other trace elements in the water could also cause problems.

85. Frederick J. Stare, Daniel Bernstein, Constantine Hampers, and James Dunning, "Fluoridation and 'New Facts,'" *Saturday Review*, May 3, 1969, 57-59.

86. Memorandum for the Record by Tula S. Brocard, November 13, 1969, Sue Burrough's Fluoridation File, Box 1, "Fluoridation," NIDR IO; "Spotlight:

Fluoridation Census 1969," April 1970, Division of Associated and Dental Health Programs Notebook, Dr. Louden's Files, PHS; "Referenda Reported for 1969," Sue Burrough's Fluoridation File, Box 1, "Fluoridation—Resource Material," NIDR IO; Annabelle Bender Motz, "The Fluoridation Issue as Studied by Social Scientists," in *Social Sciences and Dentistry*, 347, and Kegeles and Cohen, "Role of Social Sciences in Dentistry," ibid., 369.

87. Dr. Seymour J. Kreshover, director, NIDR, to Donald Dinwiddie, editorial director, *Consumers Union*, Mount Vernon, New York, June 19, 1969, and attachments, Sue Burrough's Fluoridation File, Box 1, "Fluoridation/Anderson/ Groth," NIDR IO.

88. Ned Groth III, California Institute of Technology, to Dr. Lloyd B. Tepper, July 10, 1974; Dr. Herschel Horowitz, chief, Community Programs Section, Caries Prevention and Research Branch, NCP, to director, NIDR, August 30, 1974; Tepper to John C. Greene, chief dental officer, Bureau of Health Resources Development, Health Resources Administration, September 10, 1974; Tepper to Groth, November 27, 1974, Sue Burrough's Fluoridation File, Box 1, "Fluoridation/Anderson/Groth 7/74," NIDR IO; "Food and Drug Administration Director Supports Community Water Fluoridation," FL-110, Scott's F Files, Box 2, "F-Positive News Releases," NIDR.

89. HEW News Release, August 1, 1979, Scott's F Files, Box 2, "F-CDC," NIDR.

90. McNeil, "America's Longest War," 150-51.

91. "National Cancer Institute Researchers Reaffirm: No Evidence of Cancer Hazard in Fluoridation," FL-75, March 1974, Sue Burrough's Fluoridation File, Box 1, "DOH Memoranda," NIDR IO; *Congressional Record*, House, July 21, 1975, H 7172-76; Dr. James P. Carlos, acting director, NIDR, to Hon. L. R. Fountain, chairman, Intergovernmental Relations and Human Resources Subcommittee, Committee on Government Operations, House of Representatives, September 9, 1975, Scott's F Files, Box 1, "Fluoridation Correspondence," NIDR; Dr. James A. Peters, director, Division of Cancer Cause and Prevention, NIH, to Dr. Sherman L. Cox, director, Division of Dentistry, Bureau of Health Manpower, Health Resources Administration, Sue Burrough's Fluoridation File, Box 1, "DOH Memoranda," NIDR IO; Dr. Donald S. Fredrickson to Hon. James J. Delaney, House of Representatives, February 6, 1976, Sue Burrough's Fluoridation File, Box 3, "Dr. Nylen F," NIDR IO.

92. John Small to Dr. Scott, September 27, 1976; chief, Laboratory of Developmental Biology and Anomalies (hereafter LDBA), NIDR, to director, NIDR, April 5, 1977, Scott's F Files, Box 3, "F Mohamed-Mutagenesis," NIDR; George R. Martin to director, NIDR, April 11, 1977, Scott's F Files, Box 2, "F-Positive News Releases," NIDR; "Research Shows No Mutagenic Effects from Fluoride," FL-95, September 1977, Scott's F Files, Box 2, "F-Cancer," NIDR; communication from John Small, NIDR. Drs. Beverly White, a cytogeneticist from the National Institute of Arthritis and Metabolic Diseases; Donald Taves, a fluoride specialist from the University of Rochester; and George Martin, chief of the LDBA, NIDR, visited Mohamed at his University laboratory. After another scientist reported genetic change from sodium flu-

oride in 1984, another team led by J. Cole conducted additional animal testing. They found some effects only at high, toxic concentrations of sodium fluoride and concluded that available knowledge provided "no reason to expect any genotoxic effects in human tissues at levels of fluoride ions to which they are currently exposed in the general population." See J. Cole, W. J. Muriel, and B. A. Bridges, "The Mutagenicity of Sodium Fluoride to L5178Y [Wild-Type and TK+/-(3.7.2c)] Mouse Lymphoma Cells," *Mutagenesis* 1 (Oxford, England: IRL Press Limited, 1986), and Lawrence J. Furman, chief, Dental Disease Prevention Activity, Center for Prevention Services, June 1987, to Dear Colleague, "CDC," John Small's Files, NIDR.

93. Jimmy L. Pedigo, director, Personnel Management Office, Department of Health, Education and Welfare, to John Small, December 23, 1975, "CDC," John Small's Files, NIDR; Greene to Regional Health Administrator, Region I-X, March 25, 1976, Scott's F Files, Box 1, "Fluoridation Correspondence," NIDR.

94. Undated memorandum no. 9 by John Small, "CDC," John Small's Files, NIDR.

95. U.S. Cong., House, *The National Cancer Program (Part 2 - Fluoridation of Public Drinking Water). Hearings before a Subcommittee of the Committee on Government Operations, House of Representatives*, 95th Cong., 1st sess., September 21 and October 12, 1977; "Fluoridated Water Will Kill 500,000: Scientists," *Chicago Tribune*, September 22, 1977, 8; communication from Dr. Lois Cohen of December 1987; Dr. Harald Löe to Mrs. Russell J. Hale, executive secretary, llinois Pure Water Committee, Alton, Illinois, May 16, 1985, Files of Office of the Director, National Institute of Dental Research (hereafter OD NIDR), 1985.

96. FL-105, November 1977, Scott's F Files, Box 2, "F-Positive News Releases," NIDR IO; ADA *Daily Bulletin*, October 10, 1977; HEW News Release, August 1, 1979; Stephen B. Corbin, "PHS Directions in Oral Health: Health Promotion and Disease Prevention," *Journal of Public Health Dentistry* 45 (Fall 1985): 234-37.

97. FL-90, February 1977, Scott's F Files, Box 1, "Fluoride," NIDR IO.

98. McNeil, "America's Longest War," 151; William Bradford for Dr. J. Michael Lane to director for Prevention Services, CDC, "Statement on Fluoridation," November 7, 1984, "NIDR 1984," OD NIH; John Small to Dr. Scott, January 27, 1980, attached to FL-110, "Food and Drug Administration Director Supports Community Water Fluoridation," Scott's F Files, Box 2, "F-Positive News Releases," NIDR IO.

99. Harald Löe, "Fluoridation Status of U.S. Public Water Supplies," "Contributions, Public Health Reports (Fluoridation Articles), 3/86," Anne Atlee's Files, NIDR; Motz, "The Fluoridation Issue as Studied by Social Scientists," 359; McNeil, "America's Longest War," 153.

100. C. Everett Koop, M.D., "Water Fluoridation," February 8, 1983, CDO PHS; Koop to William D. Ruckelshaus, January 23, 1984, Files of the Office of

Associate Director for Epidemiology and Oral Disease Prevention Program (hereafter EODPP), NIDR.

101. Löe, "Fluoridation Status of U.S. Public Water Supplies."

CHAPTER SIX. *The Struggles For Growth In Dental Research*

1. *Washington Post*, August 19, 1956, E4.

2. U.S. Cong., House, *Biographical Directory of the American Congress 1774-1961*, 85th Cong., 2d sess., H. Doc. 442 (Washington: GPO, 1961), 1054; *ADA News Letter* 19 (July 25, 1966): 1.

3. *Biographical Directory of the American Congress*, Fogarty, John, 90; *ADA News Letter* 20 (January 23, 1967): 1, 4; Stephen P. Strickland, *Politics, Science, & Dread Disease* (Cambridge: Harvard University Press, 1972), 80-91.

4. Director, NIH, to Office of the Surgeon General, October 1, 1948, RG 443, Box 80, Dean, H. T. Folder, NARA; *ADA News Letter* (April 1, 1949): 2; "History of National Institute of Dental Research Building," Vertical File, ADA Archives; U.S. Cong., House, *Hearings before the Subcommittee of the Committee on Appropriations*, Part 3 (Federal Security Agency) Public Health Service (Part 2), 81st Cong., 2d sess., 568-70.

5. *ADA News Letter* (April 1, 1949): 2; "History of National Institute of Dental Research Building," Vertical File, ADA Archives; *ADA News Letter* 2 (July 1, 1949): 3.

6. *Hearings on Federal Security Agency Appropriations for Fiscal Year 1951*, 568-70; *ADA News Letter* 3 (March 15, 1950): 1; *Transactions of the American Dental Association*, 91st Annual Session, Atlantic City, New Jersey, October 30-November 2, 1950, 106; "History of National Institute of Dental Research Building," "Statement of the American Dental Association to the Senate Appropriations Committee," May 15, 1951, by Dr. E. Harold Gale, Notebook: "ADA Statements, 81st through 85th Congresses," ADA DC; *Transactions of the American Dental Association*, 92d Annual Session, Washington, D.C., October 15-18, 1951, 91; "National Institute of Dental Research—Building," 1955, "Historical Files," NIDR IO; *1985 NIH Almanac*, 143-51. Dr. Harold Gale, the association's legislative chairman in 1951, however, observed that despite the wartime situation, Congress had allowed some construction funding for building on the NIH campus for other institutes. Construction that proceeded during the Korean War at the Bethesda location included maintenance facilities, animal housing and laboratories, and apartments for occupancy by "certain NIH personnel." See Gale "Statement" cited above.

7. Director, NIDR, to director, NIH, February 1, 1955; Professional Staff of National Institute of Dental Research, September 30, 1955, "NIDR Professional Staff Listing Back Issues—1958-Present," NIDR IO; *1983 NIH Almanac*, NIH Publication No. 83-5, 140-41; National Advisory Dental Research

Council, Minutes of Meeting, February 17, 1950, 1; director, NIDR, to director, NIH, February 1, 1955, "Legislation Supporting for National Institute of Dental Research 1956-1947 and Establishing of NIDR," no. 3 of 4, NIDR IO; National Institutes of Health, "Report for the Fiscal Year July 1, 1950-June 30, 1951," 103.

8. U.S. Cong., Senate, *Hearing before the Subcommittee on Health of the Committee on Labor and Public Welfare . . . on S. 3246*, 84th Cong., 2d sess., February 29, 1956 (hereafter *Hearing on S. 3246*). Quotation is on p. 3.

9. Ibid., 2-40.

10. Oveta Culp Hobby to Dr. Alan Waterman, January 14, 1955, and Waterman to Hobby, February 7, 1955, in "Appendix" to "Medical Research Activities of the Department of Health, Education and Welfare: Report of the Special Committee on Medical Research Appointed by the National Science Foundation at the Request of the Secretary of Health, Education and Welfare," December 1955, NLM; "Medical Research Activities of the Department of Health, Education and Welfare," 22-24. Dr. C. N. H. Long headed the National Science Foundation Committee.

11. "Construction of Building for National Institute of Dental Research, Remarks of Hon. James E. Murray," *Congressional Record*, "History of NIDR," NIDR IO; Sen. Lister Hill to Robert F. Kierstead, Lincoln, Nebraska, March 7, 1956, Lister Hill Papers, Roll 28, 57-b, Labor and Public Welfare Committee, September 1955-October 1956, NLM; *Hearing on S. 3246*, 2-7, 10-11, 16-19. Volker quotation is on p. 32.

12. *ADA News Letter* 9 (March 1, 1956): 1; *ADA News Letter* 9 (April 25, 1956): 1; U.S. Cong., House, "Increasing Authorization for Construction and Equipment at National Institute of Dental Research," 84th Cong., 2d sess., H. Rept. 2144, May 10, 1956; *ADA News Letter* 9 (July 16, 1956): 1; *Hearing on S. 3246*; *ADA News Letter* 9 (March 1, 1956), 1; O. M. Dresen, dean, Marquette University School of Dentistry, to Sen. Lister Hill, March 12, 1956, Lister Hill Papers, Roll 28, "57-b Labor and Public Welfare Committee, September 1955-October 1986," NLM; Hill to Dr. Roy O. Greep, dean, Harvard School of Dental Medicine, March 21, 1956, Lister Hill Papers, Roll 28, "57-b Labor and Public Welfare Committee, September 1955-October 1956," NLM; U.S. Cong., Senate, Report (to accompany S. 3246), 82d Cong., 2d sess., S. Rept. 1719, March 28, 1956; Committee on Labor and Public Welfare, "Minutes Executive Meeting, Tuesday, March 27, 1956," Lister Hill Papers, Box 28, "57-b Labor and Public Welfare Committee, September 1955-October 1956," NLM; *ADA News Letter* 9 (April 2, 1956): 1; *ADA News Letter* 9 (July 16, 1956): 1; M. B. Folsom to Hon. Percival F. Brundage, director, Bureau of the Budget, July 18, 1956, "WHO—Pending Legislation," Box 82, "7/19/56, NIDR," DDEL.

13. *NIH Record* 8 (August 13, 1956): 1.

14. U.S. Cong., Senate, *Hearings before the Subcommittee of the Committee on Appropriations . . . on H.R. 11645*, 85th Cong., 2d sess. (Washington: GPO, 1958), 1326-27; *1983 NIH Almanac*, 140.

15. Alstadt to President Dwight D. Eisenhower, December 30, 1957, White House Central File, General File, Box 1291, "182-H-7 NIDR," DDEL.

16. Adams to Alstadt, January 15, 1958, White House Central File, General File, Box 1291, "182-H-7 NIDR," DDEL; Dr. William Alstadt, telephone interview by Ruth R. Harris, April 17, 1987.

17. The ADA representatives included Camalier, the faithful supporter of the Institute; Dr. J. Claude Earnest, chairman of the Council on Legislation; Bernard J. Conway, secretary of the legislation council; and Dr. Obed Moen, chairman of the Council on International Relations. Hill and Fogarty said they wanted assurance from association officials that dentists across the nation would personally urge their own representatives and senators to approve the Institute construction funds. The association representatives committed themselves to organizing such support. Dr. William Alstadt, interview by Ruth R. Harris, April 17, 1987.

18. *ADA Information Bulletin*, March 1958, "History of NIDR," NIDR IO; *ADA News Letter* 11 (March 15, 1958): 1; *ADA News Letter*, 11 (April 15, 1958): 1; *American Dental Association Transactions 1958*, 11, 162, 167; *ADA News Letter* 11 (July 1, 1958): 1, and 11 (August 15, 1958): 2.

19. Marie T. Norris, "For the Record," "Dental Building, Cornerstone Status," NIDR IO; "Dental Health Memorandum," October 15, 1959, CDO PHS, Dental Archives.

20. *1983 NIH Almanac*, 140.

21. "Dental Health Memorandum," June 15, 1961, "Dental Building," "Dedication Ceremonies," NIDR IO; "Dedication, National Institute of Dental Research Building, National Institutes of Health," May 26, 1961, "Dedication of Dental Building," OD NIH.

22. "National Institute of Dental Research Annual Report of Administration Calendar Year 1960," 8, Dr. Kenneth Lynn's Files, NIDR.

23. "Report of Public Health Service Dental Activities Planning Group," vol. 1, 50-51, "Reorganizations DPH-DDR DHR DDH-NIDR-HSM," Dr. Louden's Files, PHS; "Report of Public Health Service Dental Activities Planning Group," vol. 2, March 23, 1960, preface, and Dr. Robert E. Greenfield and Betty Jolliffe, "Report of the Dental Fact Finding Team on Dental Activities of NIH," August 1969, 69-70, CDO PHS; "Pertinent Facts on the Division of Dental Public Health and Resources," Dr. Louden's Files, PHS.

24. Public Health Service Press Release, June 24, 1961, "Plans for Opening Dental Health Center in San Francisco," Dr. Louden's Files, PHS; "The Dental Health Center in Historical Perspective," pages unnumbered, Dr. Viron Diefenbach's Files, University of Illinois School of Public Health, Chicago (hereafter DDF).

25. Staff Meeting, April 10, 1962, notes, "Executive Dental Staff Meeting Minutes Beginning January 1963," CDO PHS; Minutes of Meeting November 7-9, 1963, of National Advisory Dental Research Council, 7, 9-10, NIDR; "Division of Dental Public Health and Resources Long Range Planning 1964-

1969," November 15, 1963, 31, 34-35, Dr. Louden's Files, PHS. Because the Public Health Service reorganization allowed Galagan's division to dispense extramural grants, the dental institute had to transfer twenty-three grants, including eleven in epidemiology, to the division in 1963.

26. Dr. Luther Terry to Deputy Chief, Bureau of State Services, May 1, 1963, Papers of Harold Hillenbrand, Paffenbarger Research Center, National Bureau of Standards (hereafter PRC NBS); "Chronology of Major Events in NBS-NIDR Interagency Agreement," "0.7.04 National Institute of Dental Research & NIH 1973," ADA DC; black book on a proposal for reorganization of dental activities (DDH), pages unnumbered, CDO PHS; "The Dental Health Center in Historical Perspective," DDF. Terry wanted the money to go toward strengthening the Institute's intramural and extramural research programs and to expand existing activities of Galagan's division.

27. "The Case for a New Dental Organization," CDO PHS; "The Development of Dental Activities in the Public Health Service, Submitted by Helen M. Riches 9 September 1966," Helen Riches to director, NIDR, September 9, 1966, "The Development of Dental Archives in the Public Health Service," Dr. Lynn's Files, NIDR; surgeon general to the Honorable John Jarman, chairman, Subcommittee on Public Health and Welfare, House Committee on Interstate and Foreign Commerce, December 22, 1967, and attachments, Legal 1-9, PL 89-749 (Implementation of Comprehensive Health Plan Program 67 and 68), OD NIH. According to the recollection of some Institute officers, several thought Fogarty sided with Galagan.

28. "Research Plans of the National Institute of Dental Research March 1973," Dr. Lynn's Files, NIDR. Members of the Ad Hoc Advisory Committee on Reorganization were Dr. Ivan L. Bennett, Jr., deputy director, Office of Science and Technology, Executive Office of the President; Dr. Maynard K. Hine, dean, School of Dentistry, Indiana University; Dr. Alvin L. Morris, assistant vice-president for the Medical Center, University of Kentucky; and Dr. Joseph F. Volker, vice-president, University of Alabama.

29. Ibid.; director, Division of Dental Health, BHM, to director, NIH, December 18, 1968, and Christensen to Hillenbrand, December 20, 1968, "0.7.04—National Institute of Dental Research and NIH 1969," ADA DC.

30. Deputy director, NIH, to director, NIH, January 29, 1969, Blue Binder, DDF; Marston to Hillenbrand, January 31, 1968, Blue Binder, DDF; director, Office of Management Policy and Review, to director, NIH, March 19, 1969, "NIDR Organizational Changes through 1969, Subsection 1969," Kirk Weaver's Files, NIDR; Robert Finch to Dr. Hillenbrand, August 20, 1969, and "Report from the Washington Office," Blue Binder, DDF; "Report of the Fact Finding Team on Dental Activities of NIH, Foreword," CDO PHS.

31. "A Study of the Organization of Dental Activities of NIH: The Report of the Dental Fact Finding Team," August 14, 1969, 26, 52-69, 74-80, 83-90, 112-16, Dr. Louden's Files, PHS. Quotations appear on pages 52 and 61.

32. Egeberg to Marston, December 12, 1969, Blue Binder, DDF; Marston to deputy director for science, NIH, and director, BEMT, January 8, 1970, Blue

Binder, DDF; Memo on Programs of the National Institute of Dental Research and the Division of Dental Health, January 9, 1970, by Dr. Thomas J. Kennedy, Jr., DDF; Deputy director for science to director, NIH, September 30, 1970, "NIDR 70," OD NIH; Richard L. Segel to director, NIH, October 30, 1970, "Reorganizations DPH-DDR, DPHR, DDH-NIDR-HSM," Dr. Louden's Files, PHS; Dr. Herschel S. Horowitz to director, NIH, November 30, 1970, Report on Relationships of Dental Activities of DDH, BEMT, NIH, and HSMSHA, Dr. Louden's Files, PHS; Marston to assistant secretary for health and scientific affairs, DHEW, December 29, 1970, Dr. Loudon's Files, PHS; Minutes of the National Advisory Dental Research Council for March 22-23, 1971, 5, NIDR; *ADA Leadership Bulletin* 3 (September 17, 1972): 1, ADA Archives.

33. Minutes of National Advisory Dental Research Council, January 10, 1949, 13, NIDR.

34. Ibid.; Joint Panel on Research and Education, "Summary Report from Panel on Dentistry," and transcript of August 12, 1952, "President's Committees, President's Commission on Health Needs," Box 2, Panel File Miscellaneous, HSTL.

35. "Statement of the American Dental Association Requesting an Appropriation to Support the Provisions of the National Dental Research Act," March 25, 1949, "Notebook: ADA Statements 81st-1949-1950," ADA DC; U.S. Cong., House, *Hearings before the Subcommittee of the Committee on Appropriations . . . Part 3 (Federal Security Agency), Public Health Service (Part 2)*, Appropriations for 1951, 81st Cong., 2d sess., January 24, 1950, 565; National Institute of Dental Research, "Data Assembled for the Special Committee on Medical Research of the National Science Foundation," August 26, 1955, "Historical Files," NIDR IO; "Extramural Research Support," "Legislation—Supporting for National Institute of Dental Research 1956-1947 and Establishing of NIDR," NIDR IO; "National Academy of Sciences—National Research Council, Committee on Dentistry (Minutes of the Nineteenth Meeting), Subcommittee on Biology, Subcommittee on Clinical Investigation, Subcommittee on Etiology and Pathology (Minutes of the Eighth Meeting), 5 February 1954," 407, National Academy of Sciences, Division of Medicine Files, "MED: Committee on Dentistry 1954-1958, Meetings: Nineteenth-twenty-seventh," NAS Archives; Minutes of National Advisory Dental Research Council, October 12, 1951, 3-4; U.S. Cong., Senate, *Hearings on . . . 1953 Fiscal Years Appropriations*, 82d Cong., 2d sess., 607.

36. F. A. Arnold, Jr., to Dr. Seymour J. Kreshover, School of Dentistry, Medical College of Virginia, July 8, 1954, "Program Planning, 1954-1959," Dr. Lynn's Files, NIDR; "Program Planning Committee," Minutes of Meeting, September 2, 1954, "Program Planning Minutes," Book 1, Brent Jaquet's Files, NIDR; Hill to "Pokey" Arnold, January 7, 1955, "Program Planning, 1954-1969," Dr. Lynn's Files, NIDR.

37. National Institute of Dental Research, "Analysis of Program Activities, 1955," 5-6, NIHL; National Institute of Dental Research, "Data Assembled for the Special Committee on Medical Research of the National Science Foundation,"

August 26, 1955, 3, "Historical Files," NIDR IO. The Council approved fifty-nine awards in 1955.

38. L. F. Neff, administrative assistant, NIDR, to H. W. Curran, assistant executive officer, OD NIH, August 13, 1953, and director, NIDR, to All NIDR Employees, September 27, 1954, NIDR IO; *1983 NIH Almanac*, 140; *Federal Services: Expenditures for Research,*" Dean Papers, NIDR IO; *1983 NIH Almanac*, 76.

39. U.S. Cong., House, *Hearings on . . . 1954 Appropriations*, 83d Cong., 1st sess., 1075-76.

40. National Institute of Dental Research, "Analysis of Program Activities, 1955," 1-6, appendix, NIHL.

41. National Institute of Dental Research, "Analysis of Program Activities, 1955," 1-6, appendix, NIHL; "Data Assembled for the Special Committee on Medical Research," 3-4; Dr. Robert Stephan, interview by Laura Kells, February 17, 1987, and Dr. Seymour Kreshover, interview by Ruth R. Harris, September 29, 1986.

42. *1983 NIH Almanac*, 76.

43. *1985 NIH Almanac*, Publication No. 85-5, 39, 53, 59, 75, 87, 100; Dr. Harold Hillenbrand, ADA executive secretary, to the Honorable Marion Folsom, secretary, Department of Health, Education and Welfare, October 8, 1955, "Legislation—Supporting for National Institute of Dental Research 1956-1947 and Establishing of NIDR," no. 3 of 4, NIDR IO; National Institute of Dental Research, "Report of Program Activities, Summary of Research Activity," January-December 1956, 5, NIHL; *ADA News Letter* 9 (March 1, 1956): 1, and 9 (April 2, 1956): 2; NIDR Direct Research Organizational-Staffing Information as of January 14, 1955, "Legislation—Supporting for National Institute of Dental Research 1956-1947 and Establishing of NIDR," no. 3 of 4, NIDR IO. G. Byron McCandless, information officer in 1956, may have been the first Institute information officer. See McCandless to Bill Carrigan, Scientific Reports Branch, Division of Research Services, August 1, 1956, NIDR IO.

44. *1985 NIH Almanac*, 39, 53, 59, 75, 87, 100; Dr. Harold Hillenbrand to the Honorable Marion Folsom, October 8, 1955, "Legislation Supporting for National Institute of Dental Research 1956-1947 and Establishing of NIDR," no. 3 of 4, NIDR IO; National Institute of Dental Research, "Report of Program Activities, Summary of Research Activity," January-December 1956, 5, NIHL; *ADA News Letter* 9 (March 1, 1956): 1, and 9 (April 2, 1956): 2.

45. Director, NIDR, to director, NIH, November 10, 1959, "History of NIDR," NIDR IO; NIDR organizational charts of November 7, 1949; March 13, 1956; July 6, 1959; March 1, 1960; March 1, 1961; July 1, 1962; March 1, 1965, and April 1, 1967, Kirk Weaver's Files, NIDR; *1983 NIH Almanac*, 131.

46. "Summary Statement by Director, National Institute of Dental Research, before Committee on Appropriations for 'Dental Health Activities, Public Health Service,'" "Opening Statements," NIDR IO; director, NIDR, to direc-

tor, NIH, November 4, 1959, "Weekly Reports" 1956-1962, vol. 1, Brent Jaquet's Files, NIDR IO; "The National Institute of Dental Research, Annual Report on Extramural Research, Calendar Year 1960," 34, Dr. Lynn's Files, NIDR.

47. "The National Institute of Dental Research, Annual Report, Calendar Year 1960," 1, Dr. Lynn's Files, NIDR; Dr. Rachel Harris Larson, interview by Ruth R. Harris, March 10, 1987, and Dr. Karl Piez, interview by Ruth R. Harris, December 29, 1986.

48. "National Institute of Dental Research, Annual Report of Administration, Calendar Year 1960," same for Calendar Year 1961, Dr. Lynn's Files, NIDR; Minutes of Meeting of February 29, March 1-2, 1960, of National Advisory Dental Research Council, 4; Dr. Seymour J. Kreshover, "The Annual Report of the Scientific Director, The National Institute of Dental Research, Calendar Year 1962," Dr. Lynn's Files, NIDR.

49. Dr. Michael Roberts, interview by Laura Kells, December 15, 1986; associate director for clinical care administration, NIH, and director, NIDR, to director, NIH, March 16, 1964, "Dental Clinic History," Dr. Michael Roberts' Files, NIDR; executive officer, PHS, to surgeon general, April 14, 1964, "NIDR Organizational Changes through 1969, Subsection 1964," Kirk Weaver's Files, NIDR; *NIH Record* 16 (April 21, 1964): 1.

50. Seymour J. Kreshover, "Report of the Director, The National Institute of Dental Research, July 1, 1965-June 30, 1966," 4, Dr. Lynn's Files, NIDR; *American Dental Association Transactions 1963*, 50-51; Francis A. Arnold, Jr., "Report of the Director, The National Institute of Dental Research, January 1, 1963-June 30, 1964," 5, Dr. Lynn's Files, NIDR.

51. "Report of the Director, The National Institute of Dental Research, July 1, 1965-June 30, 1966," 21, Dr. Lynn's Files, NIDR; *National Institutes of Health Scientific Directory* 1964 and 1966 (hereafter *NIH Scientific Directory*), NIDR.

52. Seymour J. Kreshover, "Report of the Director, The National Institute of Dental Research, July 1, 1965-June 30, 1966," 1, Dr. Lynn's Files, NIDR; Minutes of June 20-22, 1966, Meeting of the National Advisory Dental Research Council, 5-6, NIDR.

53. Dr. Seymour J. Kreshover, interview by Ruth R. Harris, September 29, 1986; *American Men and Women of Science*, 15th ed., Kreshover, Seymour J.; *1983 NIH Almanac*, 77-78.

54. Seymour J. Kreshover, "Programs of the National Institute of Dental Research," address prepared for the 1967 Conference of Dental School Deans, Miami, Florida, October 10-12, 1967, "Kreshover, Seymour," NIDR Files, Speeches, February 1986, NIDR.

55. Irving J. Lewis to Douglass Cater, August 10, 1966, and attachments, EX FG 165-6-1, 11/22/62-8/10/66, Container 249, Lyndon B. Johnson Library, Austin, Texas (hereafter LBJL); Dr. Seymour Kreshover, interview by Ruth R. Harris, September 29, 1986.

56. *NIH Record* 18 (November 30, 1966): 5.

57. *NIH Scientific Directory*, 1965, 1966, 1967, NIDR; Minutes of Program Planning Committee, May 24, 1966, Program Planning Minutes, Book II, NIDR IO; *NIH Scientific Directory*, 1969, 1970, NIDR; Chief, Human Genetics Branch, NIDR, to director, Intramural Research, NIDR, December 9, 1969, "NIDR Organizational Changes through 1969, Subsection 1969," NIDR.

58. *NIH Scientific Directory* 1972, NIDR; *1983 NIH Almanac*, 76.

59. *NIH Scientific Directory*, 1972, 1973, NIDR; Dr. Robert W. Berliner to director, NIDR, July 24, 1973, "NIDR 1973," OD NIH; director, NIDR, to NIDR Program Leaders, August 27, 1973, "NIDR Organizational Changes 1970-1977, 1973," NIDR.

60. Director of Intramural Research, NIDR, to director, NIDR, November 5, 1973, "Reorganization," and chiefs, Laboratory of Biochemistry, Laboratory of Microbiology and Immunology, and Connective Tissue Section, November 8, 1973, "Craniofacial Anomalies," LDBA, NIDR; director, NIDR, to deputy director, NIH, December 14, 1973, "Reorganizations, DDH-NIDR-HSM," binder, Dr. Louden's Files, PHS; *1983 NIH Almanac*, 122, 141.

61. Chad Leyshon, interview by Ruth R. Harris and Laura Kells, August 11, 1986; *NIH Scientific Directory* 1973, 1974, NIDR.

62. *NIH Scientific Directory* 1975, 1976, NIDR.

63. Ibid.

64. Dr. David B. Scott, interview by Ruth R. Harris, September 3, 1986; *1983 NIH Almanac*, 78.

65. *NIH Scientific Directory*, 1975, 1976, 1977, NIDR; Dr. Robert Stephan, interview by Laura Kells, February 17, 1987, and Chad Leyshon, interview by Ruth R. Harris and Laura Kells, August 11, 1986.

66. Acting director to director, NIH, September 13, 1982, and executive officer, NIDR, to director, Division of Management Policy, March 9, 1982, "O & M2-Y Organization of NIDR," OD NIH; *NIH Scientific Directory* 1983, NIDR; Goggins to acting director, NIH, January 29, 1982, "NIDR Organizational Changes 1981-Present 1982," Kirk Weaver's Files, NIDR.

67. *1985 NIH Almanac*, 88; Dr. Harald Löe, interview by Ruth R. Harris, July 2, 1987.

68. Director, NIDR, to director, NIH, December 5, 1983, "O & M2-Y Organization National Institute of Dental Research 83," OD NIH; *Federal Register* 49 (April 9, 1984): Notices.

69. "Adventures in Science," radio program presented Saturday, February 4, 1950, transcript, 3, Dean Papers, NIDR.

70. List of ADA research associates supplied by Dr. Anthony Steffek, ADA headquarters.

71. Information supplied by Dr. Marie Nylen; Dr. David E. Price to Dr. Marie J. Ussing, July 1, 1950, and Dr. Frederick L. Stone to Dr. Marie J. Ussing, July 21, 1950, Dr. Marie Nylen's Files, NIDR; *NIH Record* 33 (April 28, 1981): 4.

72. Maj. Thomas R. Tempel to director, NIDR, June 15, 1970, "Council Minutes January 1949-November 1972," November 16-17, 1970, Council Meeting, Office of Associate Director for Extramural Programs (hereafter OADEXP), NIDR. Because of a lack of records it is not possible to provide even an approximate count of the number of postdoctoral and postdental degree trainees working at the Institute. Before 1965 Institute and NIH personnel lists did not identify trainees. From 1965 through 1983 NIH referred to trainees as *associates* or *guest workers*. In 1984 *associates* became *fellows*, and *guest workers* became *guest researchers*. The count represents information drawn from *NIH Scientific Directory*, NIDR, lists from 1965 to 1985.

73. Minutes of Sixth Meeting—January 17, 1949, Committee on Dentistry, National Research Council, Division of Medical Sciences, Bulletin, Dentistry 1949, 116-19.

74. "Phase 1 NIDR Training Program Study, July 1970," 4, "NIDR Training Statistics," and "Training Grants" and "Fellowships" from FY 1949-1969, "NIDR-Training Grants-Historical Data," Dr. Thomas Valega's Files, NIDR; U.S. Cong., House, "Dental Health Activities," 84th Cong., 2d sess., February 9, 1956, 674-75, 680; Dale R. Lindsay to Files, February 21, 1956, "Program Planning, 1954-1959," Dr. Lynn's Files, NIDR; U.S. Cong., Senate, "Labor—Health, Education, and Welfare Appropriations, 1957," 84th Cong., 2d sess., 646-47, 655, 657, 658; "Appropriation History," "History of NIDR," NIDR IO.

75. Francis A. Arnold, Jr., "The Fellowship and Training Grants Program of the National Institutes of Health," *Journal of Dental Education* 23 (June 1959): 101-4; Thomas C. Hill to Pokey, Saturday morning [1956], "Program Planning, 1954-1959," Dr. Lynn's Files, NIDR; "Report of the Program Planning Committee, June 11-12 and May 3, 1956, "Program Planning, 1954-1959," Dr. Lynn's Files, NIDR; "NIDR Position Paper on Research Training," May 1979, "February 1978 to May 21-22, 1979, Council Meeting," OADEXP NIDR; Arnold to Members of the Program Planning Committee, NADRC, and Dental Study Section, September 7, 1956, "Program Planning, 1954-1959," Dr. Lynn's Files, NIDR; "First Dual Degree Clinical Research Training Program Symposium, Summary of Minutes of Meeting," September 16-17, 1969, "Dual Degree Program," Dr. Valega's Files, NIDR; Minutes of NIDR Program Planning Committee Meeting of October 2-3, 1947, and "Program Highlights in Dental Research," "Historical Files," NIDR IO; *ADA Newsletter* 15 (February 16, 1962): 1.

76. "NIDR Inaugurates Clinical Research Training Program," Research News from NIDR, no. 4, February 1964, Brent Jaquet's Files, NIDR IO.

77. "National Institute of Dental Research Trainees and Fellows: Comparison of Follow-up Surveys—1962, 1966, and 1972," August 1974, "Training Program Statistics," Dr. Valega's Files, NIDR; "Report on Career Meeting Preparatory to the National Advisory Research Council Review," January 1967, "Resource Documents Relative to NIDR Manpower Training, August 13, 1974, Dr. Gardner," 1-2, Dr. Valega's Files, NIDR; "Appropriations History"; "Phase I NIDR Training Program Study: Review of the NIDR Training

Program and Projection of the National Need for Dental Investigators and the NIDR Training Program, 1969-1976," July 1970, "NIDR Training Statistics," Dr. Valega's Files, NIDR.

78. "Phase I NIDR Training Program Study," July 1970, 5, 6.

79. "National Institute of Dental Research Trainees and Fellows: Comparison of Follow-up Surveys—1962, 1966 and 1972," August 1974, and "Special Report, NIDR Supported Trainees and Fellows in Selected Professional Activities," July 1973, 1-2, "Training Program Statistics," Dr. Valega's Files, NIDR.

80. Donald S. Fredrickson, "Training Programs of the National Institutes of Health: Current Status," "Manpower Needs in FY 1979," Dr. Valega's Files, NIDR.

81. Acting director, NIDR, to director, NIH, June 23, 1972, "June 19-20, 1972, Council Meeting," Drawer—Council Minutes, January 1949-November 1972, OADEXP NIDR.

82. "Position Paper: NIDR Training Program Directors' Meetings," May 2, 1973, "Training Program Directors' Conference," Dr. Valega's Files, NIDR; "Appropriations History"; "Ph.D. Degrees Sought by Year under NIDR Fellowships & Training Grant Support," "NRSA-Past Training Record Ph.D.," Dr. Valega's Files, NIDR.

83. *American Dental Association Transactions*, 1974, 90.

84. Assistant secretary for health to Stone, July 20, 1973, "Training Grants—Background Data," and Dr. Donald Fredrickson, "Training Programs of the National Institutes of Health: Current Status," "Manpower Needs in FY 1979," Dr. Valega's Files, NIDR.

85. "Legislative History of NIH Training," 1-14, Dr. Valega's Files, NIDR. Section 422(288a) of the amended Public Health Service Act provided for NIDR clinical training and instruction.

86. "NIDR Position Paper on Research Training," May 1979, 1, 2, 5, 6, 7, OADEXP NIDR.

87. William A. Ayer, Helen Gift, Daniel B. Green, Ann Howe, Barry C. Grossman, "Dental Researchers in the United States," December 1, 1982, 1, 77, 79-80, ADA Archives; Dr. P. A. Littleton, Jr., L. J. Brown, E. S. Solomon, "The Relationship between National Institute of Dental Research (NIDR) Supported Research Training and Careers in Dental Research," n.d., "Training, Fellows, and Career Development," Dr. James Lipton's Files, NIDR.

88. "NIH Guide for Grants and Contracts" Announcement, June 1984, "Board File-Training, January-July 1984," OADEXP 4NIDR; National Institute of Dental Research, *Dentist Scientist Award—National Institute of Dental Research*, March 1987. Participating institutions included Louisiana State University, the State University of New York at Buffalo, the University of Connecticut, the University of Iowa, the University of North Carolina, the University of Rochester, the University of Texas Health Science Center at San Antonio, the University of Washington, and Virginia Commonwealth University.

89. National Advisory Dental Research Council Minutes of Meetings for November 23-25, 1959, 3, NIDR.

90. National Advisory Dental Research Council Minutes for June 16-18, 1960, 5, and November 21-23, 1960, 5, NIDR; *ADA News Letter* 17 (September 14, 1964): 1; *NIH Record* 16 (September 6, 1964): 5; *Dental Health Memorandum*, October 15, 1964, "Dental Health Memoranda January 1963-March 1965," CDO PHS.

91. U.S. Cong., Senate, *Hearings before the Subcommittee of the Committee on Appropriations on H.R. 10904*, 87th Cong., 2d sess. (Washington: GPO, 1964), 1668; U.S. Cong., Senate, *Hearings before the Subcommittee of the Committee on Appropriations . . . on H.R. 5888*, Part II, 88th Cong., 1st sess., 1207; National Advisory Dental Research Council Minutes of Meeting, March 9-11, 1964, 5, NIDR; *ADA News Letter* 17 (July 6, 1964): 1, 4; "Clinical Research Centers (Dental)," "Special Reports Miscellaneous," Anne Atlee's Files, NIDR IO; associate director, NIDR, to director, NIH, December 23, 1965, "NIDR-1 Dental Research Institutes/ Centers 1965," OD NIH; "Special Report: Dental Research Institutes," "Special Reports Miscellaneous," Anne Atlee's Files, NIDR IO.

92. "Guidelines for Dental Research Institutes," May 1967, "Guidelines Dental Research Institutes 5/67," Evaluation of Dental Research Institutes," OADEXP NIDR.

93. S. J. Kreshover to Dr. John V. Olson, dean, University of Texas Dental Branch, Houston, April 20, 1967, "NIDR-1 Dental Research Institute/Centers 1967-68," OD NIH; *NIH Record* 18 (June 1, 1966): 4.

94. "Research News from NIDR," no. 37, February 1967, Brent Jaquet's Notebook, "Research News from NIDR No. 2," NIDR IO; June 23, 1967, HEW-Q83, Press Release, "Press Releases Old-1963," Anne Atlee's Files, NIDR IO.

95. *Evaluation of the NIDR Periodontal Disease Research Activity: Report of the Ad Hoc Scientific Evaluation Panel to the Director National Institute of Dental Research*, [NIDR], April 1976, 61, 63-65.

96. Grace M. Carter, Clara S. Lai, and Carolyn L. Lee, *A Comparison of Large Grants and Research Project Grants Awarded by the National Institutes of Health*, R-2228-1-NIH, October 1978, v-x, 1, 13, 29, 30, 52-56.

97. Seymour Kreshover, director, NIDR, to director, NIH, "Annual Review Material for November 15-16, 1971 Dental Council Meeting, Council Minutes January 1949-November 1972, November 15-16, 1971 Council Meeting," OADEXP NIDR; "NIDR Research News," November 1977, "Research News from NIDR No. 4," January 1974 to October 1978, Brent Jaquet's Files, NIDR IO; Question and Answer dated 3/6/82 in Chronological File—1/82, OADEXP NIDR; Harald Löe to Sen. William Proxmire, May 24, 1984, "OD/NIDR Correspondence 1982-1985," OD NIDR, and A. A. Rizzo, "Definitions and Descriptions of Types of Centers," August 23, 1984, "Board File July-Dec. 1984 Rizzo," OADEXP NIDR.

98. Dr. Harald Löe to the Hon. James T. Broyhill, July 8, 1983, "Correspondence 1982-1985," OD NIDR.

99. Minutes of Dental Research Institute and Centers Meeting held August 16, 1983, "Board File-Centers April 1983-1984," OADEXP NIDR; A. A. Rizzo, "Definitions and Descriptions of Types of Centers," August 23, 1984, "Board File July-Dec. 1984 Rizzo," OADEXP NIDR.

100. John F. Goggins to Dr. Roy C. Page, director, Center for Research in Oral Biology, University of Washington, Seattle, September 7, 1983, "Ext Res 2-1-b Closure of Selected General Cl. Res. Centers 84," OD NIH; Dr. Joel Rosenbloom, University of Pennsylvania, to Dr. James Wyngaarden, director, NIH, September 19, 1983, "Board Files-Center-April 1983-June 1984," OADEXP NIDR; James K. Avery, director, Dental Research Institute, and Richard L. Christiansen, dean, School of Dentistry, University of Michigan, to Dr. James B. Wyngaarden, October 6, 1983, "NIDR 83," OD NIH; Roy C. Page to Dr. Harald Löe, November 10, 1983, and attachment; John F. Goggins to Dr. Joel Rosenbloom, December 7, 1983, "Board File-Centers April 1983-June 1984," OADEXP NIDR; Harald Löe to Rep. James T. Broyhill, July 8, 1983, "OD/NIDR Correspondence 1982-1985," OD NIDR; Dr. James Wyngaarden to Hon. Thomas Foley, May 29, 1984, "Ext. Res 2-1-b Closure of Selected General Cl. Res. Centers 84," OD NIH; Sens. Howard Heflin, Jeremiah Denton, Donald W. Riegle, Carl Levin, John Heinz, and Arlen Specter to Dr. James Wyngaarden, January 13, 1984, "Ext Res 2-1-6 Closure of Selected General Cl. Res. Centers," OD NIH; Wyngaarden to Senator, "Board File - A. A. Rizzo January-June 1984," OADEXP NIDR; Anne Houser to Judy Lewis on "Meeting between National Institute for Dental Research and House and Senate Appropriations Staff," February 1, 1984, "OD/NIDR Correspondence 1982-1985," OD NIDR.

101. *NIH Record* 36 (February 26, 1985): 8; "NIH Guide Supplement for Grants and Contracts," 84-DE-02, 84-DE-01, and 84-DE-3, "Dr. Niswander's Files, RFA," Epidemiology Branch, NIDR.

102. Harald Löe to William F. Raub, deputy director, NIH, "Progress Report to the Senate Appropriations Committee on NIDR Center/Large Grant Program," November 26, 1986, 100.00 Daily Board October-December [1986], OD NIDR; National Institute of Dental Research, *Programs*, Fiscal Year 1986 Funds, 100-17, NIDR.

CHAPTER SEVEN. *Fighting Dental Decay*

1. Thomas B. Hartzell to Dr. Fredrick P. Gay, chairman of the Medical Section of the National Research Council, and members of the Medical Section, "MED: Committee on Dental Investigations 1919-1923," Central Files, NAS; Rodriguez, "Studies in the Specific Bacteriology of Dental Caries," 200.

2. Robert Morhart and Robert Fitzgerald, "Composition and Ecology of the Oral Flora," in *The Biologic Basis of Dental Caries: An Oral Biology Textbook*, ed. Lewis Menaker (Hagerstown: Harper and Row, 1980), 263; J. Kilian Clarke, "On the Bacterial Factor in the Aeiology of Dental Caries," *British Journal of Experimental Pathology* 5 (June 1924): 141-47. Quotation is on p. 145.

3. L. Hektoen, chairman, Division of Medical Sciences, National Academy of Sciences, to Capt. F. E. Rodriguez, Army Medical School, Washington, D.C., January 22, 1925, "MED: Committee on Dental Investigations 1924-1926," Central Files, NAS; Robert J. Fitzgerald, "Brief History of *Streptococcus Mutans*," *Streptococcus Mutans and Dental Caries*, 73d Annual Meeting, American Society for Microbiology, May 10, 1972, DHEW Pub. No. (NIH) 74-186, 1-2.

4. Fitzgerald in "Brief History of *Streptococcus Mutans*," 1, said, "Neither Clarke nor McLean defined the organism very well as far as biochemical characteristics were concerned."

5. Dr. Thomas Parran, surgeon general, to Dr. P. C. Lowery, chairman, Research Commission, ADA, March 10, 1937, RG 90, Box 159, 1950 American Dental Association Folder, NARA.

6. H. T. Dean to Dr. D. T. Smithwick, Louisburg, N.C., March 5, 1932, and Carl Voegtlin, acting director, to Dr. Russell Bunting, June 21, 1932, Dean Papers, NLM; Philip Jay, Mary Crowley, Faith P. Hadley, and R. W. Bunting, "Bacteriologic and Immunologic Studies on Dental Caries," *JADA* (December 1933): 2130-48.

7. Carl Voegtlin to Bunting, June 21, 1932, Dean Papers, NLM.

8. Dean to the surgeon general, February 3, 1937, RG 443, Box 76, Arnold, Francis A. (Jr.) Folder, NARA.

9. H. Trendley Dean, Philip Jay, Francis A. Arnold, Jr., and Elias Elvove, "Domestic Water and Dental Caries. II. A Study of 2,832 White Children, Aged 12-14 Years, of 8 Suburban Chicago Communities, Including *Lactobacillus acidophilus* Studies of 1,761 Children," *PHR* 56 (April 11, 1941): 761-92. Consequently, when the federal government and Michigan officials started the Grand Rapids fluoridation project in 1945, they listed among the objectives the bacteriological study of saliva of the children and *Lactobacillus acidophilus* counts in deep decay of teeth.

10. Frank J. Orland, J. Roy Blaney, R. Wendell Harrison, James A. Reyniers, Philip C. Trexler, Robert F. Ervin, Helmut A. Gordon, and Morris Wagner, "Experimental Caries in Germ-free Rats Inoculated with Enterococci," *JADA* 50 (March 1955): 260-61.

11. Dr. Marie Nylen, interview by Ruth R. Harris, May 28, 1987.

12. *NIH Record* 8 (January 30, 1956): 1, and 22 (March 31, 1970): 1.

13. R. M. Stephan, "The Development of Caries on the Buccal and Lingual Tooth Surfaces of Rats as well as Proximal and Fissure Caries," *Journal of Dental Research* 30 (1951): 484; F. J. McClure, "Experimental Dental Caries in Rats," *Journal of Nutrition* 43 (February 1951): 303-12. Dr. Rachel Larson provided this appraisal and observed that "the development of smooth surface lesions in the rat was a real landmark in caries research."

14. R. M. Stephan, R. J. Fitzgerald, F. J. McClure, Mr. Harris, and H. Jordan, "The Comparative Effects of Penicillin, Bacitracin, Chloromycetin, Aureomy-

cin and Streptomycin on Experimental Dental Caries and on Certain Oral
Bacteria in the Rat," *Journal of Dental Research* 31 (1952): 421; Dr. Robert J.
Fitzgerald, interview by Ruth R. Harris, September 24, 1986.

15. Dr. Robert J. Fitzgerald, interview by Ruth R. Harris, September 24, 1986.
    Gram-positive bacteria retain color after a test; gram-negative bacteria easily
    decolorize with the same test.

16. Ibid.; *NIH Record* 8 (February 21, 1985): 2.

17. Orland et al., "Experimental Caries in Germ-free Rats Inoculated with Entero-
    cocci."

18. Robert M. Stephan and M. Rachel Harris, "Location of Experimental Caries on
    Different Tooth Surfaces in the Norway Rat," *Advances in Experimental Caries
    Research* (Washington, D.C.: American Association for the Advance of Science,
    1955), 47-65; Dr. Rachel Harris Larson, interview by Ruth R. Harris, March
    10, 1987; *NIH Record* 3 (February 5, 1951): 2, and 8 (January 30, 1956): 2.

19. *NIH Record* 33 (September 15, 1981): 7, and 9 (January 7, 1957): 2; Dr.
    Anthony Rizzo, interview by Ruth R. Harris, November 3, 1987.

20. Associate director, NIDR, to director, NIH, July 3, 1957, "Weekly Reports
    1956-1962," vol. 1, Brent Jaquet's Files, NIDR IO.

21. R. J. Fitzgerald, H. V. Jordan, and H. R. Stanley, "Experimental Caries and
    Gingival Pathologic Changes in the Gnotobiotic Rat," *Journal of Dental Re-
    search* 39 (September-October 1960): 923-35. Quotation is on p. 934.

22. P. H. Keyes, "Dental Caries in Syrian Hamster. VIII. Induction of Rampant
    Caries Activity in Albino and Golden Animals," *Journal of Dental Research* 38
    (May-June 1959): 525; director, NIDR, to director, NIH, December 9, 1959,
    "Weekly Reports 1956-1962," vol. 1, Brent Jaquet's Files, NIDR IO.

23. Dr. Anthony Rizzo, interview by Ruth R. Harris, November 3, 1987.

24. Robert J. Fitzgerald and Paul H. Keyes, "Demonstration of the Etiologic Role
    of Streptococci in Experimental Caries in the Hamster," *JADA* 61 (July 1960):
    9-19.

25. Ibid.

26. News Summary of March 24, 1961, of the National Institute of Dental Re-
    search, "NIDR History," NIDR IO; Dr. Robert J. Fitzgerald, interview by
    Ruth R. Harris, September 24, 1986.

27. Robert J. Fitzgerald, "Microbiological Aspects of Dental Caries," *JADA* 66
    (May 1963): 597-99.

28. 1962 NIDR *Annual Report*, 32, Dr. Lynn's Files, NIDR; *NIH Record* 14
    (August 14, 1962): 3.

29. *NIH Record Science Section* 12 (September 27, 1960): 3, and (November 8,
    1960): 5.

30. "Highlights of Progress in Research in Oral Diseases 1962," 2, "Research
    Highlights 1953-1973," Anne Atlee's Files, NIDR IO.

31. *NIH Record* 12 (May 10, 1960): 5; "Highlights of Progress in Research in Oral Diseases 1962," 2, "Research Highlights 1953-1973," Anne Atlee's Files, NIDR IO.

32. Director, NIDR, to director, NIH, November 4, 1964, "Weekly Reports 1963-1968," vol. 2, Brent Jaquet's Files, NIDR IO; *NIH Record* 16 (November 18, 1964); H. R. Englander and P. H. Keyes, "The Prevention of Dental Caries in the Syrian Hamster Following Repeated Topical Application of Fluoride Gels," *JADA* 73 (December 1966): 1342-47; H. R. Englander, J. P. Carlos, R. S. Senning, and J. R. Mellberg, "Residual Anticaries Effect of Repeated Topical Sodium Fluoride Applications by Mouthpieces," *JADA* 78 (1969): 783-87.

33. Fitzgerald, "Brief History of *Streptococcus Mutans*"; information supplied by Dr. Robert Fitzgerald to Ruth R. Harris.

34. Stephen P. Strickland, *Politics, Science, and Dread Disease: A Short History of United States Medical Research Policy* (Cambridge: Harvard University Press, 1972), 182; *Biomedical Science and Its Administration: A Study of the National Institutes of Health* (White House: February 1965), 1.

35. *Biomedical Science and Its Administration*, 1-20.

36. S. J. Kreshover, acting director, NIDR, to director, NIH, August 4, 1965, "O & M-2 Organization, Functions & Staffing 1965," OD NIH; W. K. Holl, chief, Management Policy Branch, to executive officer, NIDR, November 23, 1965, "NIDR Historical Material," Dr. Lynn's Files, NIDR. Tula S. Brocard, information officer, NIDR, to Bruce Berman, Office of Research Information, September 10, 1965, "NIDR Research Accomplishments for White House," Anne Atlee's Files, NIDR IO; notes of Dr. Seymour J. Kreshover, NIDR IO.

37. Irving J. Lewis, chief, Health and Welfare Division, Bureau of the Budget, memorandum for Mr. Cater, August 10, 1966, EX FG 165-6-1, 11/22/63-8/ 10/66, Container 249, LBJL.

38. Lyndon B. Johnson's Diary File, LBJL; "11/2/66 Meeting of the National Advisory Dental Research Council to Discuss Report to White House on Progress against Disease," "NIDR Report to the President," Anne Atlee's Files, NIDR IO; notes of Dr. Samuel J. Kreshover, NIDR IO.

39. Irving J. Lewis to Douglass Cater, August 10, 1966, and attachments, EX FG 165-6-1, 11/22/62-8/10/66, Container 249, LBJL. The politics and the National Caries Program are discussed more fully in the next chapter.

40. Director, NIH, to the secretary, July 26, 1966, attached to Mike Gorman to Douglass Cater, the White House, August 8, 1966, and director, NIH, to the secretary, HEW, and the surgeon general, July 13, 1966, NIH-OD-OFF, EX FG 165-6-1, 11/22/63-8/10/66, Container 149, LBJL.

41. "NIDR Report to the President," Anne Atlee's Files, NIDR IO; *The Advancement of Knowledge for the Nation's Health: A Report to the President on the Research Programs of the National Institute of Health*, 263-406 0-67-6, 73.

42. *NIH Record* 19 (August 10, 1967): 1, 8.

43. Minutes of Program Planning Committee Meeting, October 25, 1967, "Pro-

gram Planning Minutes Book II," Brent Jaquet's Files, NIDR IO.

44. American Dental Association Press Release, February 1, 1968, "Press Releases," "Fitzgerald and Keyes Dextranase 1968," Anne Atlee's Files, NIDR IO; *NIH Record* 20 (February 20, 1968).

45. NIDR Board of Scientific Counselors, Minutes of Meeting, April 1-2, 1968, 2; *1985 NIH Almanac*, 87.

46. "Remarks of Dr. Seymour J. Kreshover, Director, National Institute of Dental Research," June 4, 1968, "NIDR Press Kit 6/68," NIDR IO; *NIH Record* 20 (June 11, 1968): 1, 5; "Research News from NIDR," no. 53, June 1968, NIDR 20th Anniversary Press Clippings, NIDR IO; NIDR Board of Scientific Counselors, Minutes of Meeting, October 21-November 1, 1968, 4, "Agenda, Minutes, and Roster—1963-1969," Office of the Scientific Director, NIDR.

47. NIDR Board of Scientific Counselors, Minutes of Meeting, April 1-2, 1968, "Agenda, Minutes, and Roster—1963-1979," Office of the Scientific Director, NIDR; "Preliminary Report, Caries Task Force, National Institute of Dental Research," January 1969, and News Release, NIDR, April 7, 1969, "National Caries Program," Sally Wilberding's Files, NIDR IO. Members of the panel included Dr. Basil Bibby, director of the Eastman Dental Center, Rochester, New York; Dr. George W. Burnett, professor of microbiology, School of Dentistry, Medical College of Georgia; Dr. Charles J. Donnelly, chief, Dental Caries and Hard Tissues Program of the Institute's extramural programs; Dr. Robert S. Harris, professor of nutritional biochemistry, Massachusetts Institute of Technology; Dr. John W. Knutson, professor of preventive dentistry, School of Dentistry, University of California; Fitzgerald, retired from the Institute to work in research at the Veterans Administration Hospital in Miami, Florida; and Dr. John Greene, deputy director of the Division of Dental Health of the Public Health Service.

48. William E. Rogers, *The National Caries Program: The First Ten Years*," 5. The panel supported the Division of Dental Health proposal for a new federal grants-in-aid program to assist fluoride-deficient communities with less than 100,000 population to install fluoridation equipment. Despite the panel's endorsement Congress did not appropriate the funds for such a program.

49. Rogers, *The National Caries Program*, 5-6.

50. U.S. Cong., Senate, *Senate Hearings before the Committee on Appropriations, Department of Labor and Health, Education and Welfare Appropriations*, 91st Cong., 1st sess., H.R. 1311, October 31, 1969, 1261-66; HEW News Release, October 16, 1969, "Press Releases. Buonocure, Sealant for ADA Release 2/70," Anne Atlee's Files, NIDR IO; Associated Press Release on "Dental Decay" by Frank Carey, WE 1019AES, December 29, 1969, in NIH Ticker Takes from A.P. and U.P.I., "National Caries Program," Sally Wilberding's Files, NIDR IO.

51. Rogers, *The National Caries Program*, 7; "A National Caries Program of the National Institute of Dental Research: Ten-Year Program of Research and Development," January 1970, Sally Wilberding's Files, NIDR IO.

52. *The Budget for Fiscal Year 1971: The Budget Message of the President*, 375-9470-70-3, 37; *NIH Record* 22 (February 17, 1970): 7.

53. "National Caries Program Brief Chronology," "National Caries Program—Historical, Publicity," EODPP NIDR.

54. Tula Brocard to Peter C. Goulding, assistant secretary for public information, ADA, September 30, 1970, "National Caries Program," Sally Wilberding's Files, NIDR IO.

55. NIDR Board of Scientific Counselors, Minutes of Meeting, October 26-27, 1970, "Agenda, Minutes, and Roster—1963-1979," Office of the Scientific Director, NIDR.

56. *NIDR Annual Report, July 1, 1970-June 30, 1971*, 1; NIDR Board of Scientific Counselors, Minutes of Meeting, May 25, 1972, 3, "Agenda, Minutes and Roster—1963-1969," Office of the Scientific Director, NIDR.

57. Minutes of the Caries Task Force, NIDR, Meeting, October 19-20, NIDR IO; *NIDR Annual Report, July 1, 1970-June 30, 1971*, 1; Marston to assistant secretary for health and scientific affairs, DHEW, December 19, 1970, "Report on Relationships of Dental Activities of DDH, BEMT, NIH, and HSMSHA," Dr. Louden's Files, PHS.

58. "Oral Disease: Target for the 70's," December 30, 1970, 5-9, Anne Atlee's Files, NIDR IO; NIDR Board of Scientific Counselors, Minutes of Meeting, November 4-5, 1971, "Agenda, Minutes, and Roster—1963-1979," Office of the Scientific Director, NIDR.

59. "National Caries Program Status Report," March 1971, "Research-NIDR," OD NIH.

60. James P. Carlos, "The Prevention of Dental Caries: Ten Years Later," *JADA* 104 (February 1982): 193; "Opportunities for Participation in the National Caries Program through Research Contracts," October 1971, EODPP NIDR.

61. Dr. James Carlos, interview by Ruth R. Harris, October 20, 1987.

62. "National Caries Program National Institute of Dental Research Status Report," March 1971, "Research-NIDR," OD NIH; "FY 1972 Appropriations Hearings," May 5, 1971, 459; National Institute of Dental Research News Release, November 11, 1971, "National Caries Program," Sally Wilberding's Files, NIDR IO; Dr. James P. Carlos, "Present Trends for Control of Dental Caries," November 30-December 6, 1971, 1, 3-4, 7-8, "Presentations Dr. Carlos 1969-1973," Epidemiology Branch, NIDR; Rogers, *The National Caries Program*, 17.

63. Kreshover to NIDR program leaders, March 17, 1972, "NIDR Organizational Changes 1972," Kirk Weaver's Files, NIDR; *JADA* 108 (March 1984): 312; McClure, *Fluoridation*, 159.

64. *NIH Record* 36 (April 24, 1984): 10; Horowitz to director, NIH, November 30, 1970, "Report on Relationships of Dental Activities of DDH, BEMT, NIH, and HSMHA," Dr. Louden's Files, PHS; Rogers, *The National Caries Program*,

15-16. Bibby served as acting chief of the NIDR Caries Prevention and Research Branch in 1973.

65. Director, Division of Administrative Services, to chairman, National Caries Program Advisory Committee, July 23, 1976, "NCP-Park Building," EODPP NIDR; *1985 NIH Almanac*, 29.

66. Rogers, *The National Caries Program*, 17-18; Dr. James Carlos, interview by Ruth R. Harris, October 20, 1987.

67. "Announcement: NIDR Initiates Community Caries Prevention Projects," "Press Releases Old—1963," Anne Atlee's Files, NIDR IO; R. H. Larson and others, "Caries Inhibition in the Rat by Water-borne and Enamel-borne Fluoride," *Caries Research* 10 (1976): 321-31; Carlos, "The Prevention of Dental Caries," 194-95.

68. "National Research Service Award Institutional Research Training Grant in Cariology," "National Caries Program," Sally Wilberding's Files, NIDR IO.

69. Carlos, "The Prevention of Dental Caries"; "Summary Report of a Workshop on New Approaches in the Development of Pit and Fissure Sealants," September 17, 1976, EODPP NIDR.

70. Scott's notes at Caries Committee Meeting, Monday, November 8, 1976, "GAO F Study," Box 2, Scott's F Files, NIDR.

71. Dr. Ann J. Miller for the record, January 21, 1977, "General Accounting Office," EODPP NIDR.

72. John W. Hein to Dr. James P. Carlos, March 1, 1977, "GAO F Study," Box 2, Scott's F Files, NIDR; Carlos to Thomas J. McGrane, U.S. General Accounting Office, Boston Regional Office, March 2, 1977, "Reading File—1977," EODPP NIDR.

73. Associate director for National Caries Program to staff members, January 3, 1977, and James P. Carlos to Dr. Gordon Watson, executive director, ADA, Chicago, "Reading File—1977," EODPP NIDR. Alice Horowitz and Dr. Ann Miller of the Institute prepared the promotional materials.

74. Assistant to associate director for National Caries Program, NIDR, to the Record, July 13, 1977, "GAO F Study," Box 2, Scott's F Files, NIDR.

75. Carlos to director, Division of Management Survey and Review AO R, August 23, 1977, "Reading File—1977," EODPP NIDR; Fredrickson to Ellsworth H. Morse, Jr., assistant comptroller general, September 8, 1977, "GAO F Study," Box 2, Scott's F Files, NIDR; Dr. Louis F. Szwejda, mouthrinse project director, to Carlos, September 15, 1977, "General Accounting Office," EODPP NIDR.

76. Dr. Ann J. Miller to Dr. James P. Carlos, January 9, 1978, "General Accounting Office," and Press Summary for Release, July 17, 1978, "NCP-Press Releases," EODPP NIDR; "Press Releases Fluoride Mouthrinsing Press Briefing July 1978," Anne Atlee's Files, NIDR IO; *Congressional Record*—Extension of Remarks, July 25, 1978, E4052.

77. *Reducing Tooth Decay - More Emphasis on Fluoridation Needed: Report to the Congress by the Comptroller General of the United States*, Rpt. no. HRD 79-3 (Washington: GAO, April 13, 1979), 4-16. The report stated that data collected on the school-based mouthrinsings lacked scientific and economic validity and that the Institute had misled Congress on the potentials of sealants and several fluoride products.

78. "Comments of the Department of Health, Education and Welfare on the Comptroller General's Draft Report to the Congress of the United States Entitled 'Research Effort to Prevent Tooth Decay Should Be Balanced with More Emphasis on a Proven Technique—Fluoridation,'" March 20, 1979, "GAO Report," Anne Atlee's Files, NIDR IO. The HEW officials challenged the GAO comparison in costs between a private mouthrinsing supplier and the government on the school-based mouthrinsing demonstrations by pointing out that costs used for the private supplier did not include the salaries of school personnel in each community. In addition, department officers noted that the GAO analysis based some of its statements on reports of sealants rejected as unsatisfactory by the NCP scientists.

79. HEW Press Release, August 1, 1979, "Press Releases, Survey of Dental Disease, Oct. 1979," NIDR IO; transcript of National Advisory Dental Research Council 96th meeting, May 22, 1979, 22, "Council Minutes February 1978 to May 21-22, 1979," Council Meeting, OADEXP NIDR.

80. Lee Merkhofer and Fred L. Offensend, Decision Analysis Group, Stanford Research Institute, to Dr. James Carlos, July 20, 1978, "Stanford Research Institute," EODPP NIDR; Carlos, "The Prevention of Dental Caries"; associate director for National Caries Program, NIDR, to the Record, November 9, 1977, "Reading File—1977," EODPP NIDR; NIH Current Clips, November 16, 1977, "Press Releases Xylitol—1977," Anne Atlee's Files, NIDR IO; special assistant to the director, NIDR, to chief, Program Planning Branch, DPA/NIH, November 1, 1978, "NCP Program Planning," and "NIH Research and Legislative Plans, FY 81-83, CARIES," EODPP NIDR.

81. John P. Patterson to Ms. Tergel, March 20, 1979, and attachments, 18, "GAO Report," Anne Atlee's Files, NIDR IO.

82. February 1-2, 1979, council meeting, rough transcript, OADEXP NIDR; *Evaluation of the National Institute of Dental Research National Caries Program*, 3 vols. (Washington: U.S. Dept. of Health, Education and Welfare, November 1979) 1:3-5, 40.

83. *Evaluation of the . . . National Caries Program* 2:77-79.

84. *Evaluation of the . . . National Caries Program* 1:40-43.

85. James P. Carlos to director, NIDR, August 29, 1980, "Reading File—1980," EODPP NIDR.

86. Carlos, "The Prevention of Dental Caries." The work on *Streptococcus mutans* was conducted by J. R. McGhee, J. Mestecky, and R. R. R. Arnold, "Induction of Secretory Antibodies in Humans Following Ingestion of *Streptococcus mutans*," *Advances in Experimental Biology* 107 (1978): 177-84.

87. Rogers, *The National Caries Program*, 31, 34; James Carlos, interview by Ruth R. Harris, October 20, 1987.

88. Carlos, "The Prevention of Dental Caries"; W. H. Bowen and others, "A Method to Assess Cariogenic Potential of Foodstuffs," *JADA* 100 (1980): 677-81.

89. "Report of the Director, The National Institute of Dental Research, October 1, 1980-September 30, 1981," 2-1, NIDR.

90. *Evaluation of the . . . National Caries Program* 1:17-18.

91. Management Analysis Branch, Division of Management Policy, April 12, 1984, Notebook no. 5 of NIDR Organizational Changes, NIDR; *NIH Record* 36 (October 23, 1984): 4; Löe to Dr. D. T. Langford, The Wellcome Research Laboratories, London, "W″, EODPP NIDR; Philip A. Swango, D.D.S., NIDR, to Alice Steele, Peterboro, N.H., March 28, 1985, "Reading File—1985," EODPP NIDR; Dr. Harald Löe, interview by Ruth R. Harris, July 22, 1987. The National Caries Program was abolished officially on April 9, 1984.

92. Dr. John W. Hein to Dr. Edward N. Brandt, Jr., assistant secretary for health, Department of Health and Human Services, July 20, 1982, "O & M 2-Y Organization National Institute of Dental Research 1983," and Emmings to Brandt, July 8, 1983, OD NIH; Carlos to Löe, August 16, 1983, "Reading File—1983," EODPP NIDR; Summary Minutes of National Advisory Dental Research Council, October 17-18, 1983, 8, NIDR; Minutes of November 3, 1983, NIDR Programs Advisory Committee, "Board File—A. A. Rizzo, January-June 1984," OADEXP NIDR. Some former NCP personnel, such as Bowen, returned to academic life.

93. "Pit and Fissure Sealant Use: An Issue Explored," *JADA* 108 (March 1984): 310-22; Helen C. Gift and Ralph A. Frew, "Sealants: Changing Patterns," *JADA* 112 (March 1986): 391-92.

94. Dwight L. Anderson to Harald Löe, January 22, 1986, "06.20, Review of Anticaries Vaccine January 15, 1985," OD NIDR.

95. Dushanka V. Kleinman, NIDR prevention research coordinator, to NIH coordinator for disease prevention and health promotion, March 19, 1966, "Reading File, Dr. Dushanka V. Kleinman, 1/1/86-3/31/86," EODPP NIDR; Carlos to director, NIDR, June 6, 1985, "Reading File—1985," Epidemiology Branch, NIDR.

96. James P. Carlos to Thomas J. Ginley, ADA, February 18, 1986, "E & ODPP Reading File 1986," Epidemiology Branch, NIDR; Herschel Horowitz to Dr. Manuel C. W. Kau, chief, Dental Health Division, Hawaii Department of Health, Honolulu, Hawaii, February 15, 1985, "E & ODPP Reading File 1985," EODPP NIDR.

CHAPTER EIGHT. *Sleuths of Science: Basic Research at NIDR*

1. Transcript of "Adventures in Science," radio program presented on February 4, 1950, under the auspices of Science Service, over the Columbia Broadcasting System, Dean Papers, NIDR IO.

2. Ibid.

3. Ibid.

4. Ibid.

5. For discussion of the science policies of the various presidents, see U.S. Cong., House, 99th Cong., 2d sess., Jeffrey K. Stine, *A History of Science Policy in the United States, 1940-1985* (Washington: GPO, 1986), 45-48, 53-54, 66-67, 71-74.

6. The budget data, including appropriations and percentages of the total NIDR budget, came from raw data collected by Dr. James Lipton, chief, Research Data and Management Information Section, Office of Planning, Evaluation, and Communications, NIDR. The percentages on obligations for NIDR programs appear in *NIDR Programs*, 5, in each edition published for FY 1973 through FY 1983.

7. *NIDR Programs*, 5, of each edition for FY 1973 through FY 1983. The multidisciplinary research centers, which used 10 to 15 percent of the Institute yearly appropriations from 1967 to 1987, spent more than 50 percent of their annual funds on periodontal research and less than 25 percent on caries investigations. Conversely, contracts, which received from 2.8 to 13.4 percent of 1965-1987 Institute funding, used from 48 to 68 percent of their funds for caries research but only 2.5 to 11 percent on periodontal projects. The appropriations for training fluctuated wildly from $20,000 in 1948 to a peak of $7.6 million in 1969 and up and down for the next seventeen years until rising in 1987 to almost $5.3 million. The source for the appropriations is from the collection of Dr. Lipton, NIDR.

8. Information supplied by Dr. David B. Scott; D. B. Scott, H. Kaplan, and R. W. G. Wyckoff, "Replica Studies of Changes in Tooth Surfaces with Age," *Journal of Dental Research* 28 (February 1949): 31-47; D. B. Scott and R. W. G. Wyckoff, "Studies of Tooth Surface Structure by Optical and Electron Microscopy," *JADA* 39 (September 1949): 275-82.

9. NIDR organizational chart of November 7, 1949, "NIDR Professional Staff Listing," NIDR IO; information supplied by Dr. David Scott.

10. Information supplied by Dr. Marie Ussing Nylen; *NIH Record Science Section* 12 (August 16, 1970): 7.

11. *NIH Record* 8 (January 30, 1956): 1.

12. For example, see D. B. Scott, M. U. Nylen, and S. Takuma, "Electron Microscopy of Developing and Mature Calcified Tissues," *Revue Belge Science Dentaire* 14 (1959): 329; information supplied by Dr. John Termine.

13. Information supplied by Dr. Marie Ussing Nylen and Dr. John Termine.

14. Lewis Menaker, ed., *The Biologic Basis of Dental Caries: An Oral Biology Textbook* (Hagerstown, Md.: Harper & Row, 1980), 192-94; announcement of October 12, 1964, "Press Releases Old—193," Anne Atlee's Files, NIDR IO; Dr. John Termine, interview by Ruth R. Harris, July 28, 1987.

15. Information supplied by Dr. Marie Ussing Nylen; Carl J. Witkop and Robert O. Wolf, "Hypoplasia and Intrinsic Staining of Enamel Following Tetracyline Therapy," *JAMA* 185 (September 28, 1963): 100-103; M. U. Nylen, K.-A. Omnell, and C.-G. Lofgren, "Fine Structure of Tetracycline-induced Hypoplastic and Hypomineralized Defects in Rat Incisor Enamel," *Journal of Dental Research* 43 (1964): 850; Marie U. Nylen, Karl-Ake Omnell, and Claes-Goran Lofgren, "An Electron Microscopic Study of Tetracycline-induced Enamel Defects in Rat Incisor Enamel," *Scandinavian Journal of Dental Research* 80 (1972): 384-409; J. Westergaard and M. U. Nylen, "Dose and Age Dependent Variations in Effect of Tetracycline on Enamel Formation in Rat," *Scandinavian Journal of Dental Research* 83 (1975): 209-32. Although several remedies, such as capping teeth and prolonged bleaching, alleviated the staining, no permanent satisfactory correction had been devised as of 1981. By then some dentists used bonding of veneers or resins to teeth, an outgrowth of the acid etching technique, to cover up imperfections, but the ADA did not recognize that method as satisfactory. The ADA stated that "the use of the acid etch technique in conjunction with veneers and tooth painting, although advantageous, may have limited value in long-term use and thus suggests caution in its use." See ADA statement of September 3, 1981, in "Tetracycline Bleaching/Cosmetic Improvement/Bibliographies," Sally Wilberding's Files, NIDR IO.

16. "Research News from NIDR," No. 138, December 1975, "Research News from NIDR No. 4, January 1974 to October 1978," Brent Jaquet's Files, NIDR IO.

17. Dr. John Termine, interview by Laura Kells, March 2, 1987; "Highlights of Research Progress during 1967 from National Institute of Dental Research," Anne Atlee's Files, NIDR IO.

18. Information supplied by Dr. John Termine on February 10, 1988, and "National Institute of Dental Research and NBS Join in Dental Materials Program," U.S. Department of Commerce News Release of May 15, 1984, "Marie Nylen," Dental and Medical Materials Group, Polymers Division, National Bureau of Standards (hereafter DMMG PD NBS); J. D. Termine and E. D. Eanes, "Comparative Chemistry of Amorphous and Apatitic Calcium Phosphate Preparations," *Calcified Tissue Research* 10 (1972): 171-92; E. D. Eanes, J. D. Termine, and M. U. Nylen, "An Electron Microscopic Study of the Formation of Amorphous Calcium Phosphate and Its Transformation to Crystalline Apatite," *Calcified Tissue Research* 12 (1973): 143-58; J. D. Termine and E. D. Eanes, "Calcium Phosphate Deposition from Balanced Salt Solutions," *Calcified Tissue Research* 15 (1974): 81-84; *American Men and Women of Science* 2 (1986): Eanes, Edward David.

19. Dr. John Termine, interview by Laura Kells, March 2, 1987; A. B. Belcourt, A. G. Fincham, and J. D. Termine, "Acid Soluble Bovine Fetal Enamelins," *Journal of Dental Research* 61 (1982): 1031-32; A. Fincham, A. B. Belcourt, D.

Lyaruu, and J. D. Termine, "Changing Patterns of Enamel Matrix Proteins in the Developing Bovine Tooth," *Caries Research* 16 (1982): 64-71; A. Fincham, A. B. Belcourt, D. Lyaruu, and J. D. Termine, "Dental Enamel Matrix: Sequences of Two Amelogenin Polypeptides," *Bioscience Reports* 1 (1981): 771-78; A. Fincham, A. B. Belcourt, D. Lyaruu, and J. D. Termine, "The Molecular Composition of Bovine Fetal Enamel Matrix" in *The Chemistry and Biology of Mineralized Connective Tissues*, A. Veis, ed. (New York: Elsevier/North Holland, 1981), 523-30.

20. Chief, Office of Planning, Evaluation, and Communications, NIDR, to Dr. Jay Moskowitz, associate director for program planning and evaluation, NIH, June 3, 1986; conversation of John Termine with Ruth Harris on July 28, 1987; Dr. Harold C. Slavkin to Dr. Jerry D. Niswander, November 4, 1983, and Slavkin to Patricia Sheridan, NIDR, January 27, 1984, Patricia Sheridan's Files, NIDR IO; Patricia Sheridan, "Tooth Enamel Gene Identified by rDNA Technology," *JADA* 110 (March 1985): 384; H. Shimokawa, M. E. Sobel, M. Sasaki, J. D. Termine, and M. F. Young, "Heterogeneity of Amelogenin mRNA in the Bovine Tooth Germ," *Journal of Biological Chemistry* 252 (1987): 402-7. The latter team represented international and inter-NIH collaboration. In addition to Shimokawa, Sasaki also came from Japan; Sobel was a scientist from the National Cancer Institute, and Young a postdoctoral fellow at the Institute.

21. V. Hascall, ed., *Functions of the Proteoglycans* (New York: Wiley and Sons, 1986); information supplied by Dr. John D. Termine.

22. D. A. Torchia, "Solid State NMR Studies of Protein Internal Dynamics," *Annual Review of Biophysics and Bioengineering* 13 (1984), 470-78; information supplied by Dr. John D. Termine.

23. J. D. Termine, "Osteonectin and Other Newly Described Proteins of Developing Bone," in W. A. Peck, ed., *Bone and Mineral Research. Annual I: A Yearly Survey of Developments in the Field of Bone and Mineral Metabolism* (Amsterdam: Excerpta Medica, 1983), 144-56.

24. Pamela Gehron Robey and J. D. Termine, "Human Bone Cells in Vitro," *Calcified Tissues International* 37 (1985): 453-60.

25. Dr. Hari Reddi, interview by Ruth R. Harris, August 24, 1987; A. H. Reddi and C. B. Huggins, "Biochemical Sequences in the Transformation of Normal Fibroblast in Adolescent Rat," *Proceedings of the National Academy of Sciences* 69 (USA, 1972): 1601; A. H. Reddi and C. B. Huggins, "The Formation of Bone Marrow in Fibroblast Transformation Ossicles," *Proceedings of the National Academy of Sciences* 72 (1975): 2212; M. R. Urist, "Bone: Formation by Autoinduction," *Science* 150 (1965): 893-98.

26. Dr. Hari Reddi, interview by Ruth R. Harris, August 24, 1987.

27. Ibid.; A. H. Reddi, "Cell Biology and Biochemistry of Endochondral Bone Development," *Collagen Research* 1 (1981): 209-26; A. H. Reddi, S. Wientroub, and N. Muthukumaran, "Biologic Principles of Bone Induction," *Orthopedic Clinics of North America* 18 (April 1987): 207-12.

28. M. R. Urist, R. J. Delange, and G. A. M. Finerman, "Bone Cell Differentiation and Growth Factors," *Science* 220 (1983): 680-86.

29. Reddi et al., "Biologic Principles of Bone Induction," 207-12; Dr. Hari Reddi, interview by Ruth R. Harris, August 24, 1987; "Can New Bone Be Created?" *Dental Impression* 4 (Summer 1987): 7.

30. "Can New Bone Be Created," 7; director, NIDR, to employees, NIDR, November 26, 1980, "Adm 12-Organization/Reorganization, 1980-1981," Intramural Administrative Files, NIDR; conversation of Dr. John Termine with Ruth Harris on July 9, 1987.

31. Irwin D. Mandel, "The Role of Saliva in Maintaining Oral Homeostasis," 13, Joan Wilentz's Files, NIDR IO. Volker had already earned his D.D.S. and was working for a doctorate in biochemistry at the University of Rochester in 1929. See *American Men and Women of Science* 7 (1986): Volker, Joseph Francis.

32. "Twenty Years of Dental Research at the NIDR," February 19, 1968, "Summary," NIDR IO; *NIH Record* 4 (April 21, 1952): 2.

33. *The Advancement of Knowledge for the Nation's Health: A Report to the President on the Research Programs of the National Institutes of Health* (U.S. Dept. of Health, Education and Welfare, PHS, July 1967), 83.

34. Dr. Arthur Hand, interview by Ruth R. Harris, January 20, 1988.

35. Ibid.; Arthur R. Hand, "The Fine Structure of von Ebner's Gland of the Rat," *Journal of Cell Biology* 44 (1970): 340-53; Margit Hamosh and Arthur R. Hand, "Development of Secretory Activity in Serous Cells of the Rat Tongue," *Developmental Biology* 65 (1978): 100-113. Hand continued studies on lingual lipase secretions with Dr. Ruth B. Field of NIDR. The two published "Secretion of Lingual Lipase and Amylase from Rat Lingual Serous Glands," *American Journal of Physiology* 253 (1987): G217-25; *NIH Record* 30 (March 21, 1978): 1.

36. "Highlights of Research Progress during 1973," NIDR IO; Irwin D. Mandel, "The Role of Saliva in Maintaining Oral Homeostasis," 1986 Seymour J. Kreshover Lecture, NIDR, September 24, 1986.

37. Irwin D. Mandel, "Dental Caries," *American Scientist* 67 (November-December 1979): 684; Mandel, "The Role of Saliva in Maintaining Oral Homeostasis," 37.

38. M. I. Mednieks and A. R. Hand, "Nuclear cAMP-Dependent Protein Kinase in Rat Parotid Acinar Cells," *Experimental Cell Research* 149 (1983): 45-55; Arthur R. Hand and Constance Oliver, "The Role of GERL in the Secretory Process," *Cell Biology of the Secretory Process*, M. Cantin, ed. (Basel: Karger, 1984), 148-70; A. R. Hand, R. Coleman, M. R. Mazariegos, J. Lustmann, and L. V. Lotti, "Endocytosis of Proteins by Salivary Gland Duct Cells," *Journal of Dental Research* 66 (February 1987): 412-19; Ruth B. Field and Arthur R. Hand, "Secretion of Lingual Lipase and Amylase from Rat Lingual Serous Glands," *American Journal of Physiology* 253 (Gastrointestinal Liver Physiology, 1987): G217-25.

39. Information supplied by Dr. Bruce Baum; B. J. Baum, "Neurotransmitter Control of Secretion," *Journal of Dental Research* (February 1987): 628-32.

40. Chief, Office of Planning, Evaluation and Communications, NIDR, June 3, 1986, Biennial Report of the Director, NIDR, "Congressional Reports," Anne Atlee's Files, NIDR IO; "Pilocarpine Used to Stimulate Normal Saliva Production," *JADA* 111 (August 1985): 310; Mandel, "The Role of Saliva in Maintaining Oral Homeostasis," 2-3; *NIH Record* 38 (January 15, 1985): 10; *NIH Record* 34 (February 2, 1982): 12; "Pilocarpine Used to Stimulate Normal Saliva Production."

41. Mandel, "The Role of Saliva in Maintaining Oral Homeostasis."

42. Dr. Karl Piez, interview by Ruth R. Harris, December 29, 1986.

43. Ibid.

44. Ibid.; K. A. Piez, "The Separation of the Diastereoisomers of Isoleucine and Hydroxylysine Be Ion Exchange Chromatograph," *Journal of Biological Chemistry* 207 (March 1954): 77-80.

45. DeWitt Stetten, Jr., ed., *NIH: An Account of Research in Its Laboratories and Clinics* (Academic Press, 1984), 274; *American Men and Women of Science*, 12th ed., 1973, 3720, 6116; *Journal of Biological Chemistry* 229 (November 1957): 101-9. Dr. Marjorie Stetten, a biochemist in the National Institute of Arthritis and Metabolic Diseases and author of classic observations in collagen and hydroxyproline research, approved the paper for submission to the journal.

46. Ibid.; *American Men and Women of Science*, 12th ed., 2343; PHS-NIH Individual Project Report, NIDR 25, in 1958 NIDR *Annual Report*, Dr. Lynn's Files, NIDR.

47. Martin was the senior author of several articles in various scholarly journals in 1961. For instance, see G. R. Martin, J. Gross, K. A Piez, and M. S. Lewis, "On the Intramolecular Crosslinking of Collagen in Lathyritic Rats," *Biochimica et Biophysica Acta* 53 (November 11, 1961): 599-601; G. R. Martin, S. E. Mergenhagen, and D. B. Scott, "Relation of Ionizing Groups to the Structure of the Collagen Fibril," *Biochimica et Biophysica Acta* 49 (May 13, 1961): 245-50.

48. Stetten, *NIH: An Account of Research*, 274-75; *American Men and Women of Science*, vol. 5, 15th ed.: George Martin; K. A. Piez, M. S. Lewis, G. R. Martin, and J. Gross, "Subunits of the Collagen Molecule," *Biochimica et Biophysica Acta* 53 (November 11, 1961): 596-98; information supplied by Drs. Karl Piez and George Martin; director of intramural research, NIDR, to acting deputy director for science, NIH, May 7, 1982, "O & M 2-Y Organization of NIDR," OD NIH.

49. *NIH Record* 15 (July 30, 1963): 5.

50. Stetten, *NIH: An Account of Research*, 275; Anthony J. Steffek, "The American Dental Association and Basic Research: A Historical Perspective," ADA, Chicago; *American Men and Women of Science*, 16th ed., 1986, 688; 12th ed., 1972, 1691, 4271; 1971, 829. The group included Drs. Edward J. Miller, an ADA

research associate with a Ph.D. from the University of Rochester; William T. Butler, with a doctorate from Vanderbilt; and Merry Sherman, who earned her Ph.D. in endocrine biochemistry from the University of California at Berkeley. Andrew H. Kang, Yutaka Nagai, Joseph M. Lane, Peter P. Fietzek, Jens Vuust, Robert C. Siegel, and John R. Daniels also participated in the research.

51. "Press Summary, 44th Annual Meeting, International Association for Dental Research," Anne Atlee's Files, NIDR IO.

52. Ibid.; *NIH Scientific Directory*, 1969, 1970, 1971; H. Small and E. Greenlee, "Collagen Research in the 1970s," *Scientometrics* 10 (1986), 102-3; *American Men and Women of Science*, 12th ed., 4153-4.

53. Small and Greenlee, "Collagen Research in the 1970s," 103-5; Stetten, *NIH: An Account of Research*, 276.

54. Small and Greenlee, "Collagen Research in the 1970s," 95-117; "Research News from NIDR," No. 77, November 1970, NIDR; *NIDR Annual Report, July 1, 1965-June 30, 1966*, 217; *NIDR Annual Report, July 1, 1970-June 30, 1971*, Serial No. NIDR-14 (62).

55. "The Laboratory of Developmental Biology and Anomalies (LBDA) 1974: Structure, Program and Personnel," Dr. George Martin's Papers, NIDR; Karl A. Piez and Andrew Miller, "The Structure of Collagen Fibrils," *Journal of Supramolecular Structure* 2 (1974): 121-37; *NIH Research Advances* 1976 (U.S. Dept. of Health, Education and Welfare. DHEW Publication No. (NIH) 76-3): 59; Stetten, *NIH: An Account of Research*, 176; "Laboratory of Biochemistry: Report of the Advisory Committee to the Scientific Director," attached to Marie U. Nylen to director of intramural research, NIH, May 7, 1982, "O & M 2-Y Organization of NIDR," OD NIH.

56. *NIH Research Advances* 1976, 60; *NIH Science Directory* 1976, 166-67; "Research Advances Year Ending June 30, 1975, for Budget for Congress," "Research Advances," Anne Atlee's Files, NIDR IO.

57. "Research News from NIDR," No. 4, July 1978, Brent Jaquet's Files, NIDR IO.

58. "NIDR Research News," July 1978, "Research News from NIDR No. 4, January 1974 to October 1978," Brent Jaquet's Files, NIDR IO; *American Men and Women of Science*, 16th ed., 1986, 373; Chief, LBDA, NIDR, to April 3, 1985, "Adm 12-Organization/Reorganization 1985," Intramural Files, NIDR.

59. *Evaluation of the NIDR Periodontal Disease Research Activity: Report of the Ad Hoc Scientific Evaluation Panel to the Director National Institute of Dental Research* (NIDR, April 1976), 63; National Advisory Dental Research Council Summary of Meeting, June 17-18, 1976, 7, NIDR IO.

60. J. R. Hassell, P. Gehron Robey, J. H. Barrach, J. Wilczek, S. I. Rennard, and G. R. Martin, "Isolation of a Heparan Sulfate-Containing Proteoglycan from Basement Membrane," *Proceedings of the National Academy of Sciences USA* 77 (1980): 4494-98.

61. Jeanette Graf, Hynda Kleinman, Makoto Sasaki, Yukihido Iwamoto, George Martin, Frank Robey, and Yoshikiki Yamada, "YIGSR, a Synthetic Laminin Pencapeptide, Inhibits Experimental Metastasis Formation," *Science* 238 (November 20, 1987): 1132-34.

62. A. Szarfman, J. R. Hassell, D. H. Rohrbach, J. R. Stanley, and G. R. Martin, "Components of Basement Membranes: Their Properties, Functions, and Alterations in Disease States," in *New Trends in Basement Membrane Research* (New York: Raven Press, 1982), 265-75; information supplied by Dr. Hynda Kleinman.

63. Information supplied by Dr. Hynda Kleinman; "Dental Researchers Report Peptide Blocks Cancer Metastasis in Laboratory Studies," "NIDR Research News," November 23, 1987, NIDR IO.

64. "NIDR Scientists Win Award for Test That Reduces Need for Animal Studies," "NIDR Research News," November 5, 1987, NIDR IO.

65. Chief, LBDA, NIDR, to director, IR, NIDR, April 3, 1985, "Adm 12-Organization/Reorganization 1985," Intramural Administrative Files, NIDR; information supplied by Dr. Hynda Kleinman; information supplied by Dr. George R. Martin; Collaborative Research Incorporated, "Basement Membrane Matrigel," undated flyer.

66. Stetten, *NIH: An Account of Research*, 176; *NIH Scientific Directory:* National Institute of Dental Research, 1974-1985; Small and Greenlee, "Collagen Research in the 1970s." For example, between 1974 and 1985 over forty postdoctoral fellows, more than two dozen guest workers, and over three dozen visiting foreign scientists worked in collagen research at the Institute. Moreover, the Institute for Scientific Information study of *Science Citation Research* showed that only three facilities were producing significant connective tissue research publications; the same study listed seventeen such institutions by 1979.

67. Dr. John E. Folk, interview by Laura Kells, December 8, 1986.

68. Dr. John E. Folk, interview by Ruth R. Harris on June 29, 1987; *American Men of Science*, 10th ed., 1960; "NIDR Publications—Calendar Year 1955," "NIDR Publications 1960-1948," NIDR IO; J. E. Folk and M. S. Burstone, "Enzymatic Hydrolysis of Prolyl- and Hydroxyprolyl-Napthylamides, *Archives of Biochemistry and Biophysics* 61 (April 1956): 257-62.

69. G. G. Glenner, P. J. McMillan, and J. E. Folk, "A Mammalian Peptidase Specific for the Hydrolysis of Terminal Alpha-L-Glutamyl and Aspartyl Residues," *Nature* 194 (June 2, 1962): 867; J. E. Folk and E. W. Schirmer, "The Porcine Pancreatic Carboxypeptidase A System. I. Three Forms of the Active Enzyme," *Journal of Biological Chemistry* 238 (December 1963): 3884-94; J. E. Folk and E. W. Schirmer, "Chrymotrypsin C," *Journal of Biological Chemistry* 240 (January 1965): 181-91.

70. Dr. John E. Folk, interviews by Laura Kells on December 8, 1986, and by Ruth R. Harris on June 29, 1987; J. E. Folk, "Transglutaminases," *Annual Review of Biochemistry* 49 (1980): 517-31.

71. *NIH Record* 16 (March 24, 1964): 3, and 18 (June 1, 1966): 7; director of laboratories and clinics, NIH, to director, NIDR, June 27, 1966, and attachments, "O & M-2 Organization, Functions & Staffing 1966," OD NIH; "Diseases of the Mouth and Teeth," and "Highlights 1969," 22, "Research Highlights 1953-1973," Anne Atlee's Files, NIDR IO; H. M. Fullmer, G. S. Lazarus, W. A. Gibson, A. C. Stam, and C. C. Link, "The Cutaneous Tissues of Two-thirds of Individuals with Amyotrophic Lateral Sclerosis," *Lancet* 1 (1966): 1007; H. M. Fullmer, "The Existence of Collagenase in Bone and Cartilage Tissues," *Israel Journal of Medical Science* 3 (1967): 758; G. S. Lazarus, J. L. Decker, C. H. Oliver, J. R. Daniels, C. V. Multz, and H. M. Fullmer, "The Relation of Collagenase Activity to the Clinical Severity of Rheumatoid Arthritis," *New England Journal of Medicine* 279 (1968): 914; H. Fullmer, "The Source of Collagenase in Human Periodontal Tissues," *Journal of Dental Research* 48 (1969): 646; H. Fullmer, "Activation of Latent Collagenase by Microbial Plaque," *Journal of Periodontological Research* 9 (1974): 81; H. Fullmer, "The Production of Collagenase by Macrophages," *Biochimica et Biophysica Acta* 420 (1976): 428; H. Fullmer, "Stimulation of Collagenase Production by Macrophages," *Archives of Oral Biology* 21 (1976): 21.

72. Dr. Marie Nylen to acting deputy director for science, NIH, May 7, 1983, "O & M 2-Y, Organization of NIDR," OD NIH; Dr. John E. Folk, interview by Laura Kells, December 8, 1986.

73. "Academy Award Won by Dr. Hampp," *NIH Record* 2 (April 10, 1950): 1; National Advisory Dental Research Council Minutes of Meeting, June 23, 1950, 2-3; Dr. Anthony Rizzo, interview by Ruth R. Harris on November 3, 1987.

74. J. Terrell Hoffield and Stephan E. Mergenhagen, "Chronic Destructive Periodonditis: An Oral Infection/Infestation," n.d., Laboratory of Microbiology and Immunology, NIDR.

75. *Challenges for the Eighties. National Institute of Dental Research Long-Range Research Plan: FY 1985-1989*, NIH Publication No. 85-860, December 1983, 37-39.

76. Dr. Stephan E. Merganhagen, interview by Ruth R. Harris, July 1, 1987; Harald A. Löe, "Scientific Revolutions in Dentistry," *Journal of Dental Research* 58 (November 1979): 2164-68. Waerhaug spent 1968 as a visiting scientist in the Institute's Laboratory of Histology and Pathology, according to the *NIH Scientific Directory* for that year.

77. *NIH Record* 12 (March 15, 1960): 6, and 12 (September 27, 1960): 6; *American Men and Women of Science*, 15th ed. (1982).

78. *NIH Scientific Directory* 1956-1963, including 1963, 79; A. Howell, Jr., and H. V. Jordan, Jr., "A Filamentous Microorganism Isolated from Periodontal Plaque in Hamsters. II. Physical and Biochemical Characteristics," *Sabouraudia* 3 (October 1963): 93-105.

79. H. V. Jordan and P. H. Keyes, "Aerobic, Gram-positive, Filamentous Bacteria as Etiologic Agents of Experimental Periodontal Disease in Hamsters," *Archives*

of Oral Biology 9 (1964): 401-4; *NIDR Reports on Dental Research* (January 1964), 15-17; A. Howell, Jr., H. V. Jordan, L. K. George, and L. Pine, "*Odontomyces Viscous*, Gen. Nov., Spec. Nov., a Filamentous Microorganism Isolated from Periodontal Plaque in Hamsters," *Sabouraudia* 4 (June 1965): 65-68; H. V. Jordan, R. J. Fitzgerald, and H. R. Stanley, "Plaque Formation and Periodontal Pathology in Gnotobiotic Rats Infected with an Oral Actinomycete," *American Journal of Pathology* 47 (December 1965): 1157-67; Dr. Anthony Rizzo, interview by Ruth R. Harris, November 3, 1987; information supplied by Dr. Robert Fitzgerald.

80. H. Löe, E. Theilade, and S. B. Jensen, "Experimental Gingivitis in Man," *Journal of Periodontology* 36 (1965): 177-87; Sigmund Socransky, "Microbial Etiology of Periodontal Diseases: State-of-the-Science," 1-3, unpublished paper, NIDR.

81. "Oral Science Award," *Journal of Dental Research* 46 (Supplement January-February 1967): 46; acting director, NIDR, to director, NIH, August 4, 1965, "O & M-2, Organization, Functions & Staffing 1965," OD NIH.

82. *NIH Record* 20 (April 16, 1968): 4.

83. "Research News from NIDR," No. 77, November 1970, Notebook on Research News from NIDR, No. 2, Brent Jaquet's Files, NIDR IO; Dr. Stephan E. Mergenhagen, interview by Ruth R. Harris on July 1, 1987; D. M. Brunette, M. J. Simon, and M. A. Reimers, "Citation Records of Papers Published in the *Journal of Periodontology* and the *Journal of Periodontal Research*," *Journal of Periodontal Research* 13 (1978): 487-97; S. E. Mergenhagen, T. R. Tempel, and R. Snyderman, "Immunologic Reactions and Periodontal Inflammation," *Journal of Dental Research* 49 (1970): 256-61; T. R. Tempel, R. Snyderman, H. V. Jordan, and S. E. Mergenhagen, "Factors from Saliva and Oral Bacteria Chemotactic for Polymorphonuclear Leukocytes: Their Possible Role in Gingival Inflammation," *Journal of Periodontology* 41: 71.

84. "Weekly Report," March 26, 1976, "Research Advances," Anne Atlee's Files, NIDR IO.

85. *NIH Research Advances* 1976, DHEW Publication No. (NIH) 76-3, 60-61.

86. *NIH Research Advances* 1976, 61; *American Men and Women of Science*, 16th ed., 1986, 375; Organizational Listing-NIDR, 20, "Key Scientific and Administrative Staff, September 1976," NIDR; *NIH Research Advances*, 1976, DHEW Publication No. (NIH) 76-3, 61-62.

87. J. J. Oppenheim, "Lymphokines," *Federal Proceedings* 41 (1982): 257-62; J. J. Farrar and J. Fuller-Farrar, "Progress in the Purification of Murine Thmoma-Derived Interleukin 2," in *Lymphokines and Thymic Hormones: Their Potential Utilization in Cancer Therapeutics*, ed. A. Goldstein and M. A. Chirigos (New York: Raven, 1981), 49-55; S. B. Mizel and A. Ben-Zvi, "Studies on the Role of Lymphocyte Activating Factor (Interleukin 1) in Antigen-Induced Lymph Node Lymphocyte Proliferation," *Cell Immunology* 54 (1980): 382-89; for example of other works, see *NIH Scientific Directory* 1983, 206-8.

88. *Challenges for the Eighties*, 38-40; "NIDR—Chief Accomplishments of Re-

search from 1960-1980," "Research Highlights 1960-1980," Anne Atlee's Files, NIDR IO; R. J. Gibbons, "Bacterial Adherence to Mucosal Surfaces and Its Inhibition by Secretory Antibodies," in J. Mestecky and A. R. Lawton, ed., *The Immunoglobulin A System: Advances in Experimental Medicine and Biology* 45 (1974): 315-26; R. J. Gibbons, D. I. Hay, and S. K. Schluckebier, "Proline-rich Proteins are Pellicle Receptors for Type 1 Fimbriae of *A. viscosus*," *Journal of Dental Research* 65 (Special issue, 1986): 179, Abstract 84.

89. C. L. Wittenberger, A. Beaman, L. N. Lee, R. M. McCabe, and J. A. Donkersloot, "Possible Role of Streptococcus Salivarius Glucosyl Transferase in Adherence of Veillonella to Smooth Surfaces," in *Proceedings 'Microbial Aspects of Dental Caries.' Microbiology Abstracts*, ed. H. M. Stiles, W. J. Loesche, and T. C. O'Brien (Washington: American Society for Microbiology, 1977), 417-21; J. A. London, "A Demonstration of Evolutionary Relationships among the Lactic Acid Bacteria by an Immunochemical Study of Malic Enzyme and Fructose Diphosphate Adolase," in *Immunochemistry of Enzymes and Their Antibodies*, ed. M. R. H. Salton (New York: John Wiley & Sons, 1977), 58-88; J. Thompson and B. Chassy, "Uptake and Metabolism of Sucrose by Streptococcus Lactis," *Journal of Bacteriology* 147 (1981): 543-51.

90. *NIH Record* 29 (January 26, 1977): 7; "NIDR—Chief Accomplishments of Research from 1960-1980," November 1982, "Research Highlights 1960-1980," Anne Atlee's Files, NIDR IO; *NIDR Annual Report Fiscal Year 1982*, D-19. Schifmann's research group included Barbara A. Corcoran, Dr. Sharon M. Wahl, and Dr. S. Aswanikumar; telephone interview of Dr. Julius Axelrod, National Institute of Mental Health, by Ruth R. Harris, February 19, 1988.

91. Julie Ann Miller, "Oral Interactions: The Molecular Basis for Bacterial Binding," *Science News* 130 (July 1986): 12-13; J. O. Cisar, A. L. Sandberg, and S. E. Mergenhagen, "The Function and Distribution of Different Fimbriae on Strains of *Actinomyces Viscosus* and *Actinomyces Naeslundii*," *Journal of Dental Research* 63 (1984): 393-96; P. E. Kolenbrander and C. S. Phucas, "Effect of Saliva on Coaggregation of Oral Actinomyces and Streptococcus Species," *Infection and Immunity* 44 (1984): 228-33; A. S. Kagermeier, J. London, and P. E. Kolenbrander, "Evidence for the Participation of N-Acetylated Amino Sugars in the Coaggregation between *Cytophaga* Species Strain DR2001 and *Actinomyces Israelii* PK16," *Infection and Immunity* 44 (1984): 299-305; information supplied by Dr. Ann Sandberg on July 8, 1987.

92. Dr. Kenneth Lynn to Dr. John Goggins, October 21, 1982, "Arthritis Special Report," Anne Atlee's Files, NIDR IO; *NIDR Annual Report Fiscal Year 1982*, D-19; information supplied by Dr. Sharon Wahl on July 1, 1987.

93. Board of Scientific Counselors, Minutes of Meeting, November 16-18, 1981, "Agendae, Minutes U Roster - 1963-1979," Office of the Scientific Director, NIDR.

94. *NIH Record* 34 (April 13, 1982): 6.

95. "Highlights of Research Progress, National Institutes of Health, 1956," 113, NLM; "Background Information on Herpes Simplex Virus" in "Report on Herpes Simpex Virus for Senate Appropriations Committee," Dr. Abner Notkins' Files, NIDR.

96. *NIH Record* 11 (December 22, 1959): 4. For instance, see E. A. Graykowski, M. F. Barile, W. B. Lee, and H. R. Stanley, "Recurrent Aphthous Stomatitis: The Clinical, Therapeutic and Histopathologic Aspects of Apthous Stomatitis," *JAMA* 196 (May 1966): 637-44.

97. W. K. Ashe and H. W. Scherp, "Antigenic Variations in Herpes Simplex Virus Isolants from Successive Recurrences of Herpes Labialis," *Journal of Immunology* 94 (March 1965): 385-94; B. Hampar and M. L. Copeland, "Persistent Herpes Simplex Virus Infection in Vitro with Cycles of Cell Destruction and Regrowth," *Journal of Bacteriology* 90 (July 1965): 205-12; "Report of the Scientific Director, The National Institute of Dental Research, July 1, 1964-June 30, 1965," 21.

98. Dr. Abner Notkins, interview by Ruth R. Harris, July 29, 1987.

99. *Frankfurter Neue Presse*, March 15, 1986, 4, NIH Library Translation, NIHL; *American Men and Women of Science*, 15th ed., 5: Notkins, Abner; "Introductory Remarks by William F. Raub at the May 6, 1987 NIH Lecture," Dr. Notkins' Files, NIDR; Dr. Abner Notkins, interview by Ruth R. Harris, July 29, 1987.

100. "Highlights of Research Progress during 1972 from the National Institute of Dental Research," 2, "Research Highlights 1953-1972," and press release, April 19, 1973, of the Federation of American Societies for Experimental Biology, 57th Annual Meeting, "Press Summaries 1963-1980," Anne Atlee's Files, NIDR IO; A. L. Notkins, "Effect of Virus Infections on Immune Function," in *Proceedings of the Sixth International Immunopathology Symposium*, ed. P. A. Micscher (Basel, Switzerland: Schwabe and Company, 1971), 413-25.

101. "Report of the Laboratory of Oral Medicine," *NIDR Annual Report, July 1, 1973-June 30, 1974*, Dr. Lynn's Files, NIDR.

102. *NIDR Research Digest*, June 1985, and "Herpes Vaccine Successful in Animals," July 7, 1986, "Research Advances," Anne Atlee's Files, NIDR IO. Collaborators included Drs. Kenneth Cremer and Charles Wohlenberg of the dental institute and Michael Mackett of the allergy and infectious diseases institute.

103. Statement prepared for Dr. David B. Scott for presentation at Senate hearings on February 3, 1976, "Opening Statement FY 1964-1977," Anne Atlee's Files, NIDR IO; *NIH Record* 31 (April 13, 1979): 6; "Announcement," May 23, 1979, "Press Releases, Juvenile Diabetes May 79, Yoon, Onodera, Notkins & Austin," NIDR IO.

104. Jean L. Marx, "Diabetes—A Possible Autoimmune Disease," *Science* 223 (September 21, 1984): 1381-82; T. Onodera and others, "Virus-induced diabetes mellitus XX. Polyendocrinopathy and autoimmunity," *Journal of Experimental Medicine* 153 (1981): 1457-73; Ji-Won Yoon and Usha R. Ray, "Perspectives on the Role of Viruses in Insulin-Dependent Diabetes," *Diabetes Care* 8 (September-October 1985): 39-44; Fredda Ginsberg-Fellner et al., "Triad of Markers for Identifying Children at High Risk of Developing Insulin-Dependent Diabetes Mellitus," *JAMA* (September 20, 1985): 1469; 1987 NIH Lecture, May 5, 1987, by Dr. Abner Notkins, NIDR.

105. "Eulogy," NIH Library Translation, NIH-86-96.

CHAPTER NINE. *Diseases, Disorders, and Therapy*

1. Hamilton B. G. Robinson, "Editor's Viewpoint. Dental Research, 1977: Vital and Productive," *Dental Survey* (August 1977): 8, 12.

2. NIDR Appropriations, 1948-1988, Dr. James Lipton's Files, NIDR; *NIDR Programs* for 1973 through 1983, and "Executive Summary: Biennial Report of the Director National Institute of Dental Research" [1988], NIDR, and *NIH Scientific Directory* for 1957 through 1985. Data on other subjects for this period were unavailable.

3. NIH, Division of Research Grants and Fellowships, "Annual Reports of the Study Sections," August 25, 1948, Dental Study Section, 32.

4. George C. Paffenbarger, J. A. English, and Edward Hampp, "Dental Research—Current and Future," *Journal of the American College of Dentists* (1955); Harald A. Loe, "Scientific Revolutions in Dentistry," *Journal of Dental Research* 58 (November 1979): 2164-68. Waerhaug spent 1968 as a visiting scientist in the Institute's Laboratory of Histology and Pathology, according to the *NIH Scientific Directory* for that year.

5. "Wooldridge Committee Report. National Institute of Dental Research," 5, "Committees-History," NIDR IO; A. L. Russell, "A System of Classification and Scoring for Prevalence Surveys of Periodontal Disease," *Journal of Dental Research* 35 (June 1956): 350-59.

6. Director, NIDR, to director, NIH, May 7, 1958, "Weekly Reports 1956-1962," vol. I, Brent Jaquet's Files, NIDR IO; A. L. Russell, "Some Epidemiological Characteristics of Periodontal Disease in a Series of Urban Populations," *Journal of Periodontology* 28 (October 1957): 286-93; director, NIDR, to director, NIH, March 11, 1958, "Weekly Reports 1956-1962," vol. I, Brent Jaquet's Files, NIDR IO; Seymour J. Kreshover, "Dental Research at the National Institutes of Health," *Dental Practitioner* 9 (February 1959): 142; "Wooldridge Committee Report," 15-16; transcript of the Combined Clinical Staff Meeting of the National Institutes of Health, Clinical Center, May 28, 1959, 4, "Periodontal Disease," NIDR; "Items of Interest on Program Developments and Research Studies Conducted and Supported by the Institutes and Divisions of NIH. As Presented to the Congress of the United States," 109, 115, "Highlights of Research Progress, National Institutes of Health, 1956," NIDR IO; A. Russell, "International Nutrition Surveys," *American Journal of Dental Research* 42 (January-February 1963): 233-44.

7. "Minutes of Program Planning Committee Meeting," September 30-October 1, 1958, "Program Planning Minutes," Book 1, NIDR IO.

8. U.S. Department of Health, Education and Welfare, PHS, *1959 Highlights of Progress in Research on Oral Diseases*, 1; "Research Highlights, National Institutes of Health, 1959," 220, NLM; "NIDR Research Grant Program," "Historical Files," NIDR IO.

9. "Special Report: Periodontal Disease," "Special Reports Miscellaneous," Anne Atlee's Files, NIDR IO.

10. Harald Löe, "The Future of Periodontal Research," 5, speech delivered at a May 17-19, 1984, symposium at the University of Michigan School of Dentistry, OD NIDR.

11. "Special Report: Periodontal Disease," "Special Reports Miscellaneous," Anne Atlee's Files, NIDR IO; *NIH Scientific Directory*, 1968.

12. Russell, "Some Epidemiological Characteristics of Periodontal Disease," 286-93; Joseph J. Zambon, Lars A. Christersson, and Robert J. Genco, "Diagnosis and Treatment of Localized Juvenile Periodontitis," *JADA* 113 (August 1986): 295-99.

13. J. Terrell Hoffeld and Stephan E. Mergenhagen, "Chronic Destructive Periodontitis: An Oral Infection/Infestation," 7-8, NIDR IO.

14. M. G. Newman, S. Socransky, E. Savitt, D. A. Propas, and A. Crawford, "Predominant Cultivable Microbiota in Periodontitis," *Journal of Periodontal Research* 47 (1976): 373-79; M. A. Listgarten, "Structure of the Microbial Flora Associated with Periodontal Health and Disease in Man: A Light and Electron Microscopic Study," *Journal of Periodontology* 47 (1976): 1-18.

15. L. J. Cianciola, R. J. Genco, M. R. Patters, J. McKenna, and C. J. van Oss, "Defective Polymorphonuclear Leukocyte Function in a Human Periodontal Disease," *Nature* 265 (February 3, 1977): 445-47. Cianciola used the method developed by R. Snyderman, L. C. Altman, M. S. Hausman, and S. E. Mergenhagen reported in the *Journal of Immunology* 108 (1972): 857-60, and the information from such work as reported by T. R. Tempel and others in the *Journal of Periodontal Research* 7 (Supplement, 1972): 10, 26-27.

16. R. J. Genco et al., "Systemic Immune Responses to Oral Anaerobic Organisms," in *Anaerobic Bacteria: Selected Topics*, ed. D. W. Lam, R. J. Genco, and K. J. Mayberry-Carson (New York: Plenum Publishing, 1980), 277-93; R. J. Genco, L. J. Cianciola, and B. Rosling, "Treatment of Localized Juvenile Periodontitis: Results After 5 Years," *Journal of Dental Research* 60 (1981): 527.

17. R. R. Ranney et al., "Relationship between Attachment Loss and Precipitating Serum Antibody to *Actinobacillus actinomycetemcomitans* in Adolescents and Young Adults Having Severe Periodontal Destruction," *Journal of Periodontology* 53 (1982): 1-2; J. J. Zambon, L. A. Christersson, and J. Slots, "*Actinobacillus actinomycetemcomitans* in Human Periodontal Disease: Prevalence in Patient Groups and Distribution of Biotypes and Serotypes within Families," *Journal of Periodontology* 54 (1983): 707-11.

18. L. A. Christersson et al., "Microbiological and Clinical Effects of Surgical Treatment of Localized Juvenile Periodontitis," *Journal of Clinical Periodontology* 12 (1985): 465-76; Zambon et al., "Diagnosis and Treatment of Localized Juvenile Periodontitis," *JADA* 113 (August 1986): 295-99.

19. Tula Brocard to Glenn E. Medcalf, editor, ADA News, Chicago, February 24, 1972, "ADA," Anne Atlee's Files, NIDR IO; "Dental Clinic Narrative," March 25, 1975, "Dental Clinic History," Dr. Michael Roberts' Files, Clinical Investigations and Patient Care Branch, NIDR.

20. *Evaluation of the NIDR Periodontal Disease Research Activity: Report of the Ad Hoc Scientific Evaluation Panel to the Director National Institute of Dental Research (NIDR)*, April 1976, vii.

21. *Evaluation of the NIDR Periodontal Disease Research Activity*, 61-63.

22. Ibid., 64-65. The committee was referring to the 1976 fiscal year, which started on October 1, 1975.

23. Dr. Seymour J. Kreshover to deputy director for science, NIH, February 11, 1975, "O & M 2 Organization Functions and Staffing (Internal NIH) January-July 1975," OD NIH; Dr. Clair Gardner to NIDR, August 5, 1975, "NIDR Organizational Changes 1970-1977," Kirk Weaver's Files, NIDR; National Advisory Dental Research Council, Summary of Meeting, June 17-18, 1976, 6-7; "Program Announcement and Guidelines, Specialized Clinical Research Centers for Periodontal Diseases," "Council Minutes, Jan. 73-Sept. 77," "October 4-5, 1976, Council Meeting," OADEXP NIDR.

24. NIDR Research News, October 1978, "NIDR National Institute of Dental Research 1979," OD NIH; "Analysis of the Current Periodontal Disease Program Activities with Reference to the Report from the Ad Hoc Scientific Evaluation Panel," April 1979, NIDR. A current table accompanying this report and assessing projects was missing in the file.

25. NIDR Clinical Project Number 78-D-77, June 5, 1978; Dr. Dennis E. Winson, to Sen. Mark Hatfield, February 6, 1979; Judith Randal, "Spare the Scalpel and Save the Gums," Outlook section, *Washington Post*, January 21, 1979; Shellie Lengel, information officer, NIDR, to Dr. Scott, May 8, 1979, "20-25 Keyes Method," OD NIDR; David B. Scott to Hon. Mark Hatfield, March 26, 1979; Donald S. Fredrickson, M.D., director, to The Honorable Charles McC. Mathias, Jr., June 25, 1979, "NIDR 1979," OD NIH.

26. NIDR Clinical Project Number 78-D-77, June 5, 1978, "20-25 Keyes Method," OD NIDR; Paul Keyes and Thomas Rams, "A Rationale for Management of Periodontal Diseases: Rapid Identification of Microbial 'Therapeutic Target' with Phase-Contrast Microscopy," *JADA* 106 (June 1983): 803-11.

27. Memo for the Record, November 5, 1980, "20-25 Keyes Method," OD NIDR; "Surgical Therapy for Periodontitis," NADRC Summary of Meeting, June 4-5, 1981, 4; Keyes and Rams, "A Rational for Management of Periodontal Diseases: Rapid Identification," and Paul Keyes and Thomas Rams, "A Rationale for the Management of Periodontal Diseases: Effects of Tetracycline on Subgingival Bacteria," *JADA* 107 (July 1983): 37-41.

28. Dr. Edwin Barrington to Dr. Micah Krichevsky, NIDR, October 21, 1983, and "Report of the Special Committee on NIH-NIDR Study on Periodontal Therapy," September 21, 1984, "20-25 Keyes Method," OD NIDR; conversation of Ruth Harris on June 15, 1987, with Dr. Micah Krichevsky of NIDR. To protect the privacy of patients, the Institute withheld information on individuals.

29. The Alexander von Humboldt Foundation of West Germany granted Mergenhagen, the laboratory chief, the United States Senior Scientist Award in

1981, and the IADR awarded him another honor in 1982.

30. Mary Beth Spina, "Buffalo's Oral Biology Research: A Frontal Attack on Periodontal Disease," *SUNY Research* (1983): 9-13; Ira B. Lamster, Linda J. Hartley, and Richard I. Vogel, "Development of a Biochemical Profile for Gingival Crevicular Fluid," in "Approaches to the Diagnosis and Chemotherapeutic Management of the Periodontal Diseases," *Journal of Periodontology* 56 (Supplement 1985): 13-21.

31. "Progress Report Summary" by Robert J. Genco for 5R01DEO6514-01, from September 1, 1982, through August 31, 1983, "Diabetes-Related," and IADR Press Summary, February 1985, and "National Institute of Dental Research Plans for Diabetes Mellitus Research and Training, FY 1985-1990," Pat Sheridan's Files, NIDR IO; *Diabetes Dateline* 7 (May/June 1986). The diabetes investigations complied with the 1974 congressional directive that the Institute participate in diabetes research, and they meshed with other work under way at the Institute, particularly virology and autoimmunity studies of diabetes mellitus by Dr. Abner Notkins.

32. *Journal of Periodontal Research* 13 (1978): 487-97.

33. "Major New Clinical Trials—FY 1988," June 25, 1986, "NIDR Contracts— History," Dr. James Lipton's Files, NIDR; Ruth R. Harris, *American Contributions to the New Age of Dental Research* (Bethesda: National Institute of Dental Research and National Library of Medicine, May 1988), 10.

34. Harald Löe to Dr. David E. Barmes, chief, Oral Health Unit, World Health Organization, Geneva, Switzerland, June 15, 1982, "Reading Board 1983," Dr. Lois Cohen's Files, NIDR; *NIDR Research Digest*, April 1987; Data Management Files, NIDR.

35. Dr. Carl Witkop, interview by Dr. Wyndham Miles, September 27, 1966; Chad Leyshon, interview by Ruth R. Harris and Laura Kells, August 11, 1986; *NIH Record* 9 (September 23, 1957).

36. *NIH Record* 9 (September 23, 1957): 1, and 15 (July 16, 1963): 3.

37. Ibid.; director, NIDR, to director, NIH, October 21, 1958, "Weekly Reports, 1956-1962," vol. I, Brent Jaquet's Files, NIDR IO.

38. "Special Report: Activities in the Field of Genetic Research," "Special Reports Miscellaneous," Anne Atlee's Files, NIDR IO.

39. Director, NIDR, to director, NIH, June 30, 1958, "Weekly Reports 1956-1962," vol. I, Brent Jaquet's Files, NIDR IO; *NIH Record* 12 (June 7, 1960): 6, and 12 (July 19, 1960): 6; interviews with Dr. Carl Witkop and Chad Leyshon.

40. Carl J. Witkop, Jr., ed., *Genetics and Dental Health. Proceedings of an International Symposium Held at the National Institutes of Health, Bethesda, Maryland, April 4-6, 1961* (New York: McGraw-Hill Book Company, 1962), 227, 243-44; "Special Report: Activities in the Field of Genetic Research," "Special Reports Miscellaneous," Anne Atlee's Files, NIDR IO; Thomas J. Hill and Sholom Pearlman, "Symposium on Genetics Related to Dental Health: A Summary Report," *JADA* 63 (November 1961): 639-42.

41. Director, NIDR, to director, NIH, April 4, 1963, and December 3, 1964, "NIDR Organizational Changes through 1969," Kirk Weaver's Files, NIDR.

42. Dr. Richard C. Greulich, "The Report of the Director of Intramural Research, The National Institute of Dental Research, July 1, 1966-June 30, 1967," IR 4, Files of the Office of the Scientific Director, NIDR; NIDR Board of Scientific Counselors Minutes of Meeting, October 11-12, 1967, "NIDR Organizational Changes through 1969, Subsection—1967," Kirk Weaver's Files, NIDR; Dr. Richard C. Greulich, "The Report of the Director of Intramural Research, The National Institute of Dental Research, July 1, 1967-June 30, 1968," 2, Files of the Office of the Scientific Director, NIDR.

43. Greulich, "The Report of the Director of Intramural Research, The National Institute of Dental Research, July 1, 1966-June 30, 1967"; NIDR Board of Scientific Counselors, Minutes of Meeting, October 11-12, 1967; chief, Human Genetics Branch, NIDR, to director, Intramural Research, NIDR, December 9, 1969, "NIDR Organizational Changes through 1969," Kirk Weaver's Files, NIDR.

44. Greulich to Kreshover, November 5 and 7, 1973, "O & M 2 Organization, Functions, and Staffing (Internal) August-December 1974," OD NIH.

45. "Intramural Reorganization," November 5, 1973; Lowell D. Peart to executive officer, NIDR, April 24, 1974; Greulich to Kreshover, November 5 and 7, 1973, "O & M 2 Organization, Functions, and Staffing (Internal) August-December 1974," OD NIH. The reorganization process upset Greulich, who said, "I feel very badly used." He subsequently transferred out of the Institute.

46. *Index to Dental Literature* (American Dental Association), categories under "Heredity" and "Genes" and various "Genetics" for 1955 through 1986.

47. Harold C. Slavkin, "Research on Craniofacial Genetics and Developmental Biology: Implications for the Future of Academic Dentistry," *Journal of Dental Education* 47, no. 4 (1983): 231-38; "New Approaches to the Problem of Birth Defects Involving the Facial Region," "Questions and Answers—NIDR Radio and TV Programs," NIDR Media File, February 1986, NIDR (St. Elizabeth's Hospital storage).

48. *NIH Record* 12 (September 5, 1955).

49. Slavkin, "Research on Craniofacial Genetics."

50. Russell S. Poor, "Suggestions for the Establishment of a Center for Cleft Palate Research," September 22, 1960, "Program Planning Minutes Book," Brent Jaquet's Files, NIDR IO; "Notice of Grant Award," March 31, 1986, Grant no. SSSS-4(B) 2 PO1 DEO1697-24A1, Dr. John Townsley's Files, NIDR; information supplied by Dr. John D. Townsley, Institute health science administrator in charge of extramural craniofacial anomalies research in 1987.

51. "Highlights of Research Conducted by the National Institute of Dental Research," prepared as background material for submission at congressional hearings on appropriations for fiscal year 1963, "Research Highlights, 1943-1973," Anne Atlee's Files, NIDR IO.

52. "Special Report: Cleft Palate Research," Anne Atlee's Files, NIDR IO.

53. Press Release of National Institutes of Health, HEW-C32, August 27, 1964, NIDR IO; *NIH Record* 16 (September 6, 1964): 5.

54. Ibid.

55. NIDR Board of Scientific Counselors, Minutes of Meeting, October 19-20, 1964, "Agendae, Minutes, & Roster—1963-1979," Office of the Scientific Director, NIDR.

56. *NIDR Reports on Dental Research*, January 1964, 22-24.

57. Director, NIDR, to director, NIH, November 16, 1965, "NIDR Organizational Changes through 1969," Kirk Weaver's Files, NIDR; NIDR Board of Scientific Counselors, Minutes of Meeting, October 11-12, 1967, "Agendae, Minutes, & Roster—1963-1979," Office of the Scientific Director, NIDR; Dr. Anthony Steffek, interview by Ruth R. Harris, April 9, 1987, at the ADA headquarters, Chicago.

58. Minutes of Program Planning Committee Meeting, October 11-12, 1966, "Program Planning Minutes," Book II, Brent Jaquet's Files, NIDR IO.

59. K. Sune Larsson, "National Institute of Dental Research Craniofacial Anomalies Program," "Council Minutes January 17-18, 1976," OADEXP NIDR.

60. Ibid.

61. "Cleft Palate Report," September 15, 1969, "Cleft Palate Special Reports," Anne Atlee's Files, NIDR IO.

62. *NIH Record* 20 (July 23, 1968): 1, 5; "Cleft Palate Report," HBT September 1, 1969, "Cleft Palate Special Reports," Anne Atlee's Files, NIDR IO.

63. A. Burdi et al., "Etiology and Pathogenesis of Congenital Cleft Lip and Cleft Palate: An NIDR State of the Art Report," *Teratology* 6 (December 1972): 255-70.

64. "Research Plans of the National Institute of Dental Research," May 1973, "NIDR Historical Material," Dr. Lynn's Files, NIDR.

65. Richard L. Christiansen and Carla A. Evans, "Habilitation of Severe Craniofacial Anomalies—The Challenge of New Surgical Procedures: An NIDR Workshop," *Cleft Palate Journal* 12 (April 1975): 167-75.

66. *NIH Record* 25 (June 19, 1973); "Workshop on 'Psychosocial Aspects of Craniofacial Malformation,'" October 15-17, 1974, "Council Minutes January 1973 to September 1977," OADEXP NIDR.

67. Information supplied by Dr. John Townsley; Grant Application IRG SSS 5, Appl. No. 2 PO1 DE03568-12, Dr. Townsley's Files, NIDR.

68. Seymour J. Kreshover, "1. Craniofacial Anomalies: Past, Present, and Future Priorities for Development and Molecular Biology," in *Extracellular Matrix Influences on Gene Expression* (New York: Academic Press, Inc., 1975), 3-7; associate director for extramural research and training, NIH, to associate direc-

tor for program planning and evaluation, NIH, March 30, 1976, "NIDR-1976," OD NIH; *Evaluation of the NIDR Craniofacial Anomalies Research Activities*, September 1981, 4.

69. *Evaluation of the NIDR Craniofacial Anomalies Research Activities*, 3, 4, 60-63.

70. Ibid., 69-70; transcript of the 103d meeting of the National Advisory Dental Research Council, November 3, 1981, 54-55, "Council Minutes, February 1978 to NADRC Meeting November 2-3, 1981," OADEXP NIDR.

71. Minutes of the NIDR Programs Advisory Committee Meeting, May 9-10, 1985, 6-11, "Minutes of PAC Meeting," OADEXP NIDR.

72. Information supplied by Dr. John Townsley.

73. Ibid.; RFA88-DE03, NIDR.

74. Chief, Office of Planning, Evaluation and Communications, NIDR, June 3, 1986, "Congressional Reports," Anne Atlee's Files, NIDR IO; RFA87-DE01, NIDR.

75. "National Institute of Dental Research Activities in the Physical, Chemical and Biological Sciences Related to Restorative Dentistry," 5, "NIDR/NBS/ADA 1961-1964," DMMG PD NBS.

76. Dr. Harold Hillenbrand, "Role of ADA Science on Dental Research: A Retro-Prospective View," March 23, 1981, talk, Dr. Carl Verrusio's Files, ADA.

77. "National Institute of Dental Research Activities in the Physical, Chemical and Biological Sciences," 2-4.

78. "NBS Dental Research Program," PRC NBS.

79. George C. Paffenbarger, John A. Tesk, and Walter E. Brown, "Dental Research at the National Bureau of Standards: How it Changed the Practice of Dental Health Service," *JADA* 111 (July 1985): 87; "National Institute of Dental Research Activities in the Physical, Chemical and Biological Sciences," 2-3; Dr. Harold Stanley, interview by Dr. Wyndham Miles, November 17, 1964.

80. Robert A. Draughn, Rafael L. Bowen, and Joseph P. Moffa, "Composite Restorative Materials," in *Restorative Dental Materials: An Overview* 1 (London: Quintessence Publishing Company, 1985): 93, 95; information supplied by Dr. Joyce A. Reese; "ADA Statement on Acid Etch Technique," "Tetracycline, Bleaching/Cosmetic Improvement/Bibliographies," Sally Wilberding's Files, NIDR IO. The ADA approved the acid etch technique in 1972.

81. Paffenbarger et al., "Dental Research at the National Bureau of Standards," 83-89; *NIDR Research Digest* 1985.

82. See note 81 above.

83. "Chronology of Major Events in NBS-NIDR Interagency Agreement," PRC NBS; Dr. John Stanford, Head of the Council on Dental Materials, Instruments, and Equipment of the American Dental Association, interview by Ruth

R. Harris, April 17, 1987, at NIDR; *New York Times*, September 25, 1959, 14, and December 16, 1961, 17.

84. "Chronology"; "Chief Dental Officers Staff Meeting," September 25, 1962, Executive Dental Staff Meeting Minutes beginning January 1963, CDO PHS; Donald J. Galagan to William T. Sweeney, chief, Dental Research Section, NBS, August 30, 1962; Dr. Pearlman to Dr. Hillenbrand, December 4, 1962; W. T. Sweeney to Dr. Harold Hillenbrand, May 7, 1964, "NIDR/NBS/ADA 1961-1964," DMMG PD NBS. The NBS unit had an outstanding record; it had influenced dental education around the world. The dental materials courses in the nation's dental schools stemmed directly from the bureau's work; the courses' textbooks extracted as much as 22 percent directly from the section's publications by 1960. Moreover, close to a dozen of the world's leading dental educators and researchers had undergone graduate training in the unit. Since 1919 its scientists and guest workers had published over 400 basic, applied, and developmental research reports on hard tooth tissues, dental materials, and instrumentations. See "Information Relative to the Cooperative Research in Dental Materials at the National Bureau of Standards," December 1963, 25 pages, "NIDR-NBS Program History," DMMG PD NBS.

85. National Advisory Dental Research Council Minutes of Meeting, June 16-18, 1960, 6, NIDR; "Proposed Dental Materials and Technology Program of the Public Health Service," August 27, 1963, 4-5, attached to deputy surgeon general memorandum for the record, August 30, 1963, "NIDR-NBS Program History," DMMG PD NBS; Dr. Walter E. Brown to William T. Sweeney, July 10, 1963, "NIDR-NBS Contracts," NBS.

86. F. A. Arnold, Jr., to Dr. I. C. Schoonover, August 28, 1964, with attachments, "NIDR-NBS Contracts," NBS.

87. Dr. John Stanford, interview by Ruth R. Harris, April 17, 1987; undated description of ADA standards research supported by NIDR, Files of Extramural Research Dental Materials Research, NIDR.

88. Dr. John Stanford, interview by Ruth R. Harris, April 17, 1987.

89. Press release of March 7, 1966, "Press Summaries 1963-1980," Anne Atlee's Files, NIDR IO; *NIH Record* 18 (October 4, 1966): 1, 4. Press release on "Identification of Dityrosine in Adhesive Formed by the Sea Mussel, *Mytilus edulis*," "Press Summaries, 1963-1980," Anne Atlee's Files, NIDR IO.

90. William J. O'Brien, Evan Greener, and David B. Mahler, "Dental Amalgam," in *Restorative Dental Materials*, 21-22.

91. Marc A. Rosenblum, Kamal Asgar, and Karl F. Leinfelder, "Dental Prosthetic Materials," in *Restorative Dental Materials*, 129, 184.

92. Paul A. Schnitman, Joseph R. Natiella, and Franklin A. Young, "Dental Implants," in *Restorative Dental Materials*, 277-300; Leonard B. Shulman, Joseph R. Natiella, and George R. Riviere, "Tooth Replantation and Transplantation," in *Restorative Dental Materials*, 301-29; November 1972 NADRC "Biomaterials Program Report," Appendix IV, "Council Minutes January 1949-November 1972," November 27-28, 1972, Council Meeting,

OADEXP NIDR; "Research Plans of the National Institute of Dental Research," May 1973, "NIDR Historical Material," Dr. Lynn's Files, NIDR; *Tooth Implants, Transplants, and Replants,* DHEW Publication No. (NIH) 77-1143.

93. Robert A. Draughn, Rafael L. Bowen, and Joseph P. Moffa, "Composite Restorative Materials," in *Restorative Dental Materials,* 95-96; *NIDR Research Digest,* 1985.

94. Theodore H. Ingalls, M.D, Framingham Union Hospital, to Dr. Harald Löe, October 23, 1984, "NIDR 1984," OD NIH; Dr. Harald Löe to The Honorable Albert Gore, Jr., undated, "85 Congressional Correspondence," OD NIDR; Littleton to Dr. James M. Melius, director, DSHEFS, September 23, 1985, "85 Daily Board," and Marie U. Nylen to Dr. Victor Penzer, Newton, Massachusetts, June 13, 1985, OD NIDR; information supplied by Dr. Lois Cohen.

95. Dr. John Stanford, interview by Ruth R. Harris, April 17, 1987.

96. *JADA* 112 (June 1986): 879.

97. Dr. John Tesk, acting group leader, Dental and Medical Materials, Polymer Science and Standards Division, to Dr. Harald Löe, February 15, 1983, "Correspondence 1983," DMMG PD NBS; "Memorandum of Agreement between the Intramural Research Program, National Institute of Dental Research . . . and the National Bureau of Standards on a Research Associate Program at the National Bureau of Standards, Y01-DE-400002-00," "NIDR Research Associate," DMMG PD NBS; *NIDR Research News,* August 1983.

98. *Pain Research from Laboratory to Clinic,* ed. and contributing author Jody Dove (NIDR, September 1986), 1.

99. E. J. Driscoll, G. R. Christenson, and C. L. White, "Physiological Studies in General Anesthesia for Ambulatory Dental Patients," *Oral Surgery, Oral Medicine and Oral Pathology* 23 (December 1959): 1475-96; Serial No. NIDR-75 (c) (58), Individual Project Report, July 1, 1967, through June 30, 1968, "NIDR Annual Report, July 1, 1967-June 30, 1968," Dr. Lynn's Files, NIDR; "The Pain Research Clinic at NIH," *News & Features from NIH* 86, no. 3; Dr. Ronald Dubner, interview by Laura Kells, December 23, 1986.

100. "Oral Disease: Target for the 70's. Five-year Plan of the National Institute of Dental Research for Optimum Development of the Nation's Dental Research Effort," "Oral Disease-Target for the 70's (5-year plan) 12/70," Anne Atlee's Files, NIDR IO; "Background Material for Dr. Driscoll's Presentation on the Pain Control Program," "Council Minutes, June 10-11, 1971, Council Meeting," OADEXP NIDR.

101. *Challenges for the Eighties,* 94.

102. Daniel M. Laskin, "Etiology of the Pain-Dysfunction Syndrome, *JADA* 79 (July 1969): 147-53.

103. Data Management Files, NIDR; information supplied by Dr. Patricia Bryant, NIDR.

104. "Report of the Ad Hoc Committee No. 1 on Research and Faculty Training in Pain Control in Dentistry," "Resource Documents Relative to NIDR Manpower Training, August 13, 1974," "Dr. Gardner," Dr. Valega's Files, NIDR.

105. "Report of the Ad Hoc Committee No. 1 on Research and Faculty Training in Pain Control in Dentistry, "Resource Documents Relative to NIDR Manpower Training, August 13, 1974," "Dr. Gardner," Dr. Valega's Files; "Oral Disease: Target for the 70's," 1-4, NIDR.

106. "Background Material for Dr. Driscoll's Presentation on the Pain Control Program," OADEXP NIDR.

107. Ibid.

108. "Report of the Ad Hoc Committee II on Research and Faculty Training in Pain Control in Dentistry, February 9-10, 1972," "Resource Documents Relative to NIDR Manpower Training, August 13, 1974," "Dr. Gardner," Dr. Valega's Files, NIDR.

109. "Highlights of Research Programs during 1972," 5, "Research Highlights 1953-1973," Anne Atlee's Files, NIDR IO; *NIH Record* 31 (August 7, 1979): 9; Aaron Ganz and Edward J. Driscoll, "Pain—Its Mystery and Challenge," "Notebook - NIDR Scientific Findings. All Reports, November 1972-December 1975," Brent Jaquet's Files, NIDR IO.

110. Information supplied by Dr. Raymond Dionne of the NIDR Pain Clinic.

111. Dr. Ronald Dubner, interview by Laura Kells, December 23, 1986; Curriculum Vitae, 1980, NIDR.

112. *NIH Record* 36 (August 27, 1974): 3.

113. Philip S. Chen, Jr., Ph.D., assistant director for intramural affairs, NIH, to scientific directors, June 18, 1975, "Research NIDR (National Institute of Dental Research) 1975," OD NIH.

114. "AADR Release-Heft," "AADR 1977," and "Statement before Senate Hearings on February 3, 1976," "Opening Statement FY 1964-77," Anne Atlee's Files, NIDR IO.

115. Dr. Ronald Dubner, interview by Laura Kells, December 23, 1986; "AADR Release-Heft," "AADR 1977," Anne Atlee's Files, NIDR IO; R. H. Gracely, R. Dubner, P. McGrath, and M. Heft, "New Methods of Pain Measurement and Their Application to Pain Control," *International Dental Journal* 28 (1978): 52-65; *Pain Research from Laboratory to Clinic*, 16-18.

116. Patricia S. Bryant, Rosalynde K. Soble, and Lois K. Cohen, "NIDR Behavioral and Social Studies," NIDR, 54-57.

117. National Advisory Dental Research Council Summary of Meeting, May 16-17, 1977, 7, NIDR; "The Pain Research Clinic at NIH," *News & Features from NIH* 86, no. 3.

118. Dr. Ronald Dubner, interview by Laura Kells, December 23, 1986; Dr. Ronald Dubner, "Intramural Pain Program at NIDR" in "Transcript of Proceedings

. . . 102nd Meeting of the National Advisory Dental Research Council, June 5, 1981," 71-85, "NADRC Meeting June 4-5, 1981," OADEXP NIDR.

119. Acting director, NIDR, to Dr. James B. Wyngaarden, director, NIH, December 13, 1982, "O & M 2, Organization of NIDR," OD NIH; *Pain Research Newsletter*, May 1986.

120. Raymond Dionne, David S. Goldstein, and Peggy R. Wirdzek, "Effects of Diazepam and Epinephrine-Containing Local Anesthetic on Caradiovascular and Plasma Catecholamine Responses to Oral Surgery," *Anesthesia and Analgesia* 63 (1984): 640-46; information supplied by Dr. Ray Dionne.

121. Raymond Dionne, "Suppression of Dental Pain by the Preoperative Administration of Flurbipofen," *American Journal of Medicine* 80 (Supplement 3A, 1986): 41-49; *Pain Research Newsletter*, May 1986.

122. K. Hargreaves, Elizabeth A. Schmodt, Gregory P. Mueller, and Raymond Dionne, "Dexamethasone Alters Plasma Levels of Beta-endorphin and Postoperative Pain," *Clinical Pharmacology and Therapeutics* 62 (1987): 601-7; *Insight* 4 (February 1, 1988): 58.

123. Jon D. Levine, Newton C. Gordon, Richard Smith, and Richard McBryde, "Desipramine Enhances Opiate Postoperative Analgesia," *Pain* 27 (1986): 45-49.

124. Data Management Files, NIDR.

125. Dr. Dushanka V. Kleinman, legislative contact, NIDR, to director, Division of Legislative Analysis, OPPE, OD NIH, "Planning and Evaluation Reading Board, Reading File, January-June 1985," NIDR IO; director, NIH, to the assistant secretary for health and human services, "OS/NIDR Correspondence 1982-1985," OD NIDR; "NIDR Research Grants Active FY 1987," Dr. Patricia Bryant's Files, NIDR; information supplied by Dr. Patricia Bryant.

126. Information supplied by Dr. Raymond Dionne of the NIDR Pain Clinic.

127. "NIDR Research Grants Active FY 1987," Dr. Patricia Bryant's Files, NIDR.

128. Information supplied by Dr. Patricia Bryant; "Research Grants Active FY 1987," Dr. Bryant's Files, NIDR.

129. Lois K. Cohen, "Dentistry and the Behavioral/Social Sciences: An Historical Overview," *Journal of Behavioral Medicine* 4, no. 3 (1981): 247.

130. Ibid., 149; information supplied by Dr. Lois Cohen.

131. "Part 1, National Institute of Dental Research Annual Report, Office of the Director, July 1, 1976-September 30, 1977," 13-16, NIDR; Bryant et al., "NIDR Behavioral and Social Studies," 11. In 1978 Cohen reported on model building in the social sciences as a means of facilitating such large-scale projects as community water fluoridation. See Cohen, "Dentistry and the Behavioral/Social Sciences," 253.

132. "NIDR—Behavioral Research Paper for American Psychologist Magazine," "Special Reports Miscellaneous," Anne Atlee's Files, NIDR IO; information

supplied by Dr. Lois K. Cohen; Howard L. Bailit and Jacob B. Silversin, "Introduction," *Journal of Behavioral Medicine* 4 (1981): 243-46.

133. Bryant et al., "NIDR Behavioral and Social Studies"; Harald Löe, "The National Institute of Dental Research and Dental Health Services Research," *Journal of Dental Education* 47 (November 1983): 704-6; "NIDR—Behavioral Research Paper for American Psychologist Magazine," 15, Anne Atlee's Files, NIDR IO; Cohen, "Dentistry and the Behavioral/Social Sciences," 253-54; information supplied by Dr. Lois Cohen.

134. *Challenges for the Eighties*, 169; Dr. Lois Cohen, special assistant to the director, NIDR, to secretary, NIH Working Group on Health and Behavior, December 2, 1983, "Reading Board 1983," Dr. Lois Cohen's Files, NIDR; Lois K. Cohen to Dr. Marilda Riley, NIA, December 2, 1985, "Reading Board 1985," NIDR.

135. Information supplied by Dr. Lois K. Cohen. NIDR recruited Dr. James Lipton, a dentist-sociologist, in 1985 for the Office of Planning, Evaluation, and Communications. The additions to the Epidemiology and Oral Disease Prevention Program included Dr. Helen Gift, a sociologist to work on oral health promotion, and Dr. L. Jackson Brown, a dentist-economist to assess treatment needs and cost implications. Dr. Thomas Drury became deputy director of the program in 1987.

136. Dr. James Lipton's Files, NIDR.

CHAPTER TEN. *From the Past to the Future*

1. J. E. Alman, "Declining Caries Prevalence—Statistical Considerations," in "The First International Conference on the Declining Prevalence of Dental Caries," *Dental Research* (November 1982): 1361-63; K. G. Konig, "Impact of Decreasing Caries Prevalence: Implications for Dental Research," *Dental Research* (November 1982): 1378-83; "Transcript of Proceedings 102nd Meeting of the National Advisory Dental Research Council," June 5, 1981, "Council Minutes February 1978 to NADRC Meeting June 4-5, 1981," OADEXP NIDR.

2. John W. Hein to Margaret Heckler, August 31, 1983, "NIDR 83," OD NIH; information relayed by Mr. Cordero of the World Health Organization to Ruth Harris on September 10, 1987.

3. A. L. Russell, N. W. Littleton, E. C. Leatherwood, G. E. Sydow, and J. C. Greene, "Dental Surveys in Relation to Nutrition," Epidemiological Branch Clinical Trials Section, NIDR; A. L. Russell, "Dental Disease in Latin America," *Journal of the American College of Dentists* (March 1963): 41-52, 96.

4. *1985 NIH Almanac*, 109.

5. *Dental Research in the United States and Other Countries. Fiscal Year 1976 through 1980* (NIDR); information supplied by Dr. Lois K. Cohen.

6. Dr. Lois Cohen's Files, NIDR.

7. John E. Fogarty International Center for Advanced Study in the Health Sciences, *National Institutes of Health Annual Report of International Activities Fiscal Year 1977*, DHEW Publication No. (NIH) 79-62, 100-101; "NIDR Foreign Expenditures," May 16, 1983, "83 Chron File," OADEXP NIDR; Harald Löe to Dr. K. A. A. A. S. Warnakulasuriya, head, Department of Oral Medicine and Periodontology, Dental School, University of Peradeniya, November 26, 1985, "85 Daily Board," OD NIDR; "National Institute of Dental Research," "International Reports," Anne Atlee's Files, NIDR IO; *National Institutes of Health Annual Report of International Activities Fiscal Year 1979*, 139; *1980*, 161; *Annual Report of International Activities Fiscal Year 1981* (NIH Publication No. 82-62, September 1982), 75-76; *Annual Report of International Activities Fiscal Year 1982* (NIH Publication No. 83-62, July 1983), 90-91; WHO Collaborating Centers at NIH, June 11, 1985, "Reading Board 1985," Dr. Cohen's Files, NIDR; *NIDR Research Digest*, April 1987; information supplied by Dr. Lois K. Cohen; *Annual Report of International Activities Fiscal Year 1982*, 90; "Bilateral Agreements and Other Country-to-Country Activities," "Reading Board 1985," Dr. Cohen's Files, NIDR.

8. *The First Fifty-Year History of the International Association for Dental Research* (University of Chicago Printing Department, 1973), 53-54; *NIH Record* 33 (April 28, 1981): 4; *Annual Report of International Activities Fiscal Year 1981*, 75; "Bilateral Agreements and Other County-to-Country Activities," "Reading Board 1985," Dr. Cohen's Files, NIDR.

9. Special assistant to the director, NIDR, to Dr. Mark S. Beaubien, acting director, Fogarty International Center, NIH, September 26, 1983, "Reading Board 1983," Dr. Cohen's Files, NIDR; assistant director for international health, NIDR, to Dr. J. R. Schmidt, chief, International Coordination and Liaison Branch, FIC, November 23, 1984, "Reading Board 1984," Dr. Cohen's Files, NIDR; *NIH Almanac 1985*, 87; information supplied by Dr. Lois K. Cohen.

10. John W. Hein to Margaret Heckler, August 31, 1983, and Margaret M. Heckler to John W. Hein, October 13, 1983, "NIDR 83," OD NIH.

11. Report of the Director, The National Institute of Dental Research, October 1, 1980-September 30, 1981, 2-1, NIDR; *Total Loss of Teeth in Adults United States-1960-1962* (DHEW Publication No. (HRA) 74-1280), 11; chief, Office of Planning, Evaluation and Communications, NIDR, to Dr. Jay Moskowitz, associate director for program planning and evaluation, NIH, June 3, 1986, "Congressional Reports," Anne Atlee's Files, NIDR IO.

12. Information supplied by Dr. Lois K. Cohen and AADR, Washington, D.C., office; suggestion of Dr. Robert Fitzgerald; J. A. Brunelle and J. F. Carlos, "Changes in the Prevalence of Dental Caries in U.S. Schoolchildren, 1961-1980," *Dental Research* (November 1982): 1346-51. Created in 1978, the National Affairs Committee of the IADR spent most of its resources on lobbying for NIDR budgets.

13. P. A. Littleton, Jr., L. J. Brown, and E. S. Solomon, "The Relationship be-

tween National Institute of Dental Research (NIDR) Supported Research Training and Careers in Dental Research," unpublished study in "Training, Fellow, and Career Development," Dr. James Lipton's Files, NIDR; L. J. Brown and P. A. Littleton, "Relationships between NIDR-supported Research Training and Subsequent Grant Activity," *Journal of Dental Research* 64, Abstract no. 273 (March 1985): 205; P. A. Littleton, L. J. Brown, and E. S. Solomon, "Relationships between NIDR-supported Training and Careers," *Journal of Dental Research* 64, Abstract no. 274 (March 1985): 205.

14. *1983 NIH Almanac*, 130-31; information supplied by Eloise Bredder, assistant director, American Association for Dental Research, to Ruth Harris on September 11, 1987; *NIH Data Book 1986*, 40; *NIDR Programs FY 1986 Funds, Grants, Awards, Contracts and Intramural Projects*, Tables 9 and 10, 84-92. Non-U.S. members rose during the same period from 103 to 2982.

15. Stella Leche Deignan and Esther Miller, "The Support of Research in the Bio Sciences for the Fiscal Years 1952 and 1953," *Science* 119 (May 14, 1954): 666; U.S. Congress, Senate, Labor-Federal Security Appropriations for 1951, 81st Cong., 2d sess., 501-5; *1983 NIH Almanac*, 78; Margaret Heckler to Dr. John W. Hein, October 13, 1983, "NIDR 83," OD NIH; *Dental Research in the United States and Canada Fiscal Year 1970* and *1971*; *Dental Research in the United States, Canada and Great Britain Fiscal Year 1974* and *1975*; *Dental Research in the United States and Other Countries Fiscal Year 1976* through *1980*; *American Dental Association 1982 Annual Reports and Resolutions*, 151. In 1982 Secretary Heckler and the ADA Council on Dental Research estimated that the Institute supplied 80 percent of American dental research support.

16. *Research Grants Awarded by the Public Health Service*, 18-19; 1948 Publication List of NIH, RG 443, Box 105, Folder 1680, NARA; "National Institute of Dental Research National Advisory Dental Research Council Minutes of Meeting January 27-28, 1986," 7; *NIH Scientific Directory 1985* (NIH Publication No. 85-4), 256-69.

17. *National Institute of Dental Research—1948—40 Years of Progress—1988* (March 1988).

18. Tabulations of *NIH Scientific Directory 1968* through *1985*. Only a partial list of 1984 publications was available. These calculations agree with a 1981 through 1984 computerized analysis by Computer Horizons, Incorporated, which reported that a breakdown of the top subfields of intramural publications in the NIH-MEDLINE data base for 1981 through 1984 showed between 24 and 25 percent concerned with dentistry and the remainder with nondental topics. Biochemistry and molecular biology followed with almost 16 percent, and immunology with close to 14 percent. See Samuel R. Reisher and Michael G. Gallagher, "Role of the National Institute of Dental Research in the Support of U.S. and International Dental Research from 1973 through 1984," Table 23, Dr. Lipton's Files, NIDR. Reisher and Gallagher used both BID- and NIH-MEDLINE data bases to give statistical evaluations of NIDR intramural and extramural publications from 1973 to 1984.

19. "Role of the National Institute of Dental Research in the Support of U.S. and International Dental Research from 1973 through 1984," CHI Project 8612-

R, Contract NIDR 263-MD-630350, April 8, 1987, Dr. Lipton's Files, NIDR; 1948 NIH Publications, RG 443, Box 105, Folder 1680, NARA; 1949-1953 Publications, NIDR IO. Raw data from files of Dr. James Lipton, NIDR. The figures totalled more than 100 percent because some authors cited more than one source of funding. Miscellaneous sources included international groups and professional societies.

20. Grace M. Carter, Clara S. Lai, and Carolyn L. Lee, *A Comparison of Large Grants and Research Project Grants Awarded by the National Institutes of Health*, R-2228-1-NIH, October 1978, ix; *NIH Almanac 1983*.

21. Personnel files of NIDR; "NIDR Intramural Contributions to Biomedical Sciences and to the Nation's Public Health: 1946-1972," "Highlights 1945-1975," Anne Atlee's Files, NIDR IO. The list included nine nondental journals, such as the *Journal of Infectious Diseases* and the *Journal of Biological Chemistry*; *1986 ADA Annual Reports and Resolutions 127th Annual Session Miami Beach, Florida October 18-23, 1986*, 138.

22. *Extramural Trends FY 1977-1986* (IMPAC NIH 1987), 12-15; *Challenges for the Eighties*, 199; "The Production of Dental Clinical Investigators under the NRSA Program," "NIDR Ad Hoc Committee on NRSA," Dr. Lipton's Files, NIDR; William Mullen, "The Disappearing Dentist," *Chicago Tribune Magazine*, July 27, 1966, 8-18, 28-29. Changes in oral disease patterns also required more dental clinical researchers, according to Dr. Lois K. Cohen.

23. Charles A. McCallum, "Interhealth Science Relationships in Fostering Dental Research," *Journal of Dental Education* 47 (April 1983): 245.

24. *Challenges for the Eighties*, 195-96; "Transcript of Proceedings 107th Meeting of the National Advisory Dental Research Council," January 26, 1983, "Council Minutes," OADEXP NIDR.

25. *Challenges for the Eighties*, 196-97.

26. *NIDR Research Digest*, April 1987.

27. *Challenges for the Eighties*, 198.

28. Robert O. Wolf, Diagnostic Systems Branch, NIDR, to Robert N. Butler, director, NIA, March 3, 1981, "Reading Board 1981 (NIH)," Dr. Cohen's Files, NIDR; National Advisory Dental Research Council Summary of Meeting, June 7-8, 1982, 6-7, NIDR IO; Harald Löe to Robert R. Rhyne, assistant chief medical director for dentistry, Department of Medicine and Surgery, Veterans Administration, September 24, 1984, "OD/NIDR Correspondence 1982-85," OD NIDR. Dr. Lois Cohen estimated that only about one-third of the 1981 to 1985 trainees were preparing for clinical research.

29. Löe to Dr. Edward F. Rossomando, School of Dental Medicine, University of Connecticut Health Center, January 18, 1984, "OD/NIDR Correspondence 1982-85," OD NIDR; "The Production of Dental Clinical Investigators under the NRSA Program," "NIDR Ad Hoc Committee on NRSA," Dr. Lipton's Files, NIDR; IOM, *Personnel Needs and Training for Biomedical and Behavioral Research* (1985), 48; National Institute of Dental Research, *Dentist Scientist Award* (March 1987).

30. *Biennial Report of the Director, National Institutes of Health* 1 (1985-1986): 75; "First Biennial Report of the National Advisory Dental Research Council," June 25, 1986, "Congressional Reports," NIDR IO.

31. Patricia Sheridan, "Computer-aided Dentistry," *JADA* 114 (April 1987): 505.

32. Richard L. Webber, "Computers in Dental Radiography: A Scenario for the Future," *JADA* 111 (September 1985): 419-24; National Health Council NIDR Exhibit, National Research Day, September 14, 1988, at the Rayburn House Office Building, Washington, D.C. This system worked by taking a picture of a selected region in a patient's tooth or mouth at precisely the same angle at different times. Next the computer calculated the difference in size of the target, such as a dental pocket or lesion, between the earlier and later X rays.

33. Ibid.; *NIDR Research Digest*, October 1986; *Dentist* (April 1987): 11, 14; *Biennial Report of the Director, National Institutes of Health* 1 (1985-1986): 75; "First Biennial Report of the National Advisory Dental Research Council," June 25, 1986, "Congressional Reports," Anne Atlee's Files, NIDR IO.

34. "NIDR Research Grants Active FY 1987 by Long Range Plan Groups Behavioral Research," Files of Dr. Patricia Bryant, NIDR.

35. Susan Johnson, "Survey of Adult Dental Health," *JADA* 114 (June 1987): 829; same, HHS News Release, June 21, 1988, NIDR.

36. A. J. Miller, J. A. Brunelle, J. P. Carlos, L. J. Brown, and H. Löe, *Oral Health of United States Adults* (NIH Publication No. 87-2868, August 1987), 7; Susan Johnson, "Survey of Adult Dental Health," 829.

37. *Oral Health of United States Adults*, 1-11; Health Resources Administration, Public Health Service, *Vital and Health Statistics Data from the National Health Survey*, series 11, no. 27, *Total Loss of Teeth in Adults United States—1960-1962*, 11.

38. Susan Johnson, HHS News Release, June 21, 1988.

39. Ibid.

40. Untitled paper, February 1984, "AIDS Special Reports," Anne Atlee's Files, NIDR IO; "National Advisory Dental Research Council Summary Minutes," September 10-11, 1985, 6, NIDR; associate director for EODPP, NIDR, to assistant director for program operations, NIDR, October 21, 1985, "Correspondence," Epidemiology Branch (Dr. Carlos), NIDR; Sol Silverman, Jr., "Infectious and Sexually Transmitted Diseases: Implications for Dental Public Health," *Journal of Public Health Dentistry* 46 (Winter 1986): 7-12.

41. Director, NIDR, to Dr. Bruce Baum and others, October 19, 1985, "85," OD NIDR; National Advisory Dental Research Council Summary Minutes, September 10-11, 1985, 6, NIDR; chief, Office of Planning, Evaluation and Communications (OPEC), NIDR, to Dr. Jay Moskowitz, associate director for program planning and evaluation, NIH, June 3, 1986, "Congressional Reports," Anne Atlee's Files, NIDR IO; assistant director for program operations, NIDR, to executive staff, October 31, 1986, "100.00 Daily Board, Oct.-Dec. (1986)," OD NIDR; acting chief, Planning and Evaluation Section, OPEC,

NIDR, to Dennis Rodrigues, December 29, 1986, "Reading Board Planning and Evaluation 1986," Planning and Evaluation Files, NIDR; *NIDR Research Digest*, September 1987; information supplied by Dr. Lois K. Cohen.

42. Susan Johnson, "Study Finds Saliva Inhibits HIV Infectivity," *NIH Record* 40 (May 17, 1988): 1, 6; telephone conversation of October 6, 1988, of Dr. Philip Fox with the author.

43. *NIH Record* 37 (March 26, 1985): 10; chair, NIDR-Industry Relations Task Force, to NIDR-Industry Relations Task Force, July 3, 1986, "100.00 Daily Board July-September (1986)," OD NIDR; chief, Office of Planning, Evaluation and Communications, NIDR, June 3, 1986, "Congressional Reports," 39, Anne Atlee's Files, NIDR IO; "First Biennial Report of the National Advisory Dental Research Council," June 25, 1986, 8, "Congressional Reports," Anne Atlee's Files, NIDR IO.

44. *NIDR Research Digest*, August 1986.

45. "The Biennial Report of the Director, National Institute of Dental Research," 3-4, NIDR IO; 1986 speech by Dr. Harald Löe, 12, NIDR.

46. "The Biennial Report of the Director," 18-19.

47. Information supplied by Dr. Lois K. Cohen.

48. 1987 speech by Dr. Harald Löe, 8-9, "Speech File," NIDR IO.

49. 1987 speech by Dr. Harald Löe, 8-9.

50. 1987 speech by Dr. Harald Löe, 13.

51. Talk by Dr. Harald Löe at the NIH Clinical Center on September 4, 1986.

Glossary and Abbreviations

AADR.	American Association for Dental Research.
ACRF.	Ambulatory Care Research Facility.
ADA.	American Dental Association.
ADA DC.	American Dental Association, District of Columbia.
AIDS.	Acquired Immunodeficiency Syndrome.
ALCOA.	Aluminum Company of America.
ANUG.	Acute Necrotizing Ulcerative Gingivitis (commonly known as trench mouth).
A.P.	Associated Press.
Avulsed tooth.	A tooth that is torn away by trauma or surgery.
BEMT.	Bureau of Health Professions, Education and Manpower Training.
Beta endorphin.	A naturally occurring peptide of the pituitary gland with morphinelike effects on pain.
CDC.	Centers for Disease Control.
CDO PHS.	Chief Dental Officer, Public Health Service.
CDP.	Chronic Destructive Periodontitis.
CMT.	Chemically Modified Tetracycline.
CT.	Computerized tomography or X ray photography of a selected plane in the body.
DDEL.	Dwight D. Eisenhower Library.
DDF.	Dr. Viron Diefenbach's Files, University of Illinois School of Public Health, Chicago.
DDH.	Division of Dental Health.
DDPH.	Division of Dental Public Health.

451

DDR.	Division of Dental Resources.
Dental caries.	A tooth cavity.
DHEF SHSW.	Dental Health Education Files, State Historical Society of Wisconsin.
DHEW.	Department of Health, Education and Welfare.
DMFS.	Decayed, Missing, or Filled Surfaces of Teeth.
DMMGPD NBS.	Dental and Medical Materials Group, Polymers Science and Standards Division, National Bureau of Standards.
DPA.	Division of Program Analysis, National Institutes of Health.
DPH.	Division of Dental Public Health.
DPHR.	Division of Dental Public Health and Resources.
DRIC.	Dental Research Institutes and Centers.
Edentulous.	A loss of all of an individual's natural teeth.
EODPP NIDR.	Office of Associate Director for Epidemiology and Oral Disease Prevention Program, NIDR.
Epidemiology.	The investigation of mass aspects of epidemic diseases.
Etiology.	The study of causes of diseases.
FDA.	Food and Drug Administration.
FDI.	Fédération Dentaire Internationale.
Fluoride.	A compound of fluorine, a gas in the halogen family that is widely distributed in nature.
Fluorination.	Term used for water fluoridation, especially before 1948.
Fluorosis (dental).	Mottled tooth enamel varying from unnoticeable to severe as a result of excessive fluoride exposure.
FSA.	Federal Security Agency.
FY.	Fiscal Year.

GAO.	General Accounting Office.
Gingival.	Gum.
Gnotobiotic animals.	(Gnotobiotes) Laboratory animals free of all microorganisms except specific known bacteria.
GPO.	Government Printing Office.
HEW.	Health, Education and Welfare [Department of].
HIV.	Human Immunodeficiency Virus.
H.R.	House of Representatives.
HSM.	Health Services and Manpower.
HSMHA.	Health Services and Mental Health Administration.
HSTL.	Harry S. Truman Library.
IADR.	International Association for Dental Research.
In vitro.	Refers to a biological reaction occurring in an artificial medium.
In vivo.	Pertains to a biological reaction in an organism or live cell.
IOM.	Institute of Medicine, National Academy of Sciences.
IR.	Intramural Research.
JADA.	Journal of the American Dental Association.
JAMA.	Journal of the American Medical Association.
Lactobacillus acidophilus.	A bacteria associated with dental decay.
LBDA.	Laboratory of Developmental Biology and Anomalies.
LBJL.	Lyndon B. Johnson Library.
Leukocytes.	White blood cells.
LJP.	Localized Juvenile Periodontitis—a periodontal disease affecting teenagers.
MED.	Division of Medical Sciences Board, National Academy of Sciences.

MMT.	Monitored and Modulated Therapy.
Mottled enamel.	Discolored teeth.
NADRC.	National Advisory Dental Research Council.
NARA.	National Archives and Records Administration.
NAS.	National Academy of Sciences.
NBS.	National Bureau of Standards; changed in 1988 to the National Institute of Standards and Technology.
NCI.	National Cancer Institute.
NCP.	National Caries Program.
NCHS.	National Center for Health Statistics.
NIA.	National Institute on Aging.
NIAID.	National Institute of Allergies and Infectious Diseases.
NIAMD.	National Institute of Arthritis and Metabolic Diseases.
NIDR.	National Institute of Dental Research.
NIDR IO.	National Institute of Dental Research Information Office.
NIH.	National Institute(s) of Health.
NIHL.	National Institutes of Health Library.
NLM.	National Library of Medicine.
NLMHMD.	National Library of Medicine History of Medicine Division.
NMR.	Nuclear Magnetic Resonance Spectroscopy.
NRSA.	National Research Service Award Act.
O&M.	Organization and Management.
OADEXP NIDR.	Office of the Associate Director for Extramural Programs, National Institute of Dental Research.
OAF.	Osteoclast Activating Factor.

Occlusal repairs.	Processes, such as grinding, to make the cusps of opposing teeth of the upper and lower jaws fit together.
OD NIDR.	Office of the Director, National Institute of Dental Research.
OD NIH.	Office of the Director, National Institutes of Health.
OPPE OD NIH.	Office of Planning and Program Evaluation, Office of the Director, National Institutes of Health.
Oral flora.	Bacteria normally present in the mouth.
ORCA.	European Organization for Caries Research.
Periodontist.	A dentist specializing in the treatment of diseases of the gum and supporting structures of the teeth.
PHR.	Public Health Reports.
PHS.	Public Health Service.
ppm.	Parts per million.
PRC NBS.	Paffenbarger Research Center, National Bureau of Standards.
S.	Senate.
SSIE.	Smithsonian Science Information Exchange.
Streptococcus mutans.	Bacteria associated with tooth decay.
SUNY.	State University of New York.
UCLA.	University of California at Los Angeles.
U.P.I.	United Press International.
VA.	Veterans Administration.
Vincent's disease.	Commonly known as trench mouth.
WHO.	World Health Organization.

End H060II

Sources

Tracing the history of the National Institute of Dental Research (NIDR) proved both challenging and fascinating. Secondary sources and interviews provided background, and other primary sources and scientific articles contributed toward the main part of the history.

To obtain a historical setting of dentistry, we found it necessary to consult a variety of secondary sources. One of the most scholarly histories, Vincenzo Guerini's *History of Dentistry*, only went up to 1800, however. Other works, such as M. K. V. Bremner's *The Story of Dentistry*, covered the nineteenth and twentieth centuries but lacked documentation. Fortunately, Hamilton B. G. Robinson assembled extensive documentation for his brief summation of dental research, "Advance in Dental Science, 1900-1950," in the *Journal of the American Dental Association* (JADA). R. C. McCluggage wrote a lively, useful *History of the American Dental Association* that explained the organizational history of American dentistry. Some dental college histories, such as Isaac Sissman's *75 Years of Dentistry—University of Pittsburgh*, contained helpful information on the history of dentistry in the United States. Scheduled for 1989 publication, *The American Dentist: A Sociological and Pictorial History* by Audrey B. Davis, Richard Glenner, and Stanley B. Burns was produced too late to use in the NIDR history.

Histories of the U.S Public Health Service (PHS) and the National Institutes of Health (NIH) also provided a framework for explaining the integration of dental research into NIH. Ralph C. Williams' *The United States Public Health Service, 1798-1950*, dealt with the origins of the PHS as well as the entry of dental research into NIH. The politics and the science that led to the establishment of NIH received a thorough analysis in Victoria Harden's *Inventing the NIH*. Stephen Strickland covered the NIH biomedical politics, particularly in the post-World War II period, in *Politics, Science, and Dread Disease*.

The sections on fluoridation in this history benefited from two excellent books. Frank McClure, a pioneer twentieth century NIH scientist involved in fluoridation research, concentrated on the science in his well-written work *Water Fluoridation: The Search and the Victory*. Donald McNeil wrote a lively account of the political side in *The Fight for Fluoridation*.

Congressional documents gave insight into the political aspects of founding and operating the Institute. The political motivation for NIDR's establishment appeared in the 1944 hearings on wartime health and the 1945 hearings on S. 190, the bill that formed the basis for the 1948 act creating

456

the National Institute of Dental Research. Annual appropriations hearings showed the growing influence of the Institute on dental research, and the 1952, 1954, and 1977 hearings on fluoridation indicated the dimensions of controversy over that process.

Annual reports of NIDR and minutes of the National Advisory Dental Research Council (NADRC) also recorded developments at the Institute. The annual reports varied from extremely brief publications in the Institute's first few years to technical accounts exceeding one hundred pages by the 1960s. All of the annual reports were in the NIH Library, but a number of them were filed under annual reports of other NIH institutes. NIDR's library contained all of the NADRC minutes from 1949 to 1988.

In the custody of the National Library of Medicine (NLM) and NIDR, taped interviews of NIDR scientists provided a contemporary flavor to the history. Those conducted in 1964 by Dr. Wyndham Miles, the NIH historian, elicited details about the early days of dental research at NIH and the paths of fluoridation research and promotion. The 1980s interviews concerned Institute policies and scientific directions as viewed by current and past NIDR scientists and administrators and non-NIDR scientists who dealt with the Institute.

The archives and publications of the American Dental Association (ADA) in Chicago and the Washington, D.C., metropolitan area were especially valuable. Nineteenth and twentieth century ADA documents and issues of *Transactions of the American Dental Association* and the *ADA News Letter* recorded actions of the ADA in supporting dental research and the founding of NIDR. The ADA-sponsored Paffenbarger Research Center at the National Bureau of Standards, Gaithersburg, Maryland, contained important papers on the dental materials research funded by NIDR.

Primary sources from federal records supplied much of the information on the rise of dentistry in the Public Health Service. Particularly useful were files at the National Archives and Records Administration (NARA) in Washington, D.C., of the PHS, NIH, Federal Security Agency, and the Department of Health, Education and Welfare. File 1206 in the Central File, 1897-1923, of Record Group 90, records of the Public Health Service, revealed the early lobbying for inclusion of dentistry in the PHS. Later papers in Record Group 90, particularly those in the 0412 Dentistry folders, covered the growth of dental research at NIH and some of the fluoridation history. Dental categories in Record Group 443, files of NIH, covered administrative, research, and fluoridation developments from the 1930s to the 1950s. The political problems affecting NIDR, especially those concerning fluoridation, appeared in dental and fluoridation files of Record Group 235, the papers of the Federal Security Agency, and the Department of Health, Education and Welfare.

Offices at federal agencies also held significant papers bearing on the history. The Public Health Service's chief dental officer and Dr. Thomas Louden, acting director of the PHS Division of Associated and Dental Health Professions, had records dating back to the 1950s. At the National Bureau of Standards, the files of Dr. John Tesk, chief of the dental and medical materials group, contained over two feet of papers on the NIDR-NBS relationships on dental materials research.

Files of the director of NIH on NIDR provided insight to federal policy on dental research and the Institute. The NIH director's files were retained by NIH in Bethesda during the time we started research in 1986.

The NIDR files, also not held in NARA or the Federal Records Center, supplied essential information for the history. The Institute's central files had been dispersed in the 1970s; subsequently, we located many of these documents in over two dozen different offices and in storage at St. Elizabeth's Hospital in Washington, D.C. The NIDR Public Inquiries and Reports Section housed especially important files of approximately six cubic feet that included documents on a variety of aspects of NIH dental research from the 1930s to the 1980s. Each member of the Public Inquiries and Reports Section stored useful files, some of which spanned up to thirty years. John Small, also an NIDR information specialist, saved valuable records on fluoridation, including the documents on which McClure based his book on fluoridation. The particular location of each NIDR-held document used in this history is identified in the endnotes for each chapter.

Available papers of NIDR directors yielded considerable information. The only director's papers available at the Institute were those of Dr. Harald Löe; files of previous directors were missing. A search for the pre-1983 directors' files ultimately turned up many of the papers of Dr. H. Trendley Dean, the first director; the 1970s fluoridation files only of Dr. David B. Scott; and less than one foot of the papers of Dr. Seymour J. Kreshover. Löe's files documented his policies at the Institute in the 1980s. The Dean papers contained significant correspondence on fluoridation research in the 1930s; Scott's files supplied details on fluoridation efforts, and Kreshover's records included his notes on the meeting of NIH directors with President Lyndon B. Johnson. The NLM took custody of the Dean papers; NIDR retained the Scott fluoridation files and the Kreshover records.

A selected bibliography of key works follows. The fuller listing of sources appears in the notes to the chapters.

Selected Bibliography

Oral History Interviews

The following taped interviews, in the custody of the National Library of Medicine History of Medicine Division, were conducted by Dr. Wyndham Miles, NIH historian:

Subject	Date
Arnold, Dr. Francis A., Jr.	June 10 and 17, September 16, October 21, and December 9, 1964
Larson, Dr. Rachel	June 3, 1964
McClure, Dr. Frank	May 20, 1964
Stanley, Dr. Harold	November 17 and December 1, 1964
Witkop, Dr. Carl	September 27, 1966
Zipkin, Dr. Isadore	May 28, 1964

The following taped oral history interviews were placed in the custody of the National Institute of Dental Research:

Subject	Date	Interviewer
Carlos, Dr. James	October 20, 1987	Ruth R. Harris
Diefenbach, Dr. Viron	April 8, 1987	Ruth R. Harris
Dubner, Dr. Ronald	December 23, 1986	Laura Kells
Fitzgerald, Dr. Robert	September 24, 1986	Ruth Harris
Folk, Dr. John E.	December 8, 1986	Laura Kells
Larson, Dr. Rachel	March 10, 1987	Ruth R. Harris
Kreshover, Dr. Seymour	September 29, 1986	Ruth R. Harris
Löe, Dr. Harald	May 8, 1988	Ruth R. Harris
Piez, Dr. Karl	December 29, 1986	Ruth R. Harris
Roberts, Dr. Michael	December 15, 1986	Laura Kells
Scott, Dr. David B.	September 3, 1986	Ruth R. Harris
Stanford, Dr. John	April 17, 1987	Ruth R. Harris
Steffek, Dr. Anthony	April 9, 1987	Ruth R. Harris
Termine, Dr. John	March 2, 1987	Laura Kells
Verrusio, Dr. Carl	April 9, 1987	Ruth R. Harris

Selected Primary Sources

American Dental Association Archives, Chicago, Illinois.
American Dental Association files, Washington, D.C.
American Expeditionary Forces (World War I) 1917-1923 records, Record Group 120, NARA.
Chief Dental Officer, Public Health Service, files, Rockville, Maryland.
Dean, Dr. H. Trendley, papers, National Library of Medicine.
Department of Health, Education and Welfare and Federal Security Agency records, Record Group 235, NARA.
Dental Health Education files, State Historical Society of Wisconsin, Madison.
Diefenbach, Dr. Viron, papers, University of Illinois School of Public Health, Chicago.
Ewing, Oscar, papers, Harry S. Truman Library, Independence, Missouri.
Hill, Lister, papers, National Library of Medicine.
Hobby, Oveta Culp, papers, Dwight D. Eisenhower Library, Abilene, Kansas.
Johnson, Lyndon B., papers, Lyndon B. Johnson Library, Austin, Texas.
Kreshover, Dr. Seymour J., papers, NIDR.
Louden, Dr. Thomas, files, Public Health Service, Rockville, Maryland.
National Institute of Dental Research files, Bethesda, Maryland.
National Institutes of Health records, Record Group 443, NARA.
National Academy of Sciences Archives, Washington, D.C.
National Advisory Dental Research Council, minutes, 1949-1987, NIDR, Bethesda, Maryland.
Office of the Director, National Institutes of Health, files, Bethesda, Maryland.
Paffenbarger Research Center files, National Bureau of Standards, Gaithersburg, Maryland.
President's Secretary's File, Harry S. Truman Library, Independence, Missouri.
Public Health Service records, Record Group 90, NARA.
Truman, Harry S., papers, Harry S. Truman Library, Independence, Missouri.
White House Central File, Dwight D. Eisenhower Library, Abilene, Kansas.

Selected Published and Unpublished Sources

Annual Report of the Supervising Surgeon of the Marine-Hospital Service of the United States. Washington: GPO, 1873, 1874, 1881.
Arnold, Francis A., Jr. "The Fellowship and Training Grants Program of the National Institutes of Health." *Journal of Dental Education* 23 (June 1959): 101-4.
Ayer, William A.; Gift, Helen; Green, Daniel B.; Howe, Anne; and Grossman, Barry C. "Dental Researchers in the United States." Unpublished manuscript completed December 1, 1982, ADA Archives, Chicago, Illinois.
Baum, B. J. "Neurotransmitter Control of Secretion." *Journal of Dental Research* (February 1987): 628-32.

Biomedical Science and Its Administration: A Study of the National Institutes of Health. White House, 1965.

Bremner, M. D. K. *The Story of Dentistry. From the Dawn of Civilization to the Present. With Special Emphasis on the American Scene.* New York: Dental Items of Interest Publishing Company, 1954.

Brown, L. J., and Littleton, P. A. "Relationships between NIDR-supported Research Training and Subsequent Grant Activity." *Journal of Dental Research* 64 (March 1985): 205.

Camalier, C. Willard, Sr. *100 Years of Dental Progress in the Nation's Capital.* Washington, 1966.

Carlos, James P. "The Prevention of Dental Caries: Ten Years Later." *JADA* 104 (February 1982): 193-97.

Carter, Grace M.; Lai, Clara S.; and Lee, Carolyn L. *A Comparison of Large Grants and Research Project Grants Awarded by the National Institutes of Health.* R-2228-1-NIH, October 1978.

Churchill, H. V. "Occurrence of Fluorides in Some Waters of the United States." *Industrial and Engineering Chemistry* 23 (September 1931): 996-98.

Cohen, Lois K. "Dentistry and the Behavioral/Social Sciences: An Historical Overview." *Journal of Behavioral Medicine* 4, no. 3 (1981): 247-375.

Commission on the Survey of Dentistry in the United States. *The Survey of Dentistry: The Final Report.* Washington: American Council on Education, 1961.

de Solla Price, Derek J. *Little Science Big Science.* New York: Columbia University Press, 1963.

Dean, H. Trendley; Arnold, Francis A., Jr.; Jay, Philip; and Knutson, John W. "Studies on Mass Control of Dental Caries through Fluoridation of the Public Water Supply." *PHR* 65 (October 27, 1950): 1403-8.

Dean, H. Trendley, and Elias Elvove. "Chronic Endemic Dental Fluorosis." *Journal of the American Medical Association* 107 (October 17, 1936): 1269-72.

Dickson, George, and Cassel, James M., eds. *Dental Materials Research.* NBS Publication 354, July 1972.

Dove, Jody; Dubner, Ronald; Dionne, Raymond; Max, Mitchell; Singer, Elyse; Hargreaves, Kenneth; Gracely, Richard; and Schafer, Susan. *Pain Research from Laboratory to Clinic.* NIDR, September 1986.

Evaluation of the NIDR Craniofacial Anomalies Research Activities. [NIDR], September 1981.

Evaluation of the National Institute of Dental Research National Caries Program. 3 vols. Washington: U.S. Dept. of Health, Education and Welfare, November 1979.

Evaluation of the NIDR Periodontal Research Activity: Report of the Ad Hoc Scientific Evaluation Panel to the Director National Institute of Dental Research, [NIDR], April 1976.

The First Fifty-Year History of the International Association for Dental Research. Chicago: University of Chicago Printing Dept., 1973.

Fitzgerald, Robert J. "Brief History of *Streptococcus Mutans.*" *Streptococcus Mutans and Dental Caries.* DHEW Publication No. (NIH) 74-186, 1972.

Fitzgerald, Robert J., and Keyes, Paul H. "Demonstration of the Etiologic Role of Streptococci in Experimental Caries in the Hamster." *JADA* 61 (July 1960): 9-19.

Foley, Gardner P. H. "Periodical Literature—Key in the Progress of Dentistry, 1901-1920." *JADA* 84 (March 1972): 501-2.

Garrington, George, M.D. "A History of the Dental Corps of the United States Public Health Service." Unpublished manuscript, NIDR.

Gibbons, R. J. "Bacterial Adherence to Mucosal Surfaces and Its Inhibition by Secretory Antibodies." In *The Immunoglobin A System: Advances in Experimental Medicine and Biology* 45, edited by J. Mestecky and A. R. Lawton, 315-26. 1974.

Gies, William J. *Dental Education in the United States and Canada: A Report to the Carnegie Foundation for the Advancement of Teaching.* New York: Carnegie Foundation for the Advancement of Teaching, 1926.

Guerini, Vincenzo. *History of Dentistry from the Most Ancient Times until the End of the 18th Century.* New York: Lea & Febiger, 1909.

Hand, Arthur R. "The Fine Structure of von Ebner's Gland of the Rat." *Journal of Cell Biology* 44 (1970): 340-53.

Harden, Victoria. *Inventing the NIH: Federal Biomedical Research Policy, 1887-1937.* Baltimore: The Johns Hopkins University Press, 1986.

Hassell, J. R.; Gehron Robey, P. J.; Barrach, J. H.; Wilczek, J.; Rennard, S. I.; and Martin, G. R. "Isolation of a Heparan Sulfate-Containing Proteoglycan from Basement Membrane." *Proceedings of the National Academy of Sciences USA* 77 (1980): 4494-98.

Hoffman-Axthelm, Walter. *History of Dentistry.* Chicago: Quintessence Publishing Company, 1981.

Howell, A., Jr., and Jordan, H. V., Jr. "A Filamentous Microorganism Isolated from Periodontal Plaque in Hamsters. II. Physical and Biochemical Characteristics." *Sabouraudia* 3 (October 1963): 93-105.

Jeffcott, George F. *United States Army Dental Service in World War II.* Washington: Office of the Surgeon General, Dept. of the Army, 1955.

Jordan, H. V., Jr.; Fitzgerald, Robert J.; and Stanley, H. R. "Plaque Formation and Periodontal Pathology in Gnotobiotic Rats Infected with an Oral Actinomycete." *American Journal of Pathology* 47 (December 1965): 1157-67.

Keyes, Paul H. "Dental Caries in Syrian Hamster. VIII. Induction of Rampant Caries Activity in Albino and Golden Animals." *Journal of Dental Research* 38 (May-June 1959): 525.

Knutson, John W. "Studies on Dental Caries. IV. Tooth Mortality in Elementary School Children." *PHR* Reprint No. 1021 (June 1938).

Konig, K. G. "Impact of Decreasing Caries Prevalence: Implications for Dental Research." *Dental Research* (November 1982): 1378-83.

Kreshover, Seymour J. "1. Craniofacial Anomalies: Past, Present, and Future Priorities for Development and Molecular Biology." *Extracellular Matrix Influences on Gene Expression*, 3-7. New York: Academic Press, 1975.

Littleton, P. A., Jr., M.D.; Brown, L. J.; and Solomon, E. S. "The Relationship between National Institute of Dental Research (NIDR) Supported Research

Training and Careers in Dental Research." Unpublished manuscript, NIDR, n.d.

Löe, Harald A. "Scientific Revolutions in Dentistry." *Journal of Dental Research* 58 (November 1979): 2164-68.

Löe, Harald A.; Theilade, E.; and Jensen, S. B. "Experimental Gingivitis in Man." *Journal of Periodontology* 36 (1965): 177-87.

McCallum, Charles A. "Interhealth Science Relationships in Fostering Dental Research." *Journal of Dental Education* 47 (April 1983): 244-51.

McCluggage, R. W. *A History of the American Dental Association.* Chicago: ADA, 1959.

McClure, Frank J. *Water Fluoridation: The Search and the Victory.* Bethesda: NIDR, 1970.

McNeil, Donald R. *The Fight for Fluoridation.* New York: Oxford University Press, 1957.

Mandel, Irwin. "The Role of Saliva in Maintaining Oral Homeostasis." 1986 Seymour J. Kreshover Lecture, NIDR.

Martin, G. R.; Gross, J.; Piez, K. A.; and Lewis, M. S. "On the Intramolecular Crosslinking in Collagen in Lathyritic Rats." *Biochimica et Biophysica Acta* 49 (May 13, 1961): 245-50.

Marx, Jean L. "Diabetes—A Possible Autoimmune Disease." *Science* 223 (September 21, 1984): 1381-82.

Menaker, Lewis, ed. *The Biologic Basis of Dental Caries: An Oral Biology Textbook.* Hagerstown: Harper and Row, 1980.

Mergenhagen, S. E.; Tempel, T. R.; and Snyderman, R. "Immunologic Reactions and Periodontal Inflammation." *Journal of Dental Research* 49 (1970): 256-61.

Messner, C. T.; Gafafer, W. M.; Cady, F. C.; and Dean, H. Trendley. *Dental Survey of School Children, Ages 6-14 Years, Made in 1933-1934 in 26 States. Public Health Bulletin* no. 226. Washington: GPO, 1936.

Miles, Wyndham Davies. *A History of the National Library of Medicine: The Nation's Treasury of Medical Knowledge.* NIH Publication no. 85-1904, 1982.

Miller, Julie Ann. "Oral Interactions: The Molecular Basis for Bacterial Binding." *Science News* 130 (July 1986): 12-13.

NIDR Annual Reports. NIDR, 1948-1986.

NIDR Programs. NIDR, 1973 through 1983.

NIDR Research Digest. NIDR, June 1985, August 1986, and April 1987.

National Institute of Dental Research. *Challenges for the Eighties. National Institute of Dental Research Long-Range Research Plan: FY 1985-1989.* NIH Publication no. 85-860, December 1983.

————. *Dental Research in the United States and Other Countries Fiscal Year 1976 through 1980.* NIH, 1976 through 1980.

National Institutes of Health Annual Report of International Activities Fiscal Year 1977 through *1982.* DHEW Publication no. (NIH) 79-62, 1978; NIH Publication no. 82-62, September 1982, and NIH Publication no. 83-62, July 1983.

1983 NIH Almanac. NIH Publication no. 83-5, March 1983.

1985 NIH Almanac. NIH Publication no. 85-5, September 1985.

1959 Highlights of Progress in Research on Oral Diseases. U.S. Dept. of Health, Education and Welfare, PHS, 1959.

NIH Research Advances. NIH, 1976.

Norwood, William Frederick. *Medical Education in the United States before the Civil War.* New York: Arno Press & The New York Times, 1971.

Notkins, A. L. "Effect of Virus Infections on Immune Function." In *Proceedings of the Sixth International Immunopathology Symposium,*edited by P. A. Miescher, 413-25. Basel, Switzerland: Schwabe and Company, 1971.

Nylen, M. U.; Omnell, K.-A.; and Lofgren, C.-G. "Fine Structure of Tetracycline-induced Hypoplastic and Hypomineralized Defects in Rat Incisor Enamel." *Journal of Dental Research* 43 (1964): 850.

Office of Program Planning and Evaluation and Division of Research Grants, National Institutes of Health. *NIH Data Book 1986.* NIH, December 1986.

Paffenbarger, George C.; English, J. A.; and Hampp, Edward. "Dental Research—Current and Future." *Journal of the American College of Dentists* (1955): 21-29.

Paffenbarger, George C.; Tesk, John A.; and Brown, Walter E. "Dental Research at the National Bureau of Standards: How It Changed the Practice of Dental Health Service." *JADA* 111 (July 1985): 83-89.

Parmly, Levi Spear. *A Practical Guide to the Management of the Teeth Comprising Discovery of the Origin of Caries on Decay of the Teeth.* Philadelphia: Collins and Croft, 1819.

Piez, K. A.; Lewis, M. S.; Martin, G. R.; and Gross, J. "Subunits of the Collagen Molecule." *Biochimica et Biophysica Acta* 53 (November 11, 1961): 596-98.

Prinz, Hermann. *Dental Chronology. A Record of the More Important Historic Events in the Evolution of Dentistry.* Philadelphia: Lea & Febiger, 1945.

Reddi, A. H.; Wientroub, S.; and Muthukumaran, N. "Biologic Principles of Bone Induction." *Orthopedic Clinics of North America* 18 (April 1987): 207-12.

Reducing Tooth Decay—More Emphasis on Fluoridation Needed: Report to the Congress by the Comptroller General of the United States. Rept. no. HRD 79-3. Washington: GAO, April 13, 1979.

Reese, Joyce A., and Valega, Thomas M., eds. *Restorative Dental Materials. An Overview.* vol. 1. London: Fédération Dentaire Internationale and Quintessence Publishing Company, 1985.

Richards, N. D., and Cohen, Lois K., eds. *Social Sciences and Dentistry: A Critical Bibliography.* 2 vols. Fédération Dentaire Internationale, 1971.

Robinson, Ben; Faggart, Harold L.; and Morrey, Lon W. "A Synoptic History of the American Dental Association." *JADA* 58 (June 1959): 19-76.

Robinson, Hamilton B. G. "Advances in Dental Science, 1900-1950." *JADA* 40 (June 1950): 647-86.

Rodriguez, F. E. "Studies in the Specific Bacteriology of Dental Caries." *Military Dental Journal* 5 (December 1922): 199-214.

Rogers, William E. *The National Caries Program: The First Ten Years.* NIDR, 1981.

Russell, A. L. "Some Epidemiological Characteristics of Periodontal Disease in a Series of Urban Populations." *Journal of Periodontology* 28 (October 1957): 286-93.

Scott, D. B.; Kaplan, H.; and Wyckoff, R. W. G. "Replica Studies of Changes in Tooth Surfaces with Age." *Journal of Dental Research* 28 (February 1949): 31-47.

Sheridan, Patricia. "Tooth Enamel Gene Identified by rDNA Technology." *JADA* 110 (March 1985): 384.

Sissman, Isaac. *75 Years of Dentistry—University of Pittsburgh: A History of the School of Dental Medicine.* University of Pittsburgh, 1971.

Slavkin, Harold C. "Research on Craniofacial Genetics and Developmental Biology: Implications for the Future of Academic Dentistry." *Journal of Dental Education* 47, no. 4 (1983): 231-38.

Small, H., and Greenlee, E. "Collagen Research in the 1970s." *Scientometrics* 10 (1986): 95-117.

Steelman, John R. *The Nation's Medical Research.* Vol. 5, *Science and Public Policy. A Report to the President.* Washington: GPO, 1947.

Stetten, DeWitt, Jr., ed. *NIH: An Account of Research in Its Laboratories and Clinics.* Orlando: Academic Press, 1984.

Stine, Jeffrey K. *A History of Science Policy in the United States, 1940-1985.* Published for U.S. Cong., House, 99th Cong., 2d sess. Washington: GPO, 1986.

Strickland, Stephan P. *Politics, Science, & Dread Disease: A Short History of United States Medical Research Policy.* Cambridge: Harvard University Press, 1972.

Tempel, T. R.; Snyderman, R.; Jordan, H. V.; and Mergenhagen, S. E. "Factors from Saliva and Oral Bacteria Chemotactic for Polymorphonuclear Leukocytes: Their Possible Role in Gingival Inflammation." *Journal of Periodontology* 41: 71.

Termine, J. D., and Eanes, E. D. "Comparative Chemistry of Amorphous and Apatitic Calcium Phosphate Preparations." *Calcified Tissue Research* 10 (1972): 171-92.

Transactions of the American Dental Association, 1885 through 1897.

Transactions of the National Dental Association, 1898-1922.

U.S. Congress. House. *Amending the Public Health Service Act to Provide for a National Institute of Dental Research.* 80th Cong., 2d sess., June 2, 1948. H. Rept. 2158.

————. *Chemicals in Foods and Cosmetics: Hearings before the House Select Committee to Investigate the Use of Chemicals in Foods and Cosmetics . . . Pursuant to H. Res. 74 and H. Res. 447,* pt. 3. 82d Cong., 2d sess. Washington: GPO, 1952.

————. *The National Cancer Program (Part 2—Fluoridation of Public Drinking Water). Hearings before a Subcommittee of the Committee on Government Operations, House of Representatives.* 95th Cong., 1st sess., September 21 and October 12, 1977.

U.S. Congress. Senate. *Dental Research and Dental Care: Hearings before a Subcommittee of the Committee on Education and Labor . . . on S. 190.* 79th

Cong., 1st sess., June 26, 27, and 28, 1945. Washington: GPO, 1945.

————. *National Institute of Dental Research Act, May 20 (legislative day, March 5, 1946)* Report. 79th Cong., 2d sess. S. Rept. 1363.

————. *Wartime Health and Education: Hearings before a Subcommittee of the Committee on Education and Labor . . . pursuant to S. Res. 74.* 78th Cong., 2d sess., July 10, 11, and 12, 1944, pt. 5. Washington: GPO, 1944.

U.S. Public Health Service. *Public Health Reports,* 1902-1988.

Urist, M. R.; Delange, R. J.; and Finerman, G. A. M. "Bone Cell Differentiation and Growth Factors." *Science* 220 (1983): 680-86.

Ward, Howard L. "The Development of Dental Curriculum." *Journal of the American College of Dentists* (April 1972): 106-13.

Weinberger, Bernhard Wolf. *An Introduction to the History of Dentistry: With Medical and Dental Chronology and Bibliographic Data.* 2 vols. St. Louis: C. V. Mosby Company, 1948.

Williams, Ralph Chester. *The United States Public Health Service, 1798-1950.* Commissioned Officers Association of the United States Public Health Service, 1951.

Witkop, Carl J., Jr., ed. *Genetics and Dental Health. Proceedings of an International Symposium Held at the National Institutes of Health, Bethesda, Maryland, April 4-6, 1961.* New York: McGraw-Hill Book Company, 1962.

Zambon, Joseph J.; Christersson, Lars A.; and Genco, Robert J. "Diagnosis and Treatment of Localized Juvenile Periodontitis." *JADA* 113 (August 1986): 295-99.

Index